The American Republic
Since 1877

Quizzes and Tests

 **Glencoe**
McGraw-Hill

New York, New York   Columbus, Ohio   Chicago, Illinois   Peoria, Illinois   Woodland Hills, California

To The Teacher

Glencoe offers resources that accompany *The American Republic Since 1877* to expand, enrich, review, and assess every lesson you teach and for every student you teach. Now Glencoe has organized its many resources for the way you teach.

HOW THIS BOOK IS ORGANIZED

Quizzes and Tests offers assessment blackline masters at unit, chapter, and section levels. We have organized this book so that all tests and quizzes appear at the point when you will most likely use them—unit pretests followed by section quizzes, followed by chapter tests, followed by unit posttests.

A COMPLETE ANSWER KEY

A complete answer key appears at the back of this book. This answer key includes answers for every test and quiz in this book, in the order in which they appear in the book.

Creating a Customized File

There are a variety of ways to organize Glencoe Social Studies teaching aids. Several alternatives in creating your own files are given below.

- Organize by category (all activities, all tests, etc.)

- Organize by category and chapter (all Chapter 1 activities, all Chapter 1 tests and quizzes, etc.)

- Organize sequentially by lesson (activities, quizzes, tests, for Chapter 1/Section 1, Chapter 1/Section 2, etc.)

No matter what organization you use, you can pull out individual worksheets from these booklets for your files, or you may photocopy directly from the booklet and file the photocopies. You will then be able to keep the original booklets intact and in a safe place.

Glencoe/McGraw-Hill

A Division of The **McGraw·Hill** *Companies*

Send all inquiries to:
Glencoe/McGraw-Hill
8787 Orion Place
Columbus, OH 43240

ISBN 0-07-828970-X

Printed in the United States of America

2 3 4 5 6 7 8 9 10   108   08 07 06 05 04 03

Table of Contents

Unit 3 Tests and Quizzes

Unit 4 Tests and Quizzes

Unit 5 Tests and Quizzes

Unit 6 Tests and Quizzes

Unit 7 Tests and Quizzes

Unit 8 Tests and Quizzes

⭐ **Unit 1 Pretest, Form A**

Score

Foundations of Liberty

DIRECTIONS: Matching Match each item in Column A with the items in Column B.
Write the correct letters in the blanks. *(4 points each)*

Column A

_____ **1.** not explicitly listed in the Constitution but necessary for
the government to do its job

_____ **2.** people whose religious beliefs differed from the majority
and were considered a threat to Puritan communities

_____ **3.** heads of government departments that advise the
president

_____ **4.** a 1700s religious revival

_____ **5.** immediate end to slavery

_____ **6.** dramatic changes in business that began in Great Britain in
the mid-1700s

_____ **7.** large cattle ranches

_____ **8.** early migrants to the Americas who continually moved
from place to place

_____ **9.** means for each branch of government to monitor and limit
the power of the others

_____ **10.** group that opposed war and whose leader, William Penn,
founded Pennsylvania

Column B

A. abolition

B. Quakers

C. checks and
balances

D. cabinet

E. nomads

F. heretics

G. Great Awakening

H. implied powers

I. Industrial
Revolution

J. haciendas

DIRECTIONS: Multiple Choice Choose the item that best completes each statement
or answers each question. Write the letter in the blank. *(4 points each)*

_____ **11.** The first Europeans to arrive in the Americas were the
    A. English.   **C.** Portuguese.
    B. Spanish.   **D.** Vikings.

_____ **12.** Christopher Columbus landed in the Americas for the first time in
    A. San Salvador.   **C.** Massachusetts.
    B. Cuba.   **D.** Virginia.

_____ **13.** The earliest Americans probably came from
    A. Asia.   **C.** Africa.
    B. Europe.   **D.** Australia.

_____ **14.** The Pilgrims immigrated to America to escape
    A. famine in England.   **C.** religious persecution.
    B. unfair taxation.   **D.** forced enlistment in the English
                 military.

(continued)

★ **Unit 1 Pretest, Form A**

_____ **15.** What product did the Jamestown colony produce and sell to England for a profit?

    A. fur clothing   **C.** gold jewelry

    B. cotton   **D.** tobacco

_____ **16.** The Bill of Rights had _____ amendments.

    A. five   **C.** twelve

    B. ten   **D.** twenty

_____ **17.** The U.S. government is a federal system because it

    A. divides power between national and state governments.

    B. gives the national government the majority of the power.

    C. divides the national government into three branches.

    D. prevents any branch of government from becoming too powerful.

_____ **18.** The expedition that gave the United States claim to the Oregon Territory was led by

    A. Zebulon Pike.   **C.** Lewis and Clark.

    B. Napoleon.   **D.** Tecumseh.

_____ **19.** The two basic labor systems used to organize enslaved African Americans working in the fields were

    A. group and task.   **C.** task and gang.

    B. driver and gang.   **D.** driver and planter.

_____ **20.** The battle of the Alamo took place during

    A. the war between the United States and Mexico.

    B. Texas's fight for independence from Mexico.

    C. the War of 1812.

    D. the French and Indian War.

DIRECTIONS: Essay Answer one of the following questions on a separate sheet of paper. *(20 points)*

21. What kinds of things do you think Europeans and Native Americans exchanged with each other?

22. Compare and contrast the lives of enslaved and free African Americans in the colonies.

⭐ **Unit 1 Pretest, Form B**

Foundations of Liberty

DIRECTIONS: Matching Match each item in Column A with the items in Column B. Write the correct letters in the blanks. *(4 points each)*

Column A

_____ **1.** first people to build a civilization in America

_____ **2.** established the city of Tenochtitlán where Mexico City now stands

_____ **3.** named by Walter Raleigh in honor of Queen Elizabeth

_____ **4.** colony named for King George III who established the colony as a place where debtors could start over

_____ **5.** elderly at the time of the Constitutional Convention, his good humor helped smooth the debates

_____ **6.** appointed by the Second Continental Congress to lead the Continental Army

_____ **7.** smuggled goods

_____ **8.** person living in a country who is not a citizen

_____ **9.** dramatic changes in business that began in Britain in the mid-1700s

_____ **10.** name given to Texas by Benjamin Edwards

Column B

A. Virginia

B. Industrial Revolution

C. Georgia

D. George Washington

E. Fredonia

F. Aztec

G. Olmec

H. Benjamin Franklin

I. contraband

J. alien

DIRECTIONS: Multiple Choice Choose the item that best completes each sentence or answers each question. Write the letter in the blank. *(4 points each)*

_____ **11.** The efforts to free Christianity's holy places from the Muslims were known as the
  A. feudal system.
  B. Middle Passage.
  C. English Civil War.
  D. Crusades.

_____ **12.** Spanish forts built in the Southwest to protect settlers and to serve as trading posts were called
  A. outposts.
  B. vaqueros.
  C. haciendas.
  D. presidios.

_____ **13.** New England colonists powered sawmills with
  A. coal.
  B. wood-burning stoves.
  C. waterfalls.
  D. oil made from whale blubber.

(continued)

_____ **14.** Enlightenment thinkers emphasized
  A. dependence on God.
  B. religious freedom.
  C. logic and reason.
  D. the right of self-government.

_____ **15.** To help the British East India Company sell its tea, Parliament passed the
  A. Townshend Act.
  B. Tea Act of 1773.
  C. Virginia Resolves.
  D. nonimportation agreement.

_____ **16.** Through the practice of _____, the British seized American sailors and forced them to work on British ships.
  A. sedition
  B. impressment
  C. impeachment
  D. embargo

_____ **17.** Southern leaders did not want to abolish slavery because
  A. they believed that enslaved Africans were better off on plantations.
  B. they believed that enslaved Africans were intellectually inferior to whites.
  C. the South relied on enslaved labor to sustain its agricultural economy.
  D. enslaved Africans from the South had fought with the British in the Revolution.

_____ **18.** The Native American group that protected its land by clashing with American settlers in southern Georgia was the
  A. Iroquois.
  B. Seminoles.
  C. Hopewells.
  D. Navajos.

_____ **19.** Andrew Jackson defended the _____ by saying that it opened up the government to more ordinary people.
  A. caucus system
  B. favorite son system
  C. spoils system
  D. diplomatic system

_____ **20.** Prison reform in the early 1800s focused on
  A. educating prisoners.
  B. strict discipline.
  C. rehabilitating prisoners.
  D. converting prisoners to Christianity.

DIRECTIONS: Essay Answer one of the following questions on a separate sheet of paper. *(20 points)*

21. What changes occurred in the 1300s and 1400s that led European and African cultures into contact with the people living in the Americas?

22. After the Revolutionary War, the thirteen colonies formed the United States of America. How did the United States expand its territory?

★ **Chapter 1**

Section Quiz 1-1

DIRECTIONS: Matching Match each item in Column A with the items in Column B.
Write the correct letters in the blanks. *(10 points each)*

Column A

_____ **1.** method used to calculate the age of material

_____ **2.** Anasazi lived here

_____ **3.** large Mississippian city

_____ **4.** good spirits

_____ **5.** built a system of irrigation canals

Column B

A. Chaco Canyon

B. kachinas

C. Cahokia

D. radiocarbon dating

E. Hohokam

DIRECTIONS: Multiple Choice In the blank at the left, write the letter of the choice
that best completes the statement or answers the question. *(10 points each)*

_____ **6.** Anthropologists think the first people to build a civilization in America
were the
  A. Anasazi.
  B. Olmec.
  C. Hohokam.
  D. Mississippian.

_____ **7.** Many groups of fishing peoples lived along the Pacific Coast from what
is now southeastern Alaska to Washington State, including the Kwakiutls
and
  A. Yakima.
  B. Iroquois.
  C. Chinook.
  D. Shoshone.

_____ **8.** The Iroquoians of New York surrounded their villages with wooden
stockades and built large rectangular
  A. longhouses.
  B. fields for crops.
  C. mounds.
  D. kachinas.

_____ **9.** Two different groups made the Far North their home: the Inuit and the
  A. Aztec.
  B. Aleut.
  C. Hohokam.
  D. Zuni.

_____ **10.** During the Ice Age, much of the earth's water froze into huge ice sheets
called
  A. savannahs.
  B. bogs.
  C. ice caps.
  D. glaciers.

★ Chapter 1

Section Quiz 1-2

DIRECTIONS: Matching Match each item in Column A with the items in Column B. Write the correct letters in the blanks. *(10 points each)*

Column A

_____ **1.** period of time from about 500 to 1400

_____ **2.** ships with the latest technology used by Portuguese explorers

_____ **3.** people who built the Songhai empire

_____ **4.** an intellectual revolution lasting from about 1350 to 1600

_____ **5.** a kind of rolling grassland

Column B

A. Renaissance

B. Sorko

C. Middle Ages

D. savannah

E. caravels

DIRECTIONS: Multiple Choice In the blank at the left, write the letter of the choice that best completes the statement or answers the question. *(10 points each)*

_____ **6.** One way the Crusades changed western European society was by bringing Europeans into contact with the Muslim and Byzantine civilizations of
   A. the Middle East.
   B. South America.
   C. China.
   D. South Africa.

_____ **7.** In the 1400s, off the west coast of Africa on the Canary and Madeira Islands, Spain and Portugal established
   A. gold mines.
   B. sugarcane plantations.
   C. salt mines.
   D. cotton plantations.

_____ **8.** What people conquered Ghana and built the empire of Mali?
   A. Malinke
   B. Soninke
   C. Sorko
   D. Portuguese

_____ **9.** Under what political system would a king give estates to nobles in exchange for their military support?
   A. states
   B. empires
   C. the Crusades
   D. feudalism

_____ **10.** The three great empires that arose in West Africa between the 400s and 1400s—Ghana, Mali, and Songhai—gained much of their prosperity by trading
   A. gold and silver.
   B. gold and silk.
   C. gold and salt.
   D. silver and salt.

⭐ **Chapter 1**

Section Quiz 1-3

DIRECTIONS: Matching Match each item in Column A with the items in Column B.
Write the correct letters in the blanks. *(10 points each)*

Column A

Column B

_____ **1.** Portuguese mariner working for Spain who discovered the strait at the southernmost tip of South America

A. Florida

B. Ferdinand Magellan

_____ **2.** imaginary north-to-south line running down the middle of the Atlantic Ocean

C. Vikings

_____ **3.** "land of flowers"

D. line of demarcation

_____ **4.** complex interactions between peoples and ecologies set in motion by the arrival of European colonists in the Americas

E. Columbian Exchange

_____ **5.** a people who came from Scandinavia

DIRECTIONS: Multiple Choice In the blank at the left, write the letter of the choice
that best completes the statement or answers the question. *(10 points each)*

_____ **6.** Native Americans introduced the Europeans to new farming methods and
    A. crops.
    B. trade.
    C. types of livestock.
    D. religions.

_____ **7.** Christopher Columbus and his three ships reached the Bahamas and probably landed on what is today
    A. Grand Bahama Island.
    B. part of Cuba.
    C. Key West.
    D. San Salvador Island.

_____ **8.** What confirmed Portugal's right to control the route around Africa to India and confirmed Spain's claim to most of the newly discovered lands of America?
    A. the Treaty of Tordesillas
    B. the Magellan Treaty
    C. the Columbian Exchange
    D. Pope Alexander VI Proclamation

_____ **9.** Who became the first European to reach the west coast of the Americas in 1513?
    A. Vasco de Balboa
    B. Christopher Columbus
    C. Claudius Ptolemy
    D. Amerigo Vespucci

_____ **10.** What were the ships called that Vikings used to venture from their homeland beginning in the late A.D. 700s?
    A. canoes
    B. longboats
    C. caravels
    D. lateen sailboats

★ Chapter 1

Section Quiz 1-4

DIRECTIONS: Matching Match each item in Column A with the items in Column B. Write the correct letters in the blanks. *(10 points each)*

Column A

_____ **1.** founded the trading post of Quebec

_____ **2.** Native American woman who became one of Cortés's closest advisers

_____ **3.** a northern water route through North America to the Pacific Ocean

_____ **4.** the men who led the expeditions to conquer Central America

_____ **5.** a road that linked missions from San Diego to San Francisco

Column B

A. Northwest Passage

B. Malinche

C. El Camino Real

D. conquistadors

E. Samuel de Champlain

DIRECTIONS: Multiple Choice In the blank at the left, write the letter of the choice that best completes the statement or answers the question. *(10 points each)*

_____ **6.** On November 8, 1519, Spanish troops peacefully entered the Aztec capital of
    A. Cholula.
    B. Cajamarca.
    C. Tenochtitlán.
    D. Cibola.

_____ **7.** In 1526 Francisco Pizarro found the Inca Empire in
    A. Mexico.
    B. Peru.
    C. Canada.
    D. New France.

_____ **8.** What became the first permanent town established by Europeans in what is today the United States?
    A. New Orleans, Louisiana
    B. St. Augustine, Florida
    C. San Diego, California
    D. San Francisco, California

_____ **9.** The St. Lawrence River was discovered and mapped by the French explorer
    A. Jacques Cartier.
    B. Louis Joliet.
    C. Jacques Marquette.
    D. Giovanni da Verrazano.

_____ **10.** Who led the Spanish march into the Aztec Empire in 1519?
    A. Hernán Cortés
    B. Francisco Pizarro
    C. Hernando de Soto
    D. Francisco Vásquez de Coronado

The American Republic Since 1877

★ Chapter 1 Test, Form A

Score

Converging Cultures

DIRECTIONS: Matching Match each item in Column A with the items in Column B. Write the correct letters in the blanks. Some items in Column B will be used more than once. *(4 points each)*

Column A

_____ **1.** developed lamps, using whale oil and blubber for fuel

_____ **2.** created a mighty empire by conquering neighboring cities

_____ **3.** constructed multi-story buildings of adobe and stone

_____ **4.** had a talent for engineering and mathematics

_____ **5.** culture whose settlements featured huge geometric earthworks

_____ **6.** developed complex and accurate calendars

_____ **7.** sculpted imposing monuments, including 8-foot-high stone heads

_____ **8.** built irrigation canals to bring water to their crops

_____ **9.** practiced slash-and-burn agriculture

_____ **10.** built Cahokia, one of the largest early American cities

Column B

A. Olmec

B. Maya

C. Hohokam

D. Aztec

E. Anasazi

F. Hopewell

G. Iroquoians

H. Aleut

I. Mississippian people

DIRECTIONS: Multiple Choice Choose the item that best completes each statement or answers each question. Write the letter in the blank. *(4 points each)*

_____ **11.** Researchers believe that people arrived in America
  A. between 5,000 and 10,000 years ago.   **C.** between 30,000 and 40,000 years ago.
  B. between 15,000 and 30,000 years ago.   **D.** between 80,000 and 100,000 years ago.

_____ **12.** Seals and walruses were among the animals hunted by the
  A. Hopi.   **C.** Sioux.
  B. Zuni.   **D.** Inuit.

_____ **13.** The West African empires of Ghana, Mali, and Songhai prospered by trading
  A. gold and silver.   **C.** gold and obsidian.
  B. copper and obsidian.   **D.** gold and salt.

_____ **14.** The Renaissance was
  A. a Crusade to the New World.
  B. a rebirth of feudalism, in which kings gave estates to nobles in exchange for loyalty and military support.
  C. a period of economic decline.
  D. a period of renewed interest in the cultures of ancient Greece and Rome.

(continued)

★ **Chapter 1 Test, Form A**

Score

_____ **15.** When Columbus landed in the Bahamas, where did he think he was?
A. China **C.** the Indies
B. America **D.** Cuba

_____ **16.** Potatoes, brought back from America, became an important crop in Europe because
A. Europeans preferred the taste of potatoes to rice.
B. potatoes were resistant to the crop-killing diseases devastating European farms at the time.
C. potatoes returned nutrients to the soil that rye had removed.
D. the same amount of land planted in potatoes instead of rye could feed four times as many people.

_____ **17.** After contact with Europeans, millions of Native Americans died because
A. the Europeans killed them to take their gold.
B. they had no immunity to European diseases.
C. they could not survive in the harsh areas where Europeans required them to live.
D. the Europeans killed off the buffalo, their main source of food.

_____ **18.** What major advantage did the Spanish have over the Native Americans in Mexico?
A. wealth **C.** guns
B. agricultural knowledge **D.** abundance of food

_____ **19.** Francisco Pizarro captured and held hostage the Inca emperor
A. Montezuma. **C.** Malinche.
B. Quetzalcóatl. **D.** Atahualpa.

_____ **20.** Under the *encomienda* system, the Spanish *encomendero* was supposed to
A. protect the Native Americans and convert them to Christianity.
B. conquer the Native Americans and ship them to Cuba to work on Spanish farms.
C. enslave the Native Americans and force them to work in Spanish mines.
D. imprison the Native Americans until they accepted Spanish rule.

DIRECTIONS: Essay Answer one of the following questions on a separate sheet of paper. *(20 points)*

21. How did gold and sugar change slavery in West Africa?

22. Complete the diagram by naming the different levels of society in the class-based Spanish colonies. Then describe the people included at each level.

Class Structure in the Spanish Colonies

The American Republic Since 1877

Chapter 1 Test, Form B

Score

Converging Cultures

DIRECTIONS: Matching Match each item in Column A with the items in Column B.
Write the correct letters in the blanks. *(4 points each)*

Column A

_____ **1.** Norse people

_____ **2.** cowhands

_____ **3.** drew maps of a round world, complete with lines of
longitude and latitude

_____ **4.** gave the Pacific Ocean its name after reaching it by sailing
around the tip of South America

_____ **5.** Portuguese ships

_____ **6.** gave Florida its name and claimed it for Spain

_____ **7.** conquered the Inca Empire of Peru

_____ **8.** after hacking his way across Central America, became the
first European known to gaze upon the Pacific Ocean

_____ **9.** explored the coast of Labrador and may have spent a
winter in Newfoundland

_____ **10.** found a water route to Asia around the tip of Africa

Column B

A. Vasco de Balboa

B. Francisco Pizarro

C. Leif Ericsson

D. caravels

E. Vasco da Gama

F. Ferdinand
Magellan

G. vaqueros

H. Juan Ponce de
Leon

I. Vikings

J. Claudius Ptolemy

DIRECTIONS: Multiple Choice Choose the item that best completes each statement
or answers each question. Write the letter in the blank. *(4 points each)*

_____ **11.** Scientists determine how old objects are through
    A. radiocalcium dating.   **C.** radiocarbon dating.
    B. microwave dating.   **D.** DNA dating.

_____ **12.** Life for the Sioux and others on the Great Plains changed dramatically
after they began to
    A. grow crops.   **C.** tame horses.
    B. hunt buffalo.   **D.** fish.

_____ **13.** What effects logically resulted from the cause shown in the diagram?
    A. Effect 1: a surplus of food; Effect 2: better pay for field workers
    B. Effect 1: increased trade; Effect 2: freedom for many serfs
    C. Effect 1: increased trade; Effect 2: the revival of the Roman Empire
    D. Effect 1: a surplus of food; Effect 2: increased trade

Cause: The invention of a better plow and the horse collar in Western Europe in A.D. 1000.	→	Effect 1	→	Effect 2

(continued)

Chapter 1 Test, Form B

Score

_____ 14. As kingdoms unified in the mid-1400s, what four strong western European states emerged?

   A. Portugal, Spain, England, and France
   B. Portugal, Spain, England, and Germany
   C. Spain, England, France, and Germany
   D. Spain, England, France, and Italy

_____ 15. The astrolabe navigational device determines direction, latitude, and local time by using the position of the

   A. sun.   **C.** North Star.
   B. magnetic north.   **D.** moon.

_____ 16. Which country financed Columbus's voyage across the Atlantic in 1492?

   A. Portugal   **C.** Italy
   B. England   **D.** Spain

_____ 17. The Treaty of Tordesillas

   A. confirmed Spain's claim to the new lands of America.
   B. confirmed Portugal's right to control Africa.
   C. granted Spain control of everything north of an imaginary dividing line.
   D. granted Portugal the exclusive right to trade with India.

_____ 18. One of the first crops that Native Americans grew to make bread was

   A. wheat.   **C.** beans.
   B. squash.   **D.** maize.

_____ 19. The heads of extended families among the Iroquoian peoples were the

   A. elder men.   **C.** tribal chiefs.
   B. elder women.   **D.** spiritual leaders.

_____ 20. Most people enslaved in African societies had

   A. committed a crime and were being punished.
   B. been sold by their families.
   C. agreed to slavery in the hope of improving their social status later through marriage.
   D. been captured in war.

DIRECTIONS: Essay Answer one of the following questions on a separate sheet of paper. *(20 points)*

21. What were some of the results of the fall of the Roman Empire?

22. What kinds of interactions occurred during the Columbian Exchange that brought change to the world's cultures?

★ **Chapter 2**

Score

Section Quiz 2-1

DIRECTIONS: Matching Match each item in Column A with the items in Column B. Write the correct letters in the blanks. *(10 points each)*

Column A

_____ **1.** wanted to purify the Anglican Church of any Catholic elements

_____ **2.** published an attack on the Catholic Church, beginning the Protestant Reformation

_____ **3.** representatives in the first general assembly in Virginia

_____ **4.** founded by colonists from England in May 1607

_____ **5.** privately owned ships licensed by the government to attack the merchant ships of other countries

Column B

A. privateers

B. Martin Luther

C. Jamestown

D. burgesses

E. Puritans

DIRECTIONS: Multiple Choice In the blank at the left, write the letter of the choice that best completes the statement or answers the question. *(10 points each)*

_____ **6.** After Sir Humphrey Gilbert was lost at sea, his half-brother, Walter Raleigh, sent two ships to scout the American coastline and they reached an island the Native Americans called
  A. Maryland.
  B. Manhattan.
  C. Croatoan.
  D. Roanoke.

_____ **7.** Maryland was founded not by another joint-stock company but by one man, George Calvert, also known as
  A. Lord Baltimore.
  B. John Rolfe.
  C. Captain John Smith.
  D. Walter Raleigh.

_____ **8.** In late 1607, with winter approaching and the colony short of food, Captain John Smith began trading goods for food with the local Native Americans, a group called the
  A. Iroquois Confederacy.
  B. Aztecs.
  C. Powhatan Confederacy.
  D. Shoshone.

_____ **9.** Although John Cabot had sailed to present-day Nova Scotia in 1497, the English made no effort to colonize America for the next
  A. 10 years.
  B. 80 years.
  C. 20 years.
  D. 200 years.

_____ **10.** In England during the 1500s, a large market for wool developed and many landowners converted their estates into sheep farms by enclosing their land and evicting thousands in what is known as
  A. the Reformation.
  B. the headright system.
  C. the enclosure movement.
  D. joint-stock companies.

Name _____ Date _____ Class _____

 Chapter 2

Score

Section Quiz 2-2

DIRECTIONS: Matching Match each item in Column A with the items in Column B.
Write the correct letters in the blanks. *(10 points each)*

Column A

_____ **1.** people who owned stock in the Massachusetts Bay
Company

_____ **2.** a Native American man who taught the Pilgrims about
their new environment

_____ **3.** people whose religious beliefs differ from the majority

_____ **4.** began separating from the Anglican Church to form their
own congregations

_____ **5.** when large numbers of people left England

Column B

A. Squanto

B. Great Migration

C. Separatists

D. freemen

E. heretics

DIRECTIONS: Multiple Choice In the blank at the left, write the letter of the choice
that best completes the statement or answers the question. *(10 points each)*

_____ **6.** Anne Hutchinson and a few followers left Massachusetts and founded
the town of
A. Boston.
B. Providence.
C. Philadelphia.
D. Portsmouth.

_____ **7.** In 1636 the Reverend Thomas Hooker asked the General Court of
Massachusetts for permission to move his entire congregation to the
A. Connecticut River valley.
B. Mississippi River valley.
C. Hudson River valley.
D. St. Lawrence River valley.

_____ **8.** Tensions between Native Americans and the English peaked in 1675
when Plymouth Colony arrested, tried, and executed three Wampanoag
for a murder, touching off what came to be called
A. the Pequot War.
B. the Great Migration.
C. Providence.
D. King Philip's War.

_____ **9.** On September 16, 1620, 102 passengers set off from England for
A. Nova Scotia.
B. Virginia.
C. Florida.
D. Boston.

_____ **10.** Under the charter of the Massachusetts Bay Company, all of the freemen
together were called the
A. Fundamental Orders.
B. Separatists.
C. General Court.
D. Pequot.

The American Republic Since 1877

★ **Chapter 2**

Section Quiz 2-3

DIRECTIONS: Matching Match each item in Column A with the items in Column B.
Write the correct letters in the blanks. *(10 points each)*

Column A

_____ **1.** opposition to war as a means of settling disputes

_____ **2.** restored the monarchy to England when he took the throne in 1660

_____ **3.** began when troops were sent into the English Parliament to arrest several Puritan leaders

_____ **4.** wealthy member of Parliament who founded Georgia

_____ **5.** Quaker who founded Pennsylvania

Column B

A. Charles II

B. William Penn

C. pacifism

D. James Oglethorpe

E. English Civil War

DIRECTIONS: Multiple Choice In the blank at the left, write the letter of the choice
that best completes the statement or answers the question. *(10 points each)*

_____ **6.** Eventually, what did the farmers in North Carolina begin to grow?
    A. tobacco   **C.** cotton
    B. sugarcane   **D.** corn

_____ **7.** After King Charles took New Netherland from the Dutch by force, it was renamed
    A. Virginia.   **C.** Philadelphia.
    B. Manhattan.   **D.** New York.

_____ **8.** In 1609 navigator Henry Hudson explored the Hudson River valley for a group of
    A. Spanish conquistadors.   **C.** English Puritans.
    B. English Quakers.   **D.** Dutch merchants.

_____ **9.** In 1682 William Penn bought three counties south of Pennsylvania, which became the colony of
    A. Delaware.   **C.** New York.
    B. South Carolina.   **D.** Quakers.

_____ **10.** The first product South Carolina exported in large quantity was
    A. deerskin.   **C.** rice.
    B. sugarcane.   **D.** tobacco.

Chapter 2

Section Quiz 2-4

DIRECTIONS: Matching Match each item in Column A with the items in Column B. Write the correct letters in the blanks. *(10 points each)*

Column A

_____ **1.** raising only enough crops to feed their families

_____ **2.** people who had money to invest in new businesses

_____ **3.** actual ownership of one human being by another

_____ **4.** wealthy plantation owners also referred to as Southern gentry

_____ **5.** open public areas where small communities of farmers centered their life

Column B

A. town commons

B. capitalists

C. subsistence farming

D. planter elite

E. chattel slavery

DIRECTIONS: Multiple Choice In the blank at the left, write the letter of the choice that best completes the statement or answers the question. *(10 points each)*

_____ **6.** What were held in New England that helped set the stage for the American Revolution and the emergence of democratic government?
   A. church covenants
   B. "Holy Watchings"
   C. capitalist meetings
   D. town meetings

_____ **7.** What was the South's first successful cash crop, or crop grown primarily for market?
   A. tobacco
   B. cotton
   C. sugarcane
   D. indigo

_____ **8.** Instead of trading directly with England, colonial merchants developed systems involving a three-way exchange of goods called
   A. bills of exchange.
   B. triangular trade.
   C. entrepreneurs.
   D. tariffs.

_____ **9.** Blessed with fertile land and a long growing season, the Middle Colonies included Delaware, New York, Pennsylvania, and
   A. Rhode Island.
   B. Maine.
   C. New Jersey.
   D. North Carolina.

_____ **10.** What event convinced many wealthy planters in Virginia that land should be made available to backcountry farmers?
   A. war with a Susquehannock group
   B. rise of triangular trade
   C. Bacon's Rebellion
   D. creation of a slave code

The American Republic Since 1877

⭐ **Chapter 2**

Section Quiz 2-5

DIRECTIONS: Matching Match each item in Column A with the items in Column B. Write the correct letters in the blanks. *(10 points each)*

Column A

_____ **1.** a set of ideas about the world economy and how it works

_____ **2.** resurgence of religious fervor in the 1700s

_____ **3.** German immigrants in Pennsylvania who often became prosperous farmers

_____ **4.** required that all goods shipped to and from the colonies be carried on English ships

_____ **5.** when a group of enslaved Africans in South Carolina rebelled against their white overseers

Column B

A. Great Awakening

B. Navigation Act of 1660

C. Pennsylvania Dutch

D. Stono Rebellion

E. mercantilism

DIRECTIONS: Multiple Choice In the blank at the left, write the letter of the choice that best completes the statement or answers the question. *(10 points each)*

_____ **6.** One idea of the English philosopher John Locke that struck a responsive chord with American colonists was that all people were born with certain
   A. sins.
   B. natural rights.
   C. restrictions in society.
   D. places in the social order.

_____ **7.** What was the name of the period during the 1700s when thinkers believed that people should use reason and natural law to shape society?
   A. the Glorious Revolution
   B. the Enlightenment
   C. the Great Awakening
   D. the Age of Reason

_____ **8.** Mercantilists believed that to become wealthy and powerful, a country had to accumulate gold and silver and also be self-sufficient in
   A. government.
   B. industry.
   C. trade.
   D. raw materials.

_____ **9.** No group in the American colonies endured lower status or hardship than the
   A. Scotch-Irish.
   B. Pennsylvania Dutch.
   C. enslaved Africans.
   D. Portuguese Jews.

_____ **10.** In 1686 the English government merged the colonies of Massachusetts, Plymouth, and Rhode Island to create a new royal province called
   A. the Dominion of New England.
   B. the Pennsylvania Dutch.
   C. the United Dominion.
   D. the Dominion of American Colonies.

★ **Chapter 2 Test, Form A**

The English Arrive in America

DIRECTIONS: Matching Match each item in Column A with the items in Column B.
Write the correct letters in the blanks. *(4 points each)*

Column A

Column B

_____ **1.** stockholder in the Massachusetts Bay Company

_____ **2.** named his territory Maine

_____ **3.** founder of Providence

_____ **4.** founded Portsmouth after being banished from
Massachusetts for heresy

_____ **5.** person who explored the region that the Dutch called New
Netherland

_____ **6.** named his capital Philadelphia, meaning "city of brotherly
love"

_____ **7.** first successful cash crop of Jamestown

_____ **8.** appointed as the first governor-general of the Dominion of
New England

_____ **9.** major product in the New England colonies

_____ **10.** people who lived in cities and used their skills to make
products

A. Henry Hudson

B. tobacco

C. skilled artisans

D. William Penn

E. Edmund Andros

F. lumber

G. John Winthrop

H. Fernando Gorges

I. Anne Hutchinson

J. Roger Williams

DIRECTIONS: Multiple Choice Choose the item that best completes each statement
or answers each question. Write the letter in the blank. *(4 points each)*

_____ **11.** The General Court of the Massachusetts Bay Colony was made up of
  A. all Puritan men.
  B. people who owned stock in the Massachusetts Bay Company.
  C. judges elected by the freemen.
  D. all freemen.

_____ **12.** The Native American Mohegan and Narraganset groups allied with John
  Mason's army to attack the
  A. Wampanoag.   **C.** Pequot.
  B. Croatoan.   **D.** Powhatan.

_____ **13.** Few Native Americans were left in New England after
  A. King Philip's War.   **C.** the Wampanoag War.
  B. the Pequot War.   **D.** the Great Migration.

(continued)

Chapter 2 Test, Form A

Score

_____ **14.** After the English Civil War, the English government viewed the colonies as
   A. risky business ventures.
   B. allies against its rival Spain.
   C. sources of raw materials.
   D. places to send criminals.

_____ **15.** William Penn acquired the land that is now Pennsylvania
   A. by inheriting it from his father.
   B. as settlement for a debt King Charles owed his father.
   C. as a reward for seizing Dutch land.
   D. by buying it from the Powhatans.

_____ **16.** Which of the following was NOT a Quaker belief?
   A. War was not an appropriate means for settling disputes.
   B. The Bible was the supreme authority.
   C. Each person had an "inner light" from God.
   D. There was no need for ministers.

_____ **17.** The people at the top of colonial New England's urban society were
   A. merchants.
   B. artisans.
   C. gentry.
   D. yeomen.

_____ **18.** The Stono Rebellion was an uprising of
   A. colonists against the Navigation Acts.
   B. enslaved Africans wanting freedom.
   C. English Protestants against James II.
   D. Southern backcountry farmers.

_____ **19.** Mercantilists believed that to become wealthy and powerful, a country had to
   A. constantly increase production.
   B. accumulate gold and silver.
   C. find new overseas markets.
   D. steadily raise prices.

_____ **20.** Africans were welcome at _____ revivals.
   A. Presbyterian
   B. Congregationalist
   C. Methodist
   D. Baptist

DIRECTIONS: Essay Answer one of the following questions on a separate sheet of paper. *(20 points)*

21. Why did the English not try to colonize America for 80 years after Cabot's arrival?

22. Identify the two movements that complete the diagram and describe each movement.

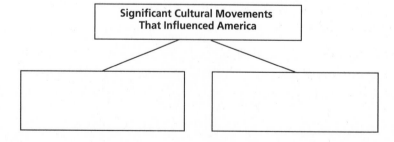

The American Republic Since 1877

⭐ **Chapter 2 Test, Form B**

Score

The English Arrive in America

DIRECTIONS: Matching Match each item in Column A with the items in Column B.
Write the correct letters in the blanks. *(4 points each)*

Column A

_____ **1.** main product of the Middle Colonies

_____ **2.** settlers who publicly uttered ideas contrary to accepted Puritan beliefs

_____ **3.** overthrow of King Charles I by Parliament troops

_____ **4.** German immigrants

_____ **5.** Separatists who fled to Holland before coming to America

_____ **6.** raids touched off when Massachusetts sent troops to punish Native Americans for the murder of two traders

_____ **7.** spread of the ideas of Martin Luther across western Europe

_____ **8.** fight touched off when the Plymouth Colony tried and executed three Native Americans for murder

_____ **9.** used to make blue dye for cloth

_____ **10.** bloodless change of power that brought Protestant rulers William and Mary to the throne of England

Column B

A. Pennsylvania Dutch

B. indigo

C. Glorious Revolution

D. Pilgrims

E. Protestant Reformation

F. wheat

G. Pequot War

H. heretics

I. King Philip's War

J. English Civil War

DIRECTIONS: Multiple Choice Choose the item that best completes each statement or answers each question. Write the letter in the blank. *(4 points each)*

_____ **11.** Along with religious persecution, the Puritans immigrated to America to escape
 A. harsh conditions in Holland where they had fled first in 1608.
 B. unfair taxation.
 C. forced enlistment in the military.
 D. depression in England's wool industry that caused them economic hardship.

_____ **12.** Thomas Hooker disagreed with the Massachusetts colony, because he believed that
 A. enslaving people was immoral.
 B. the colony's moral code was not strict enough.
 C. everyone should be allowed to vote, not just church members.
 D. men should be allowed to have more than one wife.

_____ **13.** The Georgia colony was founded as a
 A. plantation community.
 B. harbor for ships from England.
 C. refuge for Puritans.
 D. place where debtors could start over.

(continued)

★ **Chapter 2 Test, Form B**

_____ **14.** The Southern Colonies developed an economy based on
   A. manufacturing.
   B. fishing.
   C. agriculture.
   D. shipbuilding.

_____ **15.** Bacon's Rebellion convinced many wealthy planters to
   A. allow all free men to vote.
   B. build new forts along the frontier.
   C. have land available for farmers.
   D. provide more jobs for tenant farmers.

_____ **16.** To many English settlers in the early 1600s, enslaving Africans was acceptable at first because
   A. the Africans were not white.
   B. the Africans were poor.
   C. enslaved children were often freed.
   D. the Africans were not Christians.

_____ **17.** According to the map, what was the second colony to be founded in New England?
   A. Boston
   B. Portsmouth
   C. Salem
   D. New Haven

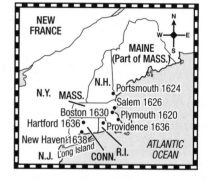

_____ **18.** The result of the Staple Act was
   A. more manufactured goods flowing to the colonies.
   B. greater trading opportunities for the colonies with Europe.
   C. greater demand for the colonies' raw materials in England.
   D. higher prices of goods the colonies imported from Europe.

_____ **19.** John Locke asserted that all people were born with the right to
   A. life, liberty, and pursuit of happiness.
   B. life, liberty, and self-government.
   C. life, liberty, and property.
   D. life and self-government.

_____ **20.** The revival of religious feeling in the 1700s was called
   A. the Enlightenment.
   B. the Glorious Revolution.
   C. the Great Awakening.
   D. the Bloodless Revolution.

DIRECTIONS: Essay Answer one of the following questions on a separate sheet of paper. *(20 points)*

21. Why did people agree to become indentured servants in the early days of Virginia and Maryland?

22. What were the benefits and drawbacks of the English mercantilist policy for the colonies?

The American Republic Since 1877

⭐ **Chapter 3**

Section Quiz 3-1

DIRECTIONS: Matching Match each item in Column A with the items in Column B.
Write the correct letters in the blanks. *(10 points each)*

Column A

_____ **1.** women's groups that began spinning their own rough cloth, called "homespun"

_____ **2.** intended to make the colonies pay more for their own defense

_____ **3.** changed the tax rates on imports of raw sugar and molasses

_____ **4.** when merchants pledged not to buy any British goods until Parliament repealed the Stamp Act

_____ **5.** a proposal that the colonies join together to form a federal government

Column B

A. nonimportation agreement

B. Quartering Act

C. Albany Plan of Union

D. Daughters of Liberty

E. Sugar Act

DIRECTIONS: Multiple Choice In the blank at the left, write the letter of the choice
that best completes the statement or answers the question. *(10 points each)*

_____ **6.** The Royal Proclamation of 1763 declared that colonists could not settle west of a line drawn north to south along the
    A. Chesapeake Bay.   **C.** Appalachian Mountains.
    B. Ohio River.   **D.** Hudson River.

_____ **7.** Parliament had imposed many taxes on trade, but what was the first direct tax Britain placed on the colonists?
    A. stamp tax   **C.** paper tax
    B. sugar tax   **D.** glass tax

_____ **8.** Fighting between the British and French that began in 1754 in North America is known as
    A. Braddock's War.   **C.** the British and French War.
    B. the Seven Years' War.   **D.** the French and Indian War.

_____ **9.** To help customs officers arrest smugglers, the Revenue Act legalized the use of general search warrants called
    A. Declaratory Acts.   **C.** customs duties.
    B. writs of assistance.   **D.** nonimportation agreements.

_____ **10.** On March 5, 1770, a crowd of colonists began taunting and throwing snowballs at a British soldier guarding a customs house, which resulted in the
    A. formation of the Sons of Liberty.   **C.** Virginia Resolves.
    B. French and Indian War.   **D.** Boston Massacre.

Chapter 3

Section Quiz 3-2

DIRECTIONS: Matching Match each item in Column A with the items in Column B. Write the correct letters in the blanks. *(10 points each)*

Column A

_____ **1.** a special unit of militia in the town of Concord

_____ **2.** where a largely untrained colonial militia stood up to one of the world's most feared armies

_____ **3.** Americans who backed Britain

_____ **4.** pamphlet written by Thomas Paine that attacked the monarchy

_____ **5.** created by each colony to communicate with the other colonies about British activities

Column B

A. Loyalists

B. *Common Sense*

C. committee of correspondence

D. Battle of Bunker Hill

E. minutemen

DIRECTIONS: Multiple Choice In the blank at the left, write the letter of the choice that best completes the statement or answers the question. *(10 points each)*

_____ **6.** With what laws did the British intend to dissuade other colonies from challenging British authority as Massachusetts had with the Boston Tea Party?
  A. Coercive Acts
  B. Tea Act
  C. Quebec Act
  D. Suffolk Resolves

_____ **7.** Where did the First Continental Congress meet on September 5, 1774?
  A. New York
  B. Albany
  C. Philadelphia
  D. Boston

_____ **8.** What document expressed loyalty to the king, but condemned the Coercive Acts and stated that the colonies would enter into a nonimportation association?
  A. Continental Association
  B. Olive Branch Petition
  C. Declaration of Independence
  D. Declaration of Rights and Grievances

_____ **9.** What became known as the Intolerable Acts in the colonies?
  A. the Tea Act and Quebec Act
  B. the Quebec Act and Coercive Acts
  C. the Coercive Acts and Tea Act
  D. the Coercive Acts and Olive Branch Petition

_____ **10.** When British troops set out for Concord on a road that took them past the town of Lexington, two men spread the alarm: Paul Revere and
  A. George Washington.
  B. John Dickinson.
  C. Joseph Galloway.
  D. William Dawes.

The American Republic Since 1877

★ **Chapter 3**

Score

Section Quiz 3-3

DIRECTIONS: Matching Match each item in Column A with the items in Column B.
Write the correct letters in the blanks. *(10 points each)*

Column A

_____ **1.** licenses to privateers

_____ **2.** wealthy Pennsylvania merchant and banker who pledged
large sums for the war effort and arranged for foreign
loans

_____ **3.** place of an unexpected turning point in the war

_____ **4.** had been an American commander early in the war but
had later sold the British military information

_____ **5.** known as the "Swamp Fox," he led the most famous
guerrilla unit in the South

Column B

A. letters of marque

B. Francis Marion

C. Robert Morris

D. Saratoga

E. Benedict Arnold

DIRECTIONS: Multiple Choice In the blank at the left, write the letter of the choice
that best completes the statement or answers the question. *(10 points each)*

_____ **6.** In the summer of 1776, the Continental Army, led by George Washington,
was unable to prevent the British from capturing
A. Boston.
B. New York City.
C. Philadelphia.
D. St. Augustine.

_____ **7.** Perhaps the most famous naval battle of the war happened near Britain
in September 1779, and involved the American naval officer
A. John Paul Jones.
B. Charles Cornwallis.
C. Patrick Ferguson.
D. George Rogers Clark.

_____ **8.** The local militias were untrained, but they were adept at tactics like
sneak attacks and hit-and-run ambushes called
A. ambushing.
B. campaigns of surprise.
C. small unit warfare.
D. guerrilla warfare.

_____ **9.** A band of "overmountain men" in the Appalachian Mountains
assembled a militia force and intercepted British cavalry officer Patrick
Ferguson and his army at
A. Charles Town.
B. Savannah.
C. Yorktown.
D. Kings Mountain.

_____ **10.** On the night of December 25, 1776, George Washington led some 2,400
men across the icy
A. Delaware River.
B. Hudson River.
C. Chesapeake Bay.
D. St. Lawrence River.

★ **Chapter 3**

Section Quiz 3-4

DIRECTIONS: Matching Match each item in Column A with the items in Column B. Write the correct letters in the blanks. *(10 points each)*

Column A

_____ **1.** better known as Molly Pitcher, she carried water to Patriot gunners during the Battle of Monmouth

_____ **2.** painted inspiring portraits of Washington and other Patriot leaders

_____ **3.** the power of a church, backed by the government, to make people worship in a certain way

_____ **4.** approval

_____ **5.** decline in the value of money

Column B

A. ratification

B. inflation

C. "ecclesiastical tyranny"

D. Mary Ludwig Hays

E. Charles Willson Peale

DIRECTIONS: Multiple Choice In the blank at the left, write the letter of the choice that best completes the statement or answers the question. *(10 points each)*

_____ **6.** Wartime debts and the trade imbalance with Britain plunged the new United States into a severe economic slowdown called
   A. an inflation.
   B. a recession.
   C. a depression.
   D. a republic.

_____ **7.** Many states attached a list of rights to their constitutions, which began in 1776 when George Mason drafted Virginia's
   A. Declaration of Rights.
   B. Bill of Rights.
   C. Articles of Confederation.
   D. Statute of Religious Freedom.

_____ **8.** Opposition to slavery had been growing steadily even before the Revolution, especially in the
   A. Appalachian Mountains.
   B. Southwest.
   C. Northern and Middle Colonies.
   D. South.

_____ **9.** What provided the basis for governing western lands and developing them into states?
   A. Articles of Confederation
   B. Confederation Congress
   C. Land Ordinance of 1785
   D. Northwest Ordinance of 1787

_____ **10.** In November 1777, the Continental Congress adopted a plan for a loose union of the states under the authority of Congress called the
   A. Constitution of the United States of America.
   B. Declaration of Independence.
   C. Bill of Rights.
   D. Articles of Confederation and Perpetual Union.

★ **Chapter 3**

Score

Section Quiz 3-5

DIRECTIONS: Matching Match each item in Column A with the items in Column B.
Write the correct letters in the blanks. *(10 points each)*

Column A

_____ **1.** rule by the people

_____ **2.** people who wanted to strengthen the central government

_____ **3.** modified the Articles of Confederation to make the central government stronger

_____ **4.** changes to the Constitution

_____ **5.** two houses of Congress that would make the laws

Column B

A. New Jersey Plan

B. legislative branch of government

C. amendments

D. popular sovereignty

E. nationalists

DIRECTIONS: Multiple Choice In the blank at the left, write the letter of the choice
that best completes the statement or answers the question. *(10 points each)*

_____ **6.** The system created as a way for each branch of government to monitor
and limit the power of the others is called

A. popular sovereignty.   **C.** checks and balances.

B. federalism.   **D.** impeachment.

_____ **7.** Arguments for ratification of the Constitution were summarized in *The
Federalist*, a collection of 85 essays written by Alexander Hamilton, John
Jay, and

A. James Madison.   **C.** Sam Adams.

B. Patrick Henry.   **D.** George Washington.

_____ **8.** The real issue, in the Antifederalists' minds, was what would be
supreme—the national government or

A. the president.   **C.** the court system.

B. state governments.   **D.** industry.

_____ **9.** To aid ratification of the Constitution, the Federalists promised to
support an amendment that would reserve for the states all powers not
specifically granted to the federal government and to attach

A. more branches of government.   **C.** new checks and balances.

B. new state borders.   **D.** a bill of rights.

_____ **10.** The compromise that stated every five enslaved people in a state would
count as three free persons for determining both representation and taxes
was called the

A. Connecticut Compromise.   **C.** system of checks and balances.

B. Federalists Plan.   **D.** Three-Fifths Compromise.

Name _____ Date _____ Class _____

Score _____

The American Revolution

DIRECTIONS: Matching Match each item in Column A with the items in Column B.
Write the correct letters in the blanks. *(4 points each)*

Column A

_____ 1. led troops that defeated the British along the Ohio River, leaving the United States in control of the region

_____ 2. surrendered to the Americans at Yorktown

_____ 3. helped win ratification in New York by delaying the final vote until news arrived that New Hampshire and Virginia had both ratified

_____ 4. main author of the Virginia Plan

_____ 5. American traitor

_____ 6. led the troops that defeated the British at Yorktown

_____ 7. Patriot whose initial objections to the Constitution eventually led to the first ten amendments

_____ 8. "No parts of His Majesty's dominions can be taxed without their consent. . . ."

_____ 9. prime minister who introduced the Sugar Act

_____ 10. "Swamp Fox"

Column B

A. James Madison

B. Alexander Hamilton

C. Charles Cornwallis

D. Sam Adams

E. George Rogers Clark

F. Anthony Wayne

G. Benedict Arnold

H. Francis Marion

I. George Grenville

J. James Otis

DIRECTIONS: Multiple Choice Choose the item that best completes each statement or answers each question. Write the letter in the blank. *(4 points each)*

_____ 11. The first skirmish of the French and Indian War occurred because
  A. the French organized Native American attacks on frontier settlements.
  B. both the French and the British wanted the Ohio River valley.
  C. the French ambushed a British detachment near Quebec City.
  D. both the French and the British claimed Louisiana.

_____ 12. The Albany Plan of Union proposed that
  A. the Iroquois join with the British.   **C.** the colonies join with the British.
  B. the colonies join together.   **D.** the colonies join with the French.

_____ 13. American forces suffered their greatest defeat of the Revolutionary War at
  A. Charles Town.   **C.** Philadelphia.
  B. New York City.   **D.** Valley Forge.

_____ 14. The Articles of Confederation gave the Confederation Congress all of the following powers EXCEPT the power to
  A. declare war.   **C.** raise armies.
  B. impose taxes.   **D.** sign treaties.

(continued)

_____ **15.** To raise money, the Confederation Congress
　　A. imposed income taxes.
　　B. regulated trade.
　　C. sold land west of the Appalachians.
　　D. required businesses to pay taxes.

_____ **16.** Loyalists could not recover the property confiscated from them during
the Revolutionary War because
　　A. the Treaty of Paris did not grant them this right.
　　B. the Confederation Congress could not compel the states to fulfill this agreement.
　　C. they owed debts to American lenders, and their property was used as repayment.
　　D. they were considered traitors with no rights of citizenship in the new nation.

_____ **17.** Shays's Rebellion started because
　　A. Massachusetts issued paper money to pay off its debts instead of raising taxes.
　　B. merchants refused to accept paper money in payment for debts.
　　C. Massachusetts raised taxes to pay off its debts instead of issuing paper money.
　　D. New York taxed goods coming into the state from Connecticut and New Jersey.

_____ **18.** The Great Compromise proposed that in the House of Representatives,
　　A. each state would have equal representation.
　　B. state legislators would choose the representatives.
　　C. the states would be represented according to the size of their populations.
　　D. all enslaved people could be counted when determining representatives.

_____ **19.** The Three-Fifths Compromise specified that
　　A. small states would have three-fifths the number of votes as large states.
　　B. every three enslaved people in a state would count as five free persons.
　　C. every five enslaved people in a state would count as three free persons.
　　D. three-fifths of enslaved people in a state could not be counted.

_____ **20.** Amending the Constitution requires
　　A. proposal and ratification.
　　B. impeachment and ratification.
　　C. unanimous approval.
　　D. unanimous ratification.

DIRECTIONS: Essay Answer one of the following questions on a separate sheet of
paper. *(20 points)*

21. Complete the diagram by naming the three branches of the federal government
set forth in the Constitution. Then describe each branch and its role.

```
          ┌──────────────────────────┐
          │  Branches of Government  │
          └──────────────────────────┘
         ┌──────────────┼──────────────┐
    ┌─────────┐    ┌─────────┐    ┌─────────┐
    │         │    │         │    │         │
    └─────────┘    └─────────┘    └─────────┘
```

22. What problems resulted from the fact that the Confederation Congress was not
allowed to regulate trade with other countries or among the states?

★ **Chapter 3 Test, Form B**

Score

The American Revolution

DIRECTIONS: Matching Match each item in Column A with the items in Column B. Write the correct letters in the blanks. *(4 points each)*

Column A

_____ **1.** required the colonies to pay more for their own defense

_____ **2.** placed new taxes on imported goods but also violated several traditional English rights

_____ **3.** prohibited colonists from settling west of an imaginary line running north to south along the Appalachian Mountains

_____ **4.** legalized the use of writs of assistance

_____ **5.** banned the use of paper money in the colonies

_____ **6.** asserted that Parliament had the power to make laws for the colonies

_____ **7.** first direct tax Britain had ever placed on the colonists

_____ **8.** arranged for foreign loans to finance the American war effort

_____ **9.** warned Concord that the British were coming

_____ **10.** voiced the idea on which the Connecticut Compromise was based

Column B

A. Stamp Act

B. Currency Act of 1764

C. Revenue Act of 1767

D. Roger Sherman

E. Declaratory Act

F. Robert Morris

G. Royal Proclamation of 1763

H. Quartering Act

I. Sugar Act

J. Samuel Prescott

DIRECTIONS: Multiple Choice Choose the item that best completes each statement or answers each question. Write the letter in the blank. *(4 points each)*

_____ **11.** The British brought temporary peace to the colonies after the Boston Massacre by repealing most of the
   A. Stamp Act.
   B. Townshend Act.
   C. Sugar Act.
   D. Quartering Act.

_____ **12.** The purpose of the Albany Conference was to negotiate
   A. a peace treaty with the British.
   B. a repeal of the Stamp Act.
   C. an alliance with the Iroquois.
   D. an end to the tea boycott.

_____ **13.** In the *Gaspee* Affair,
   A. the British seized an American ship without a warrant.
   B. the colonists burned a British ship that had run aground.
   C. the colonists seized a cargo of tea from a British ship.
   D. the colonists forced a British ship carrying tea to return home.

_____ **14.** The colonists protested the Stamp Act by
   A. refusing to sell goods to Britain.
   B. refusing to buy goods from Britain.
   C. dumping tea into Boston Harbor.
   D. dissolving the Massachusetts assembly.

(continued)

⭐ **Chapter 3 Test, Form B**

Score

_____ **15.** The American victory at Saratoga was a turning point in the war because
   A. it was the last British offensive of the war.
   B. it convinced Spain to enter the war on the American side.
   C. it convinced France to send arms and supplies to the Americans.
   D. it convinced France to commit troops to the American cause.

_____ **16.** The Virginia Statute for Religious Freedom declared that
   A. no man may be denied his rights on the basis of his religion.
   B. the state could not collect taxes for churches.
   C. churches had the right to collect taxes from their members.
   D. churches did not have to pay taxes.

_____ **17.** The laws that became known as the "Intolerable Acts" in the colonies were the Coercive Acts and the
   A. Sugar Act.   **C.** Quebec Act.
   B. Stamp Act.   **D.** Tea Act.

_____ **18.** Southern leaders showed little interest in abolishing slavery because
   A. they believed that enslaved Africans were unsuitable for freedom.
   B. the South relied on slavery to sustain its economy.
   C. enslaved Africans had fought with the British during the American Revolution.
   D. they believed enslaved Africans were better off living on plantations.

_____ **19.** The Virginia Plan would benefit
   A. small states.   **C.** large states.
   B. wealthy planters.   **D.** Southern slaveholding states.

_____ **20.** The real issue for opponents of the Constitution was whether a national government
   A. was really needed.   **C.** could regulate trade.
   B. or state governments would be supreme.   **D.** should impose taxes.

DIRECTIONS: Essay Answer one of the following questions on a separate sheet of paper. *(20 points)*

21. Why were many colonists angry about the Sugar Act?

22. The diagram shows the basic "building blocks" that form a republic. Explain what a republic is by describing the role of each of its three main parts.

Building Blocks of a Republic		
Representatives	Citizens	Constitution and Laws

★ **Chapter 4**

Score

Section Quiz 4-1

DIRECTIONS: Matching Match each item in Column A with the items in Column B.
Write the correct letters in the blanks. *(10 points each)*

Column A

_____ **1.** people living in the country who were not citizens

_____ **2.** powers specifically mentioned in the Constitution

_____ **3.** powers not explicitly listed in the Constitution but necessary for the government to do its job

_____ **4.** granted the United States the right to navigate the Mississippi and to deposit goods at the port of New Orleans

_____ **5.** paid by the manufacturer of a product and passed on to those who buy the product

Column B

A. Pinckney's Treaty

B. enumerated powers

C. excise tax

D. aliens

E. implied powers

DIRECTIONS: Multiple Choice In the blank at the left, write the letter of the choice
that best completes the statement or answers the question. *(10 points each)*

_____ **6.** During Washington's first term in office, Congress had split into factions over disagreements about Alexander Hamilton's
    A. judicial program.   **C.** foreign policies.
    B. financial program.   **D.** executive program.

_____ **7.** In 1798 the United States and France were fighting an undeclared war at sea, which came to be known as the
    A. Alien Enemies War.   **C.** XYZ Affair.
    B. Whiskey Rebellion.   **D.** Quasi-War.

_____ **8.** One of the most important acts of Congress during its first session in 1789 was the introduction of the
    A. Bill of Rights.   **C.** Bank of the United States.
    B. Sedition Act.   **D.** excise tax.

_____ **9.** The theory that if the federal government did something unconstitutional, the state could interpose between the federal government and the people to stop the action is called
    A. interposition.   **C.** implied powers.
    B. nullification.   **D.** sedition.

_____ **10.** What did John Jay persuade the British to give the United States so that Americans would not be discriminated against when they traded with Britain?
    A. enumerated powers   **C.** most-favored nation status
    B. tariffs on trade   **D.** interposition

⭐ **Chapter 4**

Section Quiz 4-2

DIRECTIONS: Matching Match each item in Column A with the items in Column B.
Write the correct letters in the blanks. *(10 points each)*

Column A

_____ **1.** the Supreme Court's power to decide whether laws passed by Congress are constitutional and to strike down those that are not

_____ **2.** a legalized form of kidnapping

_____ **3.** members of Congress who wanted to declare war on Britain

_____ **4.** a government ban on trade with other countries

_____ **5.** called for constitutional amendments to increase New England's political power

Column B

A. impressment

B. War Hawks

C. embargo

D. Hartford Convention

E. judicial review

DIRECTIONS: Multiple Choice In the blank at the left, write the letter of the choice
that best completes the statement or answers the question. *(10 points each)*

_____ **6.** Who mapped much of the upper Mississippi in 1805, and in 1806 headed west to Colorado?
   A. Meriwether Lewis
   B. Zebulon Pike
   C. William Clark
   D. Napoleon Bonaparte

_____ **7.** One of the first acts of the new Republican Congress was to repeal the Judiciary Act of 1801, abolishing the offices of the
   A. State Department.
   B. Department of the Treasury.
   C. cabinet.
   D. "midnight judges."

_____ **8.** The Lewis and Clark expedition not only provided a wealth of information about Louisiana, it also gave the United States a claim to the
   A. Yukon Territory.
   B. Oregon Territory.
   C. Northeast Territory.
   D. Great Lakes region.

_____ **9.** What stated that if either France or Britain removed its trade restrictions, the United States would stop importing goods from the other nation?
   A. Treaty of Greenville
   B. Embargo Act of 1807
   C. Macon's Bill Number Two
   D. Non-Importation Act

_____ **10.** What was the primary objective of the United States at the start of the War of 1812?
   A. conquering Britain
   B. conquering Mexico
   C. conquering France
   D. conquering Canada

The American Republic Since 1877

 **Chapter 4**

Score

Section Quiz 4-3

DIRECTIONS: Matching Match each item in Column A with the items in Column B. Write the correct letters in the blanks. *(10 points each)*

Column A

_____ **1.** a Native American group

_____ **2.** Supreme Court case that dealt with interstate commerce

_____ **3.** Chief Justice of the United States

_____ **4.** led U.S. troops into Florida in 1818

_____ **5.** protected American manufacturers by taxing imports

Column B

A. *Gibbons* v. *Ogden*

B. Andrew Jackson

C. protective tariff

D. Seminoles

E. John Marshall

DIRECTIONS: Multiple Choice In the blank at the left, write the letter of the choice that best completes the statement or answers the question. *(10 points each)*

_____ **6.** Spain ceded all of Florida to the United States in the
  A. Adams-Onís Treaty.
  B. Monroe Doctrine.
  C. McCulloch-Florida Treaty.
  D. Gibbons-Ogden Treaty.

_____ **7.** Chief Justice John Marshall interpreted the Constitution broadly to support
  A. military power.
  B. judicial power.
  C. federal power.
  D. state power.

_____ **8.** In 1816 Senator John C. Calhoun of South Carolina introduced a bill proposing the
  A. Monroe Doctrine.
  B. Second Bank of the United States.
  C. Adams-Onís Treaty.
  D. regulation of interstate commerce.

_____ **9.** The Monroe Doctrine declared that the American continents should no longer be viewed as open to
  A. foreign industry.
  B. European visitors.
  C. immigration.
  D. colonization.

_____ **10.** What did a Boston newspaper, the *Columbian Centinal*, declare had dawned after the War of 1812?
  A. Era of Good Feelings
  B. Era of Isolationism
  C. Era of the Republicans
  D. Era of Nationalism

★ **Chapter 4 Test, Form A**

Score

Federalists and Republicans

DIRECTIONS: Matching Match each item in Column A with the items in the diagram. Write the correct letters from the diagram in the blanks. *(4 points each)*

Column A

_____ **1.** Supreme Court

_____ **2.** Department of State

_____ **3.** Office of the Attorney General

_____ **4.** Department of the Treasury

_____ **5.** Department of War

A Thomas Jefferson	**B** Alexander Hamilton
	C Henry Knox
Federal Bureaucracy	
E John Jay	**D** Edmund Randolph

DIRECTIONS: Matching Match the political parties in Column B with the facts about them in Column A. Write the correct letters in the blanks. The letters will be used more than once. *(4 points each)*

Column A

_____ **6.** rights of states over the power of the federal government

_____ **7.** government should be led by the wealthy and educated

_____ **8.** manufacturing and trade are the basis of national wealth

_____ **9.** the strength of the United States is its independent farmers

_____ **10.** opposed protective tariffs

Column B

A. Federalists

B. Democratic-Republicans

DIRECTIONS: Multiple Choice Choose the item that best completes each statement or answers each question. Write the letter in the blank. *(4 points each)*

_____ **11.** The Bill of Rights that went into effect in 1791 had _____ amendments.
   A. eight
   B. ten
   C. twelve
   D. fourteen

_____ **12.** Paper notes promising to eventually repay money with interest are called
   A. stocks.
   B. tariffs.
   C. bank notes.
   D. bonds.

_____ **13.** James Madison opposed the Bank of the United States because he believed
   A. the Constitution did not give the federal government the power to create a bank.
   B. the paper money issued by the bank would soon become worthless.
   C. Southern planters would own most of the stock because only they could afford it.
   D. the Constitution forbade the federal government from creating a bank.

_____ **14.** In Jay's Treaty, the British agreed to
   A. stop seizing American ships.
   B. pay back American merchants.
   C. not discriminate against the U.S. in trade.
   D. protect Western settlements from attack.

(continued)

Chapter 4 Test, Form A

Score

_____ **15.** The XYZ Affair concerned
   A. French demands for bribes from the United States.
   B. American demands for bribes from France.
   C. British demands for bribes from the United States.
   D. American demands for bribes from Britain.

_____ **16.** The Shoshone who joined the Lewis and Clark expedition as a guide was
   A. Tenskwatawa.   **C.** Blue Jacket.
   B. Tecumseh.   **D.** Sacagawea.

_____ **17.** In 1807 President Jefferson tried to avoid going to war by asking
   Congress to instead pass the _____, halting all trade with Europe.
   A. Alien and Sedition Acts **C.** Hartford Convention
   B. Virginia Resolution   **D.** Embargo Act

_____ **18.** Macon's Bill Number Two stated that if Britain or France agreed to drop
   its restrictions on trade, the United States would
   A. stop importing from the other nation. **C.** stop seizing that nation's ships.
   B. declare war on the other nation.   **D.** support that nation's war efforts.

_____ **19.** In the Battle of Lake Erie,
   A. the British beat the U.S. fleet.   **C.** Native Americans beat U.S. troops.
   B. the U.S. fleet beat the British.   **D.** there was no clear winner.

_____ **20.** The Tariff of 1816 nurtured American manufacturers by
   A. taxing imports.
   B. taxing exports.
   C. banning certain imports from entering the country.
   D. banning certain exports from leaving the country.

DIRECTIONS: Essay Answer one of the following questions on a separate sheet of
paper. *(20 points)*

21. Study the diagram and present Alexander Hamilton's point of view.

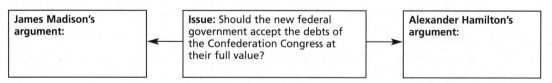

| James Madison's argument: | | Issue: Should the new federal government accept the debts of the Confederation Congress at their full value? | | Alexander Hamilton's argument: |

22. Explain the four laws that made up the Alien and Sedition Acts.

★ **Chapter 4 Test, Form B**

Federalists and Republicans

DIRECTIONS: Matching Match each item in Column A with its political party in Column B. Write the correct letters in the blanks. *(4 points each)*

Column A

_____ **1.** the strength of the U.S. was its independent farmers

_____ **2.** had a strong base in the rural South and West

_____ **3.** led by Alexander Hamilton

_____ **4.** strict interpretation of the Constitution

_____ **5.** led by Thomas Jefferson

Column B

A. Federalists

B. Democratic-Republicans

DIRECTIONS: Matching Match the Supreme Court cases in Column B with their outcomes in Column A. Write the correct letters in the blanks. *(4 points each)*

Column A

_____ **6.** asserted the Supreme Court's sovereignty over state courts

_____ **7.** Court could overturn state laws that opposed specific provisions of the Constitution

_____ **8.** concluded that "necessary and proper" clause gave Congress flexibility to enact legislation

_____ **9.** Court asserts power of judicial review

_____ **10.** ensured that federal law regulated interstate commerce

Column B

A. *Martin* v. *Hunter's Lessee*

B. *Gibbons* v. *Ogden*

C. *Marbury* v. *Madison*

D. *Fletcher* v. *Peck*

E. *McCulloch* v. *Maryland*

DIRECTIONS: Multiple Choice Choose the item that best completes each statement or answers each question. Write the letter in the blank. *(4 points each)*

_____ **11.** The last amendment in the Bill of Rights states that
   A. the people have other rights that are not listed.
   B. the people have the right to bear arms.
   C. any powers not given to the federal government are reserved for the states.
   D. the people have the right to life, liberty, and the pursuit of happiness.

_____ **12.** Hamilton's financial plan passed in Congress in exchange for
   A. the government would pay compensation to the original owners of the bonds.
   B. the capital of the United States would be moved to the North.
   C. the capital of the United States would be moved to the South.
   D. the government would impose taxes on Northern states to repay the bonds.

(continued)

⭐ **Chapter 4 Test, Form B**

Score

_____ **13.** The war between Britain and France put President Washington in a difficult position because
  A. he opposed going to war, but most Americans wanted to support Britain.
  B. he opposed going to war, but most Americans wanted to support France.
  C. a treaty required the U.S. to defend France's colonies in the Caribbean.
  D. a treaty required the U.S. to defend Britain's colonies in the Caribbean.

_____ **14.** Pinckney's Treaty gave the United States
  A. control of the Florida territory.   **C.** most-favored nation status with Spain.
  B. the right to navigate the Mississippi. **D.** the right to trade with Britain.

_____ **15.** The United States gained the Louisiana Territory by
  A. buying it from France.   **C.** winning it in the War of 1812.
  B. buying it from Spain.   **D.** winning it in the Quasi-War.

_____ **16.** Through the practice of _____, the British seized American sailors.
  A. sedition   **C.** interposition
  B. impeachment   **D.** impressment

_____ **17.** Frances Scott Key wrote "The Star-Spangled Banner" after
  A. the burning of the White House.   **C.** the bombardment of Fort McHenry.
  B. the Treaty of Ghent.   **D.** the Battle of New Orleans.

_____ **18.** Members of Congress who wanted to declare war on Britain were nicknamed the
  A. War Hawks.   **C.** Hartford Hawks.
  B. Fighting Calhouns.   **D.** Federalists.

_____ **19.** During the War of 1812, _____ secretly arranged for the construction of a fleet on the coast of Lake Erie in Ohio.
  A. William Hull   **C.** William Henry Harrison
  B. Andrew Jackson   **D.** Oliver Perry

_____ **20.** In 1816 legislation gave the Second Bank of the United States the power to
  A. make loans to state banks.   **C.** issue notes as a national currency.
  B. impose taxes to raise money.   **D.** reduce interest rates on loans.

DIRECTIONS: Essay Answer one of the following questions on a separate sheet of paper. *(20 points)*

21. Study the diagram and present James Madison's point of view.

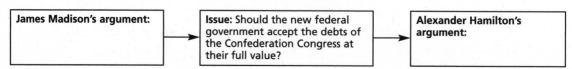

22. What was the Monroe Doctrine, what world situations prompted it, and what were its implications for the future?

The American Republic Since 1877

Copyright © by The McGraw-Hill Companies, Inc.

★ **Chapter 5**

Score

Section Quiz 5-1

DIRECTIONS: Matching Match each item in Column A with the items in Column B. Write the correct letters in the blanks. *(10 points each)*

Column A

_____ **1.** an enslaved minister who believed God had chosen him to bring his people out of bondage

_____ **2.** standard components first used in gun-making

_____ **3.** a textile worker who built a successful spinning mill

_____ **4.** engine that quickly and efficiently removed cotton seeds from the bolls

_____ **5.** developed the first successful steamboat

Column B

A. Samuel Slater

B. cotton gin

C. Nat Turner

D. Robert Fulton

E. interchangeable parts

DIRECTIONS: Multiple Choice In the blank at the left, write the letter of the choice that best completes the statement or answers the question. *(10 points each)*

_____ **6.** Communications improved, particularly when American inventor Samuel F.B. Morse developed Morse code and perfected the
  A. telephone.
  B. telegraph.
  C. radio.
  D. transistor.

_____ **7.** In the 1800s, as cotton production became more common and slavery became more widespread, many enslaved persons were organized into work groups that labored from sunup to sundown in a rigid system called the
  A. gang system.
  B. driver system.
  C. task system.
  D. chattel system.

_____ **8.** In 1806 the nation took the first steps toward a transportation revolution when Congress funded the building of a major east-west highway, the
  A. Erie Road.
  B. Vandalia Turnpike.
  C. East-West Turnpike.
  D. National Road.

_____ **9.** A preference for native-born people and a desire to limit immigration was called
  A. Know-Nothings.
  B. prejudice.
  C. nativism.
  D. nationalism.

_____ **10.** Along with dramatic changes in transportation, a revolution occurred in business and industry called the
  A. Industrial Revolution.
  B. Universal Revolution.
  C. Manufacturing Revolution.
  D. Financial Revolution.

★ **Chapter 5**

Score

Section Quiz 5-2

DIRECTIONS: Matching Match each item in Column A with the items in Column B. Write the correct letters in the blanks. *(10 points each)*

Column A

_____ **1.** President Jackson issued this order that all payments for public lands be made in silver or gold

_____ **2.** men who enjoyed popularity and political support in their home state and region

_____ **3.** temporarily settled the dispute over the westward expansion of slavery

_____ **4.** candidates attacking each other's personalities and morals

_____ **5.** practice of appointing people to government jobs based on party loyalty and support

Column B

A. mudslinging

B. Specie Circular

C. favorite sons

D. Missouri Compromise

E. spoils system

DIRECTIONS: Multiple Choice In the blank at the left, write the letter of the choice that best completes the statement or answers the question. *(10 points each)*

_____ **6.** What was the law signed by Andrew Jackson in 1830 that helped the states relocate Native Americans to largely uninhabited regions west of the Mississippi?
   A. Trail of Tears Act   **C.** Relocation Act
   B. Reservation Act   **D.** Indian Removal Act

_____ **7.** Andrew Jackson's outraged supporters decided to break with the faction of the party allied with John Quincy Adams and called themselves Democratic Republicans, later known as
   A. Democrats.   **C.** National Republicans.
   B. Republicans.   **D.** Whigs.

_____ **8.** What state threatened to secede from the Union when Congress levied a new tariff that critics called the "Tariff of Abominations"?
   A. Virginia   **C.** South Carolina
   B. Georgia   **D.** North Carolina

_____ **9.** The Whigs wanted to expand the federal government, encourage industrial and commercial development, and create a
   A. state-centered economy. **C.** deficit economy.
   B. centralized economy.   **D.** surplus economy.

_____ **10.** The Jacksonians replaced the caucus system of choosing a party's nominee with the
   A. popular vote.   **C.** national nominating convention.
   B. spoils system.   **D.** electoral college.

★ **Chapter 5**

Section Quiz 5-3

DIRECTIONS: Matching Match each item in Column A with the items in Column B. Write the correct letters in the blanks. *(10 points each)*

Column A

_____ **1.** marked the beginning of an organized woman's movement

_____ **2.** important African American abolitionist

_____ **3.** pioneered a new kind of poetry with *Leaves of Grass*

_____ **4.** based on the idea that people can transcend, or overcome, the mind's limit

_____ **5.** ideal societies

Column B

A. Sojourner Truth

B. Seneca Falls Convention

C. utopian communities

D. Transcendentalism

E. Walt Whitman

DIRECTIONS: Multiple Choice In the blank at the left, write the letter of the choice that best completes the statement or answers the question. *(10 points each)*

_____ **6.** One of the leaders of the education movement who helped create the Massachusetts Board of Education in 1837 was
  A. Horace Mann.
  B. Calvin Wiley.
  C. Ralph Waldo Emerson.
  D. Lyman Beecher.

_____ **7.** The most divisive of all the reform movements that began in the early 1800s was the movement for the immediate end to slavery, or
  A. the gag rule.
  B. temperance.
  C. utopian societies.
  D. abolition.

_____ **8.** Who did Presbyterian minister Lyman Beecher insist should take charge of building a better society?
  A. the benevolent societies
  B. the nation's citizenry
  C. the government
  D. the education system

_____ **9.** What were the groups called that preached the evils of alcohol?
  A. utopian societies
  B. transcendentalists
  C. temperance groups
  D. abolitionists

_____ **10.** The antislavery movement gained new momentum in the 1830s, thanks largely to the co-founder of the Boston newspaper, the *Liberator*,
  A. William Lloyd Garrison.
  B. Frederick Douglass.
  C. Sojourner Truth.
  D. Thomas Dew.

Chapter 5

Score

Section Quiz 5-4

DIRECTIONS: Matching Match each item in Column A with the items in Column B. Write the correct letters in the blanks. *(10 points each)*

Column A

_____ **1.** absorption

_____ **2.** famed frontiersman who died at the Alamo

_____ **3.** agents who contracted with the Mexican government to bring in a certain number of residents in exchange for large grants of Texas land

_____ **4.** settled on land they did not own

_____ **5.** the idea that the nation was meant to spread all the way to the Pacific

Column B

A. squatters

B. *empresarios*

C. Jim Bowie

D. Manifest Destiny

E. annexation

DIRECTIONS: Multiple Choice In the blank at the left, write the letter of the choice that best completes the statement or answers the question. *(10 points each)*

_____ **6.** During the election of 1844, Polk's supporters chanted "Fifty-four Forty or Fight," in reference to the boundary of
   A. Texas.
   B. Oregon.
   C. California.
   D. Alaska.

_____ **7.** The convention in San Felipe in 1832 asked Mexico to loosen the taxes on imports and reopen Texas to American
   A. trade.
   B. immigrants.
   C. politics.
   D. explorers.

_____ **8.** On May 13, 1846, the Senate voted 40 to 2 and the House 174 to 14 in favor of
   A. statehood for Texas.
   B. war with Mexico.
   C. purchasing California.
   D. signing the Treaty of Guadalupe Hidalgo.

_____ **9.** By the 1840s, several east-to-west routes had been carved out by early adventurers, and the most popular route was the
   A. Oregon Trail.
   B. Santa Fe Trail.
   C. California Trail.
   D. Old Spanish Trail.

_____ **10.** When Santa Anna's troops arrived at San Antonio in February 1836, they found about 150 rebels and 24 noncombatants holed up in a former Spanish mission called
   A. San Jacinto.
   B. San Antonio.
   C. the Alamo.
   D. Washington-on-the-Brazos.

The American Republic Since 1877

★ **Chapter 5 Test, Form A**

The Young Republic

DIRECTIONS: Matching Match each item in Column A with the items in Column B.
Write the correct letters in the blanks. *(4 points each)*

Column A

_____ **1.** president of the Second Bank of the United States

_____ **2.** perfected the telegraph in 1832

_____ **3.** transformed gun-making into an assembly-line process

_____ **4.** opened a series of mills that not only spun raw cotton into thread but also produced finished cloth

_____ **5.** built a tiny but powerful locomotive

Column B

A. Francis C. Lowell

B. Nicholas Biddle

C. Peter Cooper

D. Samuel F.B. Morse

E. Eli Whitney

DIRECTIONS: Matching The time line shows dates when five presidents were elected
or took office. Match each date to the appropriate president below. *(4 points each)*

_____ **6.** John Tyler

_____ **7.** Martin Van Buren

_____ **8.** William Henry Harrison

_____ **9.** Andrew Jackson

_____ **10.** James K. Polk

DIRECTIONS: Multiple Choice Choose the item that best completes each statement or
answers each question. Write the letter in the blank. *(4 points each)*

_____ **11.** The steamboat was an improvement over barges because it could
  A. carry more cargo.
  B. travel upstream.
  C. provide entertainment for travelers.
  D. navigate smaller rivers.

_____ **12.** The introduction of food canning was important because cans
  A. protected food from spilling.
  B. were compact.
  C. were cheaper than other packaging.
  D. prevented many foods from spoiling.

_____ **13.** The solution that emerged in the Missouri Compromise was to admit Missouri
  A. as a free state and Maine as a slave state.
  B. as a slave state and Maine as a free state.
  C. as a slave state and prohibit slavery in the rest of the western territories.
  D. as a slave state but ban free African Americans from entering the state.

(continued)

★ Chapter 5 Test, Form A

_____ **14.** John Quincy Adams won the presidency by
  A. winning the most popular votes.
  B. winning the majority of votes in the Electoral College.
  C. winning the election in the Senate.
  D. winning the election in the House of Representatives.

_____ **15.** Andrew Jackson destroyed the Second Bank of the United States by
  A. calling in the loans the Bank had made.
  B. stopping all new lending by the Bank.
  C. signing a bill that ended the Bank's charter.
  D. withdrawing the government's deposits from the Bank.

_____ **16.** By the end of the 1700s, many church leaders sensed that the doctrine of faith was being challenged by
  A. the influx of immigrants.
  B. the loss of traditional values.
  C. the growth of new religions.
  D. the growth of scientific knowledge.

_____ **17.** Normal schools were established in the early 1800s to
  A. teach all children how to read.
  B. train teachers.
  C. educate women.
  D. educate African American children.

_____ **18.** The American Colonization Society was formed to
  A. move Native Americans to reservations on the Great Plains.
  B. help new immigrants find housing and jobs in the United States.
  C. move African Americans to Africa.
  D. move African Americans to islands in the Caribbean.

_____ **19.** Manifest Destiny was the idea that
  A. white men were meant to civilize the Native Americans.
  B. the United States was meant to become the greatest nation on the earth.
  C. the nation was meant to spread all the way to the Pacific.
  D. Christianity was meant to spread across the country and around the world.

_____ **20.** The war between the United States and Mexico ended when U.S. troops took
  A. Vera Cruz.
  B. Guadalupe Hidalgo.
  C. Santa Fe.
  D. Mexico City.

DIRECTIONS: Essay Answer one of the following questions on a separate sheet of paper. *(20 points)*

21. What basic developments characterized the Industrial Revolution?

22. Discuss the reasons most Texans favored annexation and why Texas did not join the United States immediately after winning independence.

The American Republic Since 1877

⭐ **Chapter 5 Test, Form B**

Score

The Young Republic

DIRECTIONS: Matching Match each item in Column A with the items in Column B.
Write the correct letters in the blanks. *(4 points each)*

Column A

_____ **1.** leader of the Mormons

_____ **2.** led an armed uprising that killed more than 50 white people before he was caught and hanged

_____ **3.** became a prominent leader of the antislavery movement

_____ **4.** first president of the Republic of Texas

_____ **5.** accused of planning a large armed uprising but was tried, convicted, and hanged before the revolt started

_____ **6.** organization that usually focused on a single trade in the late 1820s and early 1830s

_____ **7.** went from Cumberland, Maryland, to Vandalia, Illinois

_____ **8.** connected the Hudson River to Lake Erie

_____ **9.** California's name as an independent nation

_____ **10.** name of the Texas republic before annexation

Column B

A. Denmark Vesey

B. Frederick Douglass

C. Sam Houston

D. Nat Turner

E. Joseph Smith

F. Lone Star Republic

G. Erie Canal

H. labor union

I. Bear Flag Republic

J. National Road

DIRECTIONS: Multiple Choice Choose the item that best completes each statement
or answers each question. Write the letter in the blank. *(4 points each)*

_____ **11.** Private businesses built thousands of miles of toll roads by 1821 because
   A. the Constitution did not state that the federal government could do it.
   B. the federal government lacked the money to fund road construction.
   C. the businesses wanted exclusive use of the roads to transport their goods.
   D. transporting goods by road was cheaper than by waterway.

_____ **12.** A cotton gin
   A. picks cotton.
   B. spins cotton into cloth.
   C. removes cotton seeds.
   D. bales cotton.

_____ **13.** Missouri's request to enter the Union as a slave state created a problem because
   A. it would create a new slave state north of the accepted dividing line.
   B. most Senators bitterly opposed allowing slavery in any new states.
   C. it would upset the balance of power between slave and free states in the Senate.
   D. slavery had been banned in the Louisiana Territory.

_____ **14.** According to an accepted amendment to the Missouri Compromise, slavery could
   A. not expand in Louisiana Territory north of Missouri's southern boundary.
   B. not expand into any other Western territories.
   C. expand into the Great Plains but not into the rest of the Louisiana Purchase.
   D. be allowed in a new state only if a free state entered the Union at the same time.

(continued)

Chapter 5 Test, Form B

Score

_____ **15.** John Quincy Adams was accused of winning the presidency through a "corrupt bargain," in which Adams
  A. paid Henry Clay a bribe in return for his support.
  B. gave Henry Clay a cabinet post in return for his support.
  C. agreed to fund programs favored by Henry Clay in return for his support.
  D. gave William Crawford a job in return for his support in the South.

_____ **16.** The Whig party advocated
  A. expanding the federal government.   **C.** limiting commercial development.
  B. preserving states' rights.   **D.** lowering tariffs.

_____ **17.** At the Seneca Falls Convention, Elizabeth Cady Stanton proposed
  A. equal pay for equal work.   **C.** gaining the right to vote.
  B. getting women elected to Congress.   **D.** greater workplace opportunities.

_____ **18.** In 1836 the House of Representatives passed a "gag rule" that
  A. set aside all abolitionist petitions without debate.
  B. imposed censorship on abolitionist publications.
  C. outlawed abolitionist societies.
  D. limited the circulation of abolitionist publications to the North.

_____ **19.** In the Treaty of Fort Laramie, the United States promised the Native Americans
  A. that they could continue hunting on the Great Plains.
  B. that certain territories would belong to them forever.
  C. that government troops would stop attacking them on the Great Plains.
  D. that settlers would be required to pay them for their land.

_____ **20.** In the election campaign, candidate James K. Polk promised to
  A. annex Texas, Oregon, and Louisiana.
  B. annex Texas and Oregon, and buy California from Mexico.
  C. buy Texas and California from Mexico.
  D. annex Texas, Oregon, and California.

DIRECTIONS: Essay Answer one of the following questions on a separate sheet of paper. *(20 points)*

21. Describe some of the restrictions imposed on enslaved people by slave codes.

22. Use the diagram to help you describe the sequence of events that led to the emergence of the first women's movement.

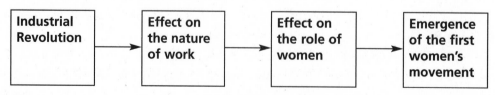

Industrial Revolution → Effect on the nature of work → Effect on the role of women → Emergence of the first women's movement

★ **Unit 1 Posttest, Form A**

Score

Foundations of Liberty

DIRECTIONS: Matching Match each item in Column A with the items in Column B. Write the correct letters in the blanks. *(4 points each)*

Column A

_____ **1.** founded colony in Massachusetts as a refuge for Puritans

_____ **2.** large Spanish cattle ranches in the Americas

_____ **3.** division of power between the national government and the state governments

_____ **4.** businesspeople who risk their own money in hopes of making a profit

_____ **5.** drafted a plan to take New England out of the Union

_____ **6.** European name for the terrible journey enslaved Africans took across the Atlantic to America

_____ **7.** plan for a loose union of the states under the authority of the Continental Congress

_____ **8.** warned Lexington that the British were coming

_____ **9.** British commander whose troops landed in New York at the start of the Revolutionary War

_____ **10.** worker organizations that pressed for improved working conditions

Column B

A. William Howe

B. entrepreneurs

C. Articles of Confederation

D. haciendas

E. Middle Passage

F. labor unions

G. federalism

H. Essex Junto

I. John Winthrop

J. Paul Revere

DIRECTIONS: Multiple Choice Choose the item that best completes each statement or answers each question. Write the letter in the blank. *(4 points each)*

_____ **11.** The most important crop of early Native American civilizations was
  A. wheat.
  B. squash.
  C. beans.
  D. maize.

_____ **12.** Few Native Americans were left in New England after
  A. the Great Migration.
  B. the Wampanoag War.
  C. the Pequot War.
  D. King Philip's War.

_____ **13.** Walter Raleigh sent ships that settled
  A. Jamestown Colony.
  B. Plymouth Colony.
  C. Roanoke.
  D. Rhode Island Colony.

_____ **14.** Jamestown experienced all of the following troubles EXCEPT
  A. none of the colonists knew how to raise livestock or grow crops.
  B. constant attacks by Native Americans discouraged new immigrants from settling there.
  C. the upper-class colonists refused to do manual labor.
  D. the land was swampy and swarming with malaria-carrying mosquitoes.

(continued)

Unit 1 Posttest, Form A

Score

_____ **15.** The Great Compromise proposed that in the House of Representatives,
  A. each state would have equal representation.
  B. the states would be represented according to the size of their population.
  C. three-fifths of enslaved Southerners would not pay taxes.
  D. each state would send a delegation of two.

_____ **16.** In Jay's Treaty, the British agreed
  A. to stop seizing American ships.
  B. to compensate American merchants for goods seized.
  C. to send more British troops to protect Western settlements from Native American attack.
  D. to not discriminate against the United States in trade.

_____ **17.** The Confederation Congress was weakened because it could not
  A. declare war.   **C.** raise armies.
  B. impose taxes.   **D.** sign treaties.

_____ **18.** Spain ceded Florida to the United States when it signed the
  A. Treaty of Greenville.   **C.** Treaty of Ghent.
  B. Adams-Onís Treaty.   **D.** Florida Compromise.

_____ **19.** The rulings of the Marshall Supreme Court established
  A. dominance of the judicial branch of government over the legislative branch.
  B. the rights of states to regulate interstate commerce.
  C. the Supreme Court as the nation's top lawmaking body.
  D. dominance of the nation over the states.

_____ **20.** At the Seneca Falls Convention, Elizabeth Cady Stanton proposed
  A. equal pay for equal work.   **C.** gaining the right to vote.
  B. getting women elected to Congress.   **D.** greater workplace opportunities.

DIRECTIONS: Essay Answer one of the following questions on a separate sheet of paper. *(20 points)*

21. Describe the reasons that sectional tensions increased in the United States after the War of 1812.

22. Alexander Hamilton and James Madison held differing views on whether the new federal government should accept the debts of the Confederation Congress at their full value. Summarize their opposing viewpoints.

⭐ **Unit 1 Posttest, Form B**

Foundations of Liberty

DIRECTIONS: Matching Match each item in Column A with the items in Column B. Write the correct letters in the blanks. *(4 points each)*

Column A

_____ **1.** popularized the use of interchangeable parts

_____ **2.** asserted Court's power of judicial review

_____ **3.** founded colony in Georgia as a place where debtors imprisoned in England could start over

_____ **4.** water route through North America to the Pacific Ocean that early explorers hoped to find

_____ **5.** government where power resides with a body of citizens entitled to vote

_____ **6.** gave the United States a claim to the Oregon Territory

_____ **7.** kidnapping of sailors

_____ **8.** in his farewell address urged Americans to avoid sectionalism

_____ **9.** first ten amendments to the Constitution

_____ **10.** founded colony at Portsmouth after being banished from the Puritan colony in Boston

Column B

A. George Washington

B. Bill of Rights

C. *Marbury* v. *Madison*

D. Eli Whitney

E. Anne Hutchinson

F. James Oglethorpe

G. Lewis and Clark expedition

H. republic

I. Northwest Passage

J. impressment

DIRECTIONS: Multiple Choice Choose the item that best completes each statement or answers each question. Write the letter in the blank. *(4 points each)*

_____ **11.** Whales and caribou were among the animals hunted by the
A. Hopi.
B. Zuni.
C. Sioux.
D. Aleut.

_____ **12.** In 1492 Columbus made his first voyage across the Atlantic with financial backing from
A. Portugal.
B. England.
C. Spain.
D. Italy.

_____ **13.** King Philip's War was a conflict between settlers and the
A. English.
B. Wampanoag.
C. Pequot.
D. Anglican Church.

_____ **14.** What did Puritans call their duty to watch over their neighbor's behavior?
A. Stage Playing
B. spying
C. Holy Watching
D. town covenant

(continued)

★ **Unit 1 Posttest, Form B**

Copyright © by The McGraw-Hill Companies, Inc.

Score

_____ **15.** What product saved the Jamestown colony?
   A. fur clothing
   B. cotton
   C. gold jewelry
   D. tobacco

_____ **16.** King George III declared the colonies "open and avowed enemies" after
   A. he read the Olive Branch Petition.
   B. the attack on British troops in Quebec.
   C. the battles of Lexington and Concord.
   D. the Boston Massacre.

_____ **17.** The Tenth Amendment to the Constitution states that
   A. the people have other rights that are not listed.
   B. the people have the right to bear arms.
   C. any powers not specifically given to the federal government are reserved for the states.
   D. the people have the right to life, liberty, and the pursuit of happiness.

_____ **18.** In the Battle of Tippecanoe
   A. U.S. troops defeated British troops.
   B. British troops defeated U.S. troops.
   C. there was no clear winner.
   D. Native Americans defeated Harrison's troops.

_____ **19.** John C. Calhoun argued that because the states had created the federal union, they had the right to declare a federal law invalid. This idea became known as
   A. sedition.
   B. nullification.
   C. secession.
   D. transcendentalism.

_____ **20.** Supporters of the idea of Manifest Destiny believed that
   A. white men were meant to civilize the Native Americans.
   B. the United States was meant to become the greatest nation on the earth.
   C. the nation was meant to spread all the way to the Pacific.
   D. Christianity was meant to spread across the country and around the world.

DIRECTIONS: Essay Answer one of the following questions on a separate sheet of paper. *(20 points)*

21. What were the benefits of becoming an indentured servant in the early days of Virginia and Maryland? Did many indentured servants get what they wanted? Why or why not?

22. Describe the problem that arose when Missouri applied for statehood, and how the Missouri Compromise solved the problem.

Unit 2 Pretest, Form A

Score

The Crisis of Union

DIRECTIONS: Matching Match each item in Column A with the items in Column B.
Write the correct letters in the blanks. *(4 points each)*

Column A

_____ **1.** white Southerners who supported Reconstruction

_____ **2.** conflict between the Union and the Confederacy

_____ **3.** proposed by Southern politicians who feared losing political power

_____ **4.** Northerners who traveled to the South and sought political power during Reconstruction

_____ **5.** imposed by Lincoln to prevent Maryland from leaving the Union

_____ **6.** farmers who paid their rent with part of their yield rather than in cash

_____ **7.** encouraged voluntary enlistment in the military

_____ **8.** formerly enslaved African Americans

_____ **9.** the idea that the people living in the territories should decide about slavery for themselves

_____ **10.** person's right not to be imprisoned without a trial

Column B

A. carpetbaggers

B. popular sovereignty

C. habeas corpus

D. Civil War

E. freedmen

F. bounty

G. scalawags

H. martial law

I. secession

J. sharecroppers

DIRECTIONS: Multiple Choice Choose the item that best completes each statement
or answers each question. Write the letter in the blank. *(4 points each)*

_____ **11.** In 1849 thousands of "Forty-Niners" came to California seeking
  A. freedom from slavery.
  B. religious freedom.
  C. cheap land offered by the government.
  D. gold.

_____ **12.** Who accused other senators of forcing Kansas into the ranks of the slave states?
  A. Andrew P. Butler
  B. Charles Sumner
  C. Frederick Douglass
  D. Simon Legree

_____ **13.** The Civil War began when
  A. Lincoln issued the Emancipation Proclamation.
  B. the Confederacy attacked Washington.
  C. the Confederacy fired on Fort Sumter.
  D. the Northern states seceded.

_____ **14.** The book *Uncle Tom's Cabin*
  A. aroused antislavery sentiment in the North.
  B. justified slavery by depicting African Americans as being happy in enslavement.
  C. justified slavery by depicting African Americans as heretics.
  D. led to better treatment of enslaved African Americans in the South.

(continued)

Unit 2 Pretest, Form A

Score

_____ **15.** A divisive issue that eventually contributed to the Civil War was whether to allow
- **A.** slavery to expand into the western territories.
- **B.** slavery to expand into the North.
- **C.** enslaved Africans to become citizens of the United States.
- **D.** the continued capturing and transporting of Africans to the United States.

_____ **16.** The Civil War began in
- **A.** 1860.
- **B.** 1871.
- **C.** 1861.
- **D.** 1886.

_____ **17.** What act created a national currency and allowed the government to issue paper money?
- **A.** Greenback Act
- **B.** Legal Tender Act
- **C.** Freeport Act
- **D.** Banking Act

_____ **18.** In the _____, Lincoln reminded his listeners that the United States was "dedicated to the proposition that all men are created equal."
- **A.** first inaugural speech
- **B.** Gettysburg Address
- **C.** Emancipation Proclamation
- **D.** second inaugural address

_____ **19.** Lincoln's goal for Reconstruction sought to
- **A.** punish the South for treason.
- **B.** create a permanent division between the North and South.
- **C.** erase the differences between the North and South.
- **D.** bring the South back into the Union.

_____ **20.** The South never regained the offensive after the battle of
- **A.** Vicksburg.
- **B.** Atlanta.
- **C.** Bull Run.
- **D.** Gettysburg.

DIRECTIONS: Essay Answer one of the following questions on a separate sheet of paper. *(20 points)*

21. What do you think happened to runaway slaves who managed to make it to the North? Were they safe? Do you think the people of the North and the courts protected them?

22. What do you think were some of the results of the Civil War? What kinds of things would the national government have to resolve to put the nation back together again?

Unit 2 Pretest, Form B

The Crisis of Union

DIRECTIONS: Matching Match each item in Column A with the items in Column B.
Write the correct letters in the blanks. *(4 points each)*

Column A

_____ **1.** arrived in California hoping to make fortunes

_____ **2.** forced ordinary citizens to turn in runaways

_____ **3.** defeated Lincoln to keep his Senate seat

_____ **4.** popular name for the Union's original plan to defeat the South

_____ **5.** common disease that killed many soldiers

_____ **6.** soldiers captured by the enemy in battle

_____ **7.** taken by siege by Grant's forces

_____ **8.** Southern state that seceded

_____ **9.** president who succeeded Lincoln and was impeached

_____ **10.** slaveholding state that did not secede

Column B

A. smallpox

B. Kentucky

C. Andrew Johnson

D. Vicksburg

E. South Carolina

F. Forty-Niners

G. prisoners of war

H. Fugitive Slave Act

I. Stephen A. Douglas

J. Anaconda Plan

DIRECTIONS: Multiple Choice Choose the item that best completes each sentence
or answers each question. Write the letter in the blank. *(4 points each)*

_____ **11.** The _____ Party was formed to oppose the spread of slavery into the western territories.
- **A.** Free-Soil
- **B.** Whig
- **C.** Democratic
- **D.** Republican

_____ **12.** Crittenden's Compromise would have
- **A.** banned slavery north of an extended Missouri Compromise line and allowed slavery south of it.
- **B.** banned slavery in Nebraska but allowed it in Kansas.
- **C.** banned slavery from expanding into the western territories but guaranteed slavery where it already existed.
- **D.** required new states to enter the Union in pairs, with one state entering as a free state and the other as a slave state.

_____ **13.** Grant ordered his troops to live off the country by _____, or searching for their own food.
- **A.** siege
- **B.** harvesting
- **C.** foraging
- **D.** mandate

(continued)

Unit 2 Pretest, Form B

_____ **14.** Who was viewed by many Northerners as a martyr for the cause of abolition?
  A. Abraham Lincoln   **C.** Frederick Douglass
  B. John Brown   **D.** Jefferson Davis

_____ **15.** The Confederate Congress chose _____ as its capital.
  A. Atlanta, Georgia   **C.** Baltimore, Maryland
  B. Richmond, Virginia   **D.** Chicago, Illinois

_____ **16.** The North had a large _____ advantage at the start of the Civil War.
  A. naval   **C.** arms
  B. military   **D.** fortifications

_____ **17.** Most of the battles of the Civil War occurred
  A. in border states.   **C.** in Union states.
  B. at sea.   **D.** in Confederate states.

_____ **18.** General Sherman's troops cut a path of destruction through Georgia on their _____.
  A. Atlantic Coast Seizure **C.** March Across Georgia
  B. Railway Bombardment   **D.** March to the Sea

_____ **19.** What political group did not want to reconcile with the South at the end of the Civil War?
  A. African Americans   **C.** Quakers
  B. Radical Republicans   **D.** Democrats

_____ **20.** What was the name for Northerners who came to the South after the war and who were viewed as intruders seeking political and financial gains?
  A. aristocrats
  B. carpetbaggers
  C. scalawags
  D. outsiders

DIRECTIONS: Essay Answer one of the following questions on a separate sheet of paper. *(20 points)*

21. How do you think the United States would be different today if the South had been allowed to secede?

22. Why do you think it was difficult for the North and South to reunite after the Civil War?

★ Chapter 6

Score

Section Quiz 6-1

DIRECTIONS: Matching Match each item in Column A with the items in Column B.
Write the correct letters in the blanks. *(10 points each)*

Column A

_____ **1.** book written by Harriet Beecher Stowe that aroused
passionate antislavery sentiment in the North

_____ **2.** taking states out of the Union

_____ **3.** armed Missourians who swarmed across the border to vote
illegally in Kansas

_____ **4.** informal but well-organized network of sympathizers who
helped thousands of enslaved persons flee north

_____ **5.** a railroad that would cross the whole country

Column B

A. transcontinental
railroad

B. *Uncle Tom's Cabin*

C. Underground
Railroad

D. secession

E. "border ruffians"

DIRECTIONS: Multiple Choice In the blank at the left, write the letter of the choice
that best completes the statement or answers the question. *(10 points each)*

_____ **6.** Southern senators made it clear that before Nebraska could be organized,
Congress would have to repeal part of the
A. Kansas-Nebraska Act.   **C.** Fugitive Slave Act.
B. Compromise of 1850.   **D.** Missouri Compromise.

_____ **7.** By the end of 1849, over 80,000 "Forty-Niners" were hoping to make
their fortunes in
A. Oregon.   **C.** Texas.
B. Kansas.   **D.** California.

_____ **8.** In 1853 Mexico accepted $10 million for the Gadsden Purchase—a 30,000-
square-mile strip of land that today is part of southern Arizona and
A. California.   **C.** New Mexico.
B. Colorado.   **D.** Texas.

_____ **9.** To Northerners, one of the most objectionable components of the
Compromise of 1850 was the
A. Fugitive Slave Act.   **C.** Wilmot Proviso.
B. Underground Railroad.   **D.** Free-Soil Party.

_____ **10.** What proposed that in any territory the United States gained from
Mexico "neither slavery nor involuntary servitude shall ever exist"?
A. Fugitive Slave Act   **C.** Compromise of 1850
B. Wilmot Proviso   **D.** Kansas-Nebraska Act

Chapter 6

Section Quiz 6-2

DIRECTIONS: Matching Match each item in Column A with the items in Column B.
Write the correct letters in the blanks. *(10 points each)*

Column A

_____ **1.** Senator from Illinois nicknamed "The Little Giant"

_____ **2.** popular vote on an issue

_____ **3.** organized from coalitions opposed to slavery

_____ **4.** rebellion

_____ **5.** a famous Western explorer nicknamed "The Pathfinder"

Column B

A. John C. Frémont

B. insurrection

C. Republican Party

D. Stephen A. Douglas

E. referendum

DIRECTIONS: Multiple Choice In the blank at the left, write the letter of the choice
that best completes the statement or answers the question. *(10 points each)*

_____ **6.** John Brown attempted to seize a federal arsenal at
   A. St. Augustine, Florida.
   B. Washington, D.C.
   C. Harpers Ferry, Virginia.
   D. Cincinnati, Ohio.

_____ **7.** The voters in Kansas overwhelmingly rejected the Lecompton
constitution, meaning they were against
   A. slavery in their midst.
   B. Northerners.
   C. referendums.
   D. the Republican Party.

_____ **8.** The American Party, better known as the Know-Nothings, was an anti-
Catholic and
   A. nativist party.
   B. liberal party.
   C. anti-Protestant party.
   D. pro-immigration party.

_____ **9.** Just two days after President Buchanan's inauguration, the Supreme
Court ruled in a landmark case involving a Missouri slave named
   A. Frederick Douglass.
   B. Harriet Tubman.
   C. John Brown.
   D. Dred Scott.

_____ **10.** In the campaign for Senate in 1858, Abraham Lincoln opposed the spread
of slavery into the western territories, while his opponent Stephen A.
Douglas supported
   A. popular sovereignty.
   B. the Missouri Compromise.
   C. secession by the South.
   D. insurrections.

★ **Chapter 6**

Section Quiz 6-3

DIRECTIONS: Matching Match each item in Column A with the items in Column B. Write the correct letters in the blanks. *(10 points each)*

Column A

_____ **1.** military rule

_____ **2.** chosen to be president of the Confederate States of America

_____ **3.** first state to secede from the Union

_____ **4.** site of John Brown's raid that was a turning point for the South

_____ **5.** state where the Confederate capital was established

Column B

A. South Carolina

B. martial law

C. Harpers Ferry

D. Virginia

E. Jefferson Davis

DIRECTIONS: Multiple Choice In the blank at the left, write the letter of the choice that best completes the statement or answers the question. *(10 points each)*

_____ **6.** Where were the first shots of the Civil War fired?
  A. Harpers Ferry
  B. Fort Sumter
  C. Washington, D.C.
  D. Richmond

_____ **7.** The newspapers called a series of amendments to the Constitution proposed by Senator John J. Crittenden of Kentucky
  A. the New Missouri Compromise.
  B. the Fort Sumter Compromise.
  C. the Kentucky Compromise.
  D. Crittenden's Compromise.

_____ **8.** Who did many Southern newspapers and politicians blame for John Brown's raid?
  A. Republicans
  B. Democrats
  C. Whigs
  D. Know-Nothings

_____ **9.** What did the Confederate Constitution guarantee in Confederate territory?
  A. slavery
  B. protective tariffs
  C. a strong federal government
  D. martial law

_____ **10.** Where did President Lincoln impose martial law so that anyone supporting secession could be arrested and held without trial?
  A. Louisville, Kentucky
  B. Washington, D.C.
  C. Baltimore, Maryland
  D. St. Louis, Missouri

⭐ **Chapter 6 Test, Form A**

Sectional Conflict Intensifies

DIRECTIONS: Matching Each item in Column B was part of the Southern way of thinking in the debate leading to the Compromise of 1850. Put these items into the proper sequence illustrated in the diagram. Write the correct sequence in Column A. *(4 points each)*

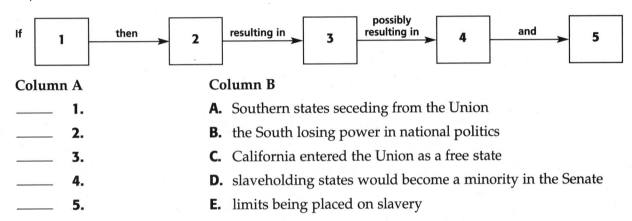

If [1] then → [2] resulting in → [3] possibly resulting in → [4] and → [5]

Column A

_____ **1.**

_____ **2.**

_____ **3.**

_____ **4.**

_____ **5.**

Column B

A. Southern states seceding from the Union

B. the South losing power in national politics

C. California entered the Union as a free state

D. slaveholding states would become a minority in the Senate

E. limits being placed on slavery

DIRECTIONS: Matching The election of 1860 featured several points of view. Match the parties in Column B with facts about them in Column A. Write the correct letters in the blanks. Some letters will be used more than once. *(4 points each)*

Column A

_____ **6.** nominated Abraham Lincoln

_____ **7.** supported popular sovereignty

_____ **8.** wanted to uphold both the Constitution and the Union

_____ **9.** supported the *Dred Scott* decision

_____ **10.** nominated Stephen A. Douglas

Column B

A. Southern Democrats

B. Northern Democrats

C. Republicans

D. Constitutional Unionists

DIRECTIONS: Multiple Choice Choose the item that best completes each statement or answers each question. Write the letter in the blank. *(4 points each)*

_____ **11.** The Wilmot Proviso, which never passed, would have

   A. prohibited slavery in any territory gained from Mexico.

   B. prevented Congress from banning slavery in any territory gained from Mexico.

   C. created a compromise by dividing the territories into free and slave states.

   D. made it easier for slaveholders to retrieve an enslaved person.

_____ **12.** The original purpose of the Gadsden Purchase was to

   A. balance the division of territory between free states and slave states.

   B. expand slavery west.

   C. balance the amount of territory included in Kansas and Nebraska.

   D. create a route for the transcontinental railroad from New Orleans.

(continued)

⭐ **Chapter 6 Test, Form A**

_____ **13.** The Know-Nothings were
- **A.** antislavery and nativist.
- **B.** antislavery and anti-Catholic.
- **C.** anti-Catholic and nativist.
- **D.** pro-slavery and anti-Catholic.

_____ **14.** By rejecting the Lecompton constitution, Kansas voters
- **A.** rejected slavery in their state.
- **B.** applied for statehood as a slave state.
- **C.** enabled Kansas to become a state.
- **D.** rejected the Kansas-Nebraska Act.

_____ **15.** Crittenden's Compromise proposed to
- **A.** extend the Missouri Compromise line and allow slavery south of it.
- **B.** prohibit slavery in Nebraska but allow it in Kansas.
- **C.** prohibit slavery from expanding into the western territories.
- **D.** require new states to enter the Union in pairs.

_____ **16.** In his inaugural speech, President Lincoln
- **A.** threatened to attack the seceded states if they did not return to the Union.
- **B.** repeated his commitment not to interfere with slavery where it already existed.
- **C.** repeated his commitment to abolishing slavery.
- **D.** threatened to attack if the South did not return the federal forts it had seized.

_____ **17.** Lincoln wanted to prevent Maryland from seceding, because if it did,
- **A.** the South would gain control of the strategically important Potomac River.
- **B.** the South would gain control of important arsenals there.
- **C.** Washington, D.C., would be surrounded by Confederate territory.
- **D.** the South would control more territory than the North.

_____ **18.** Lincoln tried to prevent Maryland's secession by
- **A.** respecting its declaration of neutrality.
- **B.** allowing slavery in Maryland.
- **C.** declaring martial law in Baltimore.
- **D.** protecting the state from invasion.

_____ **19.** The most famous conductor on the Underground Railroad was
- **A.** Harriet Beecher Stowe.
- **B.** Harriet Tubman.
- **C.** Sojourner Truth.
- **D.** Henry David Thoreau.

_____ **20.** For most Southerners, John Brown's raid offered proof that
- **A.** slaves were plotting insurrections.
- **B.** Northerners plotted to murder slaveholders.
- **C.** they had to secede from the Union.
- **D.** slavery would be banned in the South.

DIRECTIONS: Essay Answer one of the following questions on a separate sheet of paper. *(20 points)*

21. Describe Henry Clay's four pairs of resolutions that eventually became the Compromise of 1850.

22. Describe the case of *Dred Scott* v. *Sandford,* the decision, and its significance.

The American Republic Since 1877

★ ## Chapter 6 Test, Form B

Sectional Conflict Intensifies

DIRECTIONS: Matching Identify the position toward slavery taken by each person in Column A. Write the appropriate letter from Column B in the blanks provided. The letters will be used more than once. *(4 points each)*

Column A

_____ **1.** John Brown

_____ **2.** Charles Sumner

_____ **3.** John C. Calhoun

_____ **4.** Levi Coffin

_____ **5.** Roger B. Taney

_____ **6.** Preston Brooks

_____ **7.** Harriet Beecher Stowe

_____ **8.** John C. Frémont

_____ **9.** David Wilmot

_____ **10.** Frederick Douglass

Column B

A. supported slavery

B. opposed slavery

DIRECTIONS: Multiple Choice Choose the item that best completes each statement or answers each question. Write the letter in the blank. *(4 points each)*

_____ **11.** Most Free-Soilers opposed the spread of slavery because it
A. was immoral.   **C.** shifted power to the South.
B. was a territorial decision.   **D.** would take jobs from free men.

_____ **12.** After passage of the Kansas-Nebraska Act, many Northerners headed to Kansas to
A. farm the rich soil.   **C.** build the transcontinental railroad.
B. create an antislavery majority.   **D.** keep Southern immigrants out.

_____ **13.** The Kansas-Nebraska Act further inflamed sectional tensions because it
A. forbade slavery in the territories.   **C.** made both states slave states.
B. undid the Missouri Compromise.   **D.** undid the Compromise of 1850.

_____ **14.** The Whig Party and American Party both dissolved because
A. Northern and Southern members split over the slavery issue.
B. members disagreed sharply over their party's presidential nominee.
C. members polarized over the *Dred Scott* decision.
D. Western members split over popular sovereignty in the territories.

_____ **15.** John Brown's intention in raiding the arsenal at Harpers Ferry was to arm
A. slaveholders so they could defend themselves against a slave insurrection.
B. Virginians for civil war.
C. his followers so they could overthrow the federal government.
D. enslaved people and begin an insurrection against slaveholders.

(continued)

Chapter 6 Test, Form B

Score

_____ **16.** The Confederate Constitution stated that
  A. each state could impose its own protective tariffs.
  B. each state could decide for itself whether or not to accept slavery.
  C. each state was independent.
  D. the Confederate government would make the laws that would govern the states.

_____ **17.** All of the following states seceded from the Union EXCEPT
  A. North Carolina.   **C.** Arkansas.
  B. Tennessee.   **D.** Missouri.

_____ **18.** After passage of the Kansas-Nebraska Act, "border ruffians" swarmed into Kansas to
  A. vote illegally to elect a pro-slavery legislature.
  B. vote illegally to elect an antislavery legislature.
  C. organize a slave insurrection.
  D. attack pro-slavery settlers in Lawrence, Kansas.

_____ **19.** In the *Dred Scott* case, the Supreme Court ruled as unconstitutional part of the
  A. Missouri Compromise.   **C.** Fugitive Slave Act.
  B. Compromise of 1850.   **D.** Kansas-Nebraska Act.

_____ **20.** Lewis Cass proposed that the decision of slavery in the territories be made by
  A. the Supreme Court.   **C.** the citizens of the territories.
  B. Congress.   **D.** a nationwide vote.

DIRECTIONS: Essay Answer one of the following questions on a separate sheet of paper. *(20 points)*

21. Describe the provisions of the Fugitive Slave Act.

22. During a debate, Abraham Lincoln posed a question to Stephen A. Douglas that put Douglas in a dilemma. Complete the diagram by describing the dilemma and Douglas's response.

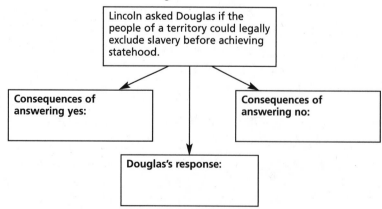

Douglas's Dilemma

Lincoln asked Douglas if the people of a territory could legally exclude slavery before achieving statehood.

Consequences of answering yes:

Consequences of answering no:

Douglas's response:

The American Republic Since 1877

⭐ **Chapter 7**

Section Quiz 7-1

DIRECTIONS: Matching Match each item in Column A with the items in Column B.
Write the correct letters in the blanks. *(10 points each)*

Column A

_____ **1.** caused worldwide interest when a ship carrying two
Confederate diplomats was intercepted by a Union
warship

_____ **2.** opposed the war and called for reuniting the states
through negotiation rather than force

_____ **3.** the wearing down of one side by the other through
exhaustion of soldiers and resources

_____ **4.** a name the Republicans called the Peace Democrats

_____ **5.** paper money

Column B

A. Peace Democrats

B. greenbacks

C. *Trent* Affair

D. attrition

E. Copperheads

DIRECTIONS: Multiple Choice In the blank at the left, write the letter of the choice
that best completes the statement or answers the question. *(10 points each)*

_____ **6.** Northern newspapers scorned Winfield Scott's strategy for defeating the
South, which they called the
A. Copperhead Plan.   **C.** War Democrat Plan.
B. Greenback Plan.   **D.** Anaconda Plan.

_____ **7.** What did Congress pass in 1862 that created a national currency and
allowed the government to issue paper money?
A. Legal Tender Act   **C.** Anaconda Plan
B. Income Tax Act   **D.** Internal Revenue Service Act

_____ **8.** Criticism greeted President Lincoln's decision to suspend a person's right
not to be imprisoned unless charged with a crime and given a trial,
which is known as
A. writ of speedy trial.   **C.** habeas corpus.
B. attrition.   **D.** conscription.

_____ **9.** One major disagreement between Republicans and Democrats concerned
the enactment in 1862 of a militia law that required states to draft people
for military service, also called
A. attrition.   **C.** habeas corpus.
B. conscription.   **D.** greenbacking.

_____ **10.** What often interfered with Jefferson Davis's ability to conduct the war?
A. the Underground Railroad   **C.** his health
B. uprisings of enslaved people   **D.** commitment to states' rights

Chapter 7

Score

Section Quiz 7-2

DIRECTIONS: Matching Match each item in Column A with the items in Column B. Write the correct letters in the blanks. *(10 points each)*

Column A

_____ **1.** sum of money given by the North as a bonus to individuals who promised three years of military service

_____ **2.** crucial victory for the Union

_____ **3.** small, fast vessels the South used to smuggle goods past the Union blockade

_____ **4.** a decree freeing all enslaved persons in states still in rebellion after January 1, 1863

_____ **5.** a series of attacks on McClellan's army by General Lee

Column B

A. blockade runners

B. Seven Days' Battle

C. Battle of Antietam

D. bounty

E. Emancipation Proclamation

DIRECTIONS: Multiple Choice In the blank at the left, write the letter of the choice that best completes the statement or answers the question. *(10 points each)*

_____ **6.** New Orleans, the South's largest city and a center of the cotton trade, was in Union hands due to a daring move made by
  A. Irwin McDowell.
  B. David G. Farragut.
  C. George B. McClellan.
  D. Ulysses S. Grant.

_____ **7.** It was clear that a large, well-trained army would be needed to defeat the South after the Union defeat at
  A. the First Battle of Bull Run.
  B. Fort Donelson.
  C. the Battle of Antietam.
  D. New Orleans.

_____ **8.** For what profession in the United States was the Civil War a turning point?
  A. teaching
  B. nursing
  C. law
  D. engineering

_____ **9.** The 54th Massachusetts, which became one of the most famous regiments in the war, was the first
  A. Southern regiment.
  B. regiment taken as prisoners of war.
  C. Northern regiment.
  D. official African American regiment.

_____ **10.** Early on April 6, 1862, Confederate forces launched a surprise attack on Grant's troops camped about 20 miles north of Corinth, Mississippi, near a small church named
  A. Murfreesboro.
  B. Bull Run.
  C. Shiloh.
  D. Antietam.

⭐ **Chapter 7**

Section Quiz 7-3

DIRECTIONS: Matching Match each item in Column A with the items in Column B.
Write the correct letters in the blanks. *(10 points each)*

Column A

_____ **1.** searching and raiding for food

_____ **2.** one of the best-known speeches in American history given
by President Lincoln

_____ **3.** became general in chief of the Union forces

_____ **4.** chosen by Lincoln to replace General Hooker

_____ **5.** to cut off food and supplies and bombard a city until its
defenders give up

Column B

A. Gettysburg
Address

B. foraging

C. George Meade

D. Ulysses S. Grant

E. siege

DIRECTIONS: Multiple Choice In the blank at the left, write the letter of the choice
that best completes the statement or answers the question. *(10 points each)*

_____ **6.** What Union victory cut the Confederacy in two?
  A. Gettysburg
  B. Fredericksburg
  C. Vicksburg
  D. Chancellorsville

_____ **7.** What was passed on January 31, 1865, banning slavery in the United
States?
  A. Thirteenth Amendment to the Constitution
  B. Appomattox Courthouse Resolve
  C. Gettysburg Address
  D. Bill of Rights Amendment to the Constitution

_____ **8.** After the Union's major victories at Vicksburg and Gettysburg, fierce
fighting erupted near Chattanooga, Tennessee, a vital
  A. sea harbor.
  B. source of ammunition.
  C. railroad junction.
  D. river port.

_____ **9.** What battle was the turning point of the war in the east?
  A. Chattanooga
  B. Cold Harbor
  C. Vicksburg
  D. Gettysburg

_____ **10.** The capture of Vicksburg had given the Union control of the Mississippi
River, while the victory at Chattanooga had secured eastern Tennessee
and cleared the way for an invasion of
  A. Florida.
  B. Georgia.
  C. Texas.
  D. Mississippi.

Chapter 7

Section Quiz 7-4

DIRECTIONS: Matching Match each item in Column A with the items in Column B. Write the correct letters in the blanks. *(10 points each)*

Column A

_____ **1.** when a president lets a session of Congress expire without signing legislation

_____ **2.** freed African Americans

_____ **3.** pardon

_____ **4.** rebuilding the nation after the war

_____ **5.** laws passed by Southern legislatures limiting the rights of African Americans in the South

Column B

A. amnesty

B. black codes

C. Reconstruction

D. pocket veto

E. freedmen

DIRECTIONS: Multiple Choice In the blank at the left, write the letter of the choice that best completes the statement or answers the question. *(10 points each)*

_____ **6.** President Lincoln's plan for Reconstruction offered a general pardon to Southerners who took an oath of loyalty to the United States and accepted the Union's proclamation concerning
   A. slavery.   **C.** prisons.
   B. elections.   **D.** food supplies.

_____ **7.** Recognizing the importance of African American suffrage, the Republican-led Congress proposed the
   A. Civil Rights Act of 1866.   **C.** Fourteenth Amendment.
   B. Thirteenth Amendment.   **D.** Fifteenth Amendment.

_____ **8.** Congressional Reconstruction began with the passage of what act that granted citizenship to all persons born in the United States except Native Americans?
   A. Fourteenth Amendment   **C.** Thirteenth Amendment
   B. Military Reconstruction Act **D.** Civil Rights Act of 1866

_____ **9.** The agency given the task of feeding and clothing war refugees in the South using surplus army supplies was called the
   A. Military Reconstruction Bureau.   **C.** Freedmen's Bureau.
   B. Radical Republicans.   **D.** Red Cross.

_____ **10.** Under the provisions of the Wade-Davis Bill, who would not be allowed the right to vote or hold office?
   A. former enslaved African Americans
   B. plantation owners
   C. former Confederate government officials and military officers
   D. any men who fought in the Confederate army

★ **Chapter 7**

Section Quiz 7-5

DIRECTIONS: Matching Match each item in Column A with the items in Column B. Write the correct letters in the blanks. *(10 points each)*

Column A

_____ **1.** Northerners who traveled to the South

_____ **2.** passed by Congress to combat the violence in the South

_____ **3.** gaining money illegally through politics

_____ **4.** paid a share of their crops to cover their rent as well as paying the cost of seeds, fertilizer, tools, and animals

_____ **5.** white Southerners who worked with the Republicans and supported Reconstruction

Column B

A. carpetbaggers

B. sharecroppers

C. graft

D. Enforcement Acts

E. scalawags

DIRECTIONS: Multiple Choice In the blank at the left, write the letter of the choice that best completes the statement or answers the question. *(10 points each)*

_____ **6.** What housed schools, hosted social events and political gatherings, and were the center of many African American communities?
  A. town halls
  B. churches
  C. plantations
  D. government buildings

_____ **7.** Southerners who called for the creation of a "New South" were convinced that the region had to develop a strong
  A. plantation system.
  B. agricultural economy.
  C. industrial economy.
  D. welfare system.

_____ **8.** A series of bad railroad investments forced the powerful banking firm of Jay Cooke and Company to declare bankruptcy and resulted in a wave of fear known as the
  A. Compromise of 1877.
  B. Ku Klux Klan.
  C. Whiskey Ring.
  D. Panic of 1873.

_____ **9.** Hundreds of formerly enslaved people served as delegates to the conventions that created the new state
  A. constitutions.
  B. laws.
  C. legislatures.
  D. voting guidelines.

_____ **10.** In April 1877, President Hayes pulled federal troops out of the South, ending
  A. the Civil War.
  B. the Compromise of 1877.
  C. the Enforcement Acts.
  D. Reconstruction.

⭐ **Chapter 7 Test, Form A**

The Civil War and Reconstruction

DIRECTIONS: Matching Match each item in Column A with the items in Column B.
Write the correct letters in the blanks. *(4 points each)*

Column A

_____ **1.** Lee surrendered to Grant

_____ **2.** taken by siege by Union forces under Grant

_____ **3.** the result of this battle convinced Lincoln that the time had come to end slavery in the South

_____ **4.** battle where "Stonewall" Jackson got his nickname

_____ **5.** led newspapers to demand that Lincoln fire Ulysses S. Grant

_____ **6.** made Southern civilians understand the horrors of war

_____ **7.** battle within 20 miles of Washington in which Lee's army forced the North to retreat, and then invaded Maryland to try to gain a victory on Northern soil

_____ **8.** Lee led a series of attacks on McClellan's army that forced McClellan to retreat

_____ **9.** Lee lost more than a third of his entire force

_____ **10.** won by the Union because of a daring move by the commander, David G. Farragut

Column B

A. Seven Days' Battle

B. Battle of Shiloh

C. Second Battle of Bull Run

D. Vicksburg

E. First Battle of Bull Run

F. New Orleans

G. Battle of Antietam

H. Battle of Gettysburg

I. March to the Sea

J. Appomattox Courthouse

DIRECTIONS: Multiple Choice Choose the item that best completes each statement or answers each question. Write the letter in the blank. *(4 points each)*

_____ **11.** Robert E. Lee did not accept command of the Union troops because
  A. he believed in slavery.
  B. he supported secession.
  C. his home state was Virginia.
  D. he was already Confederate commander.

_____ **12.** The Emancipation Proclamation
  A. decreed freedom for all enslaved people.
  B. decreed freedom for all enslaved people in the states at war with the Union.
  C. decreed freedom for all enslaved people in the Union border states.
  D. started the process of amending the Constitution to free all enslaved people.

_____ **13.** The infamous prison in the South was called
  A. Andersonville.
  B. Chancellorsville.
  C. Chickamauga.
  D. Petersburg.

_____ **14.** Benjamin Grierson's forces traveled 600 miles in two weeks in order to
  A. disrupt supply lines sustaining the city of Vicksburg.
  B. slow the advance of Grant's troops toward Vicksburg.
  C. buy time for reinforcements to reach the beleaguered defenders of Vicksburg.
  D. distract the forces defending Vicksburg so Grant could move south of the city.

(continued)

★ **Chapter 7 Test, Form A**

Score

_____ **15.** The map shows the site of the battle that was the turning point of the war in the east. That battle took place at
   A. Chattanooga.
   B. Chickamauga.
   C. Chancellorsville.
   D. Gettysburg.

PENNSYLVANIA

_____ **16.** Abraham Lincoln was assassinated while
   A. making a speech.
   B. watching a play.
   C. visiting the troops in Virginia.
   D. strolling on the White House grounds.

_____ **17.** To receive a pardon under Lincoln's Reconstruction plan, Southerners had to take an oath of loyalty to the United States and
   A. promise never to secede from the Union again.
   B. accept the Union's proclamations concerning slavery.
   C. agree to set up schools to educate formerly enslaved people.
   D. promise to pay a share of the costs of property damage done to the North.

_____ **18.** In 1866 Republicans in Congress feared that President Johnson could interfere by
   A. vetoing their laws.
   B. refusing to enforce their laws.
   C. declaring their laws unconstitutional.
   D. adding amendments to their laws.

_____ **19.** In the election of 1868, Ulysses S. Grant won several Southern states because
   A. Congress did not allow a presidential candidate from the South to enter the race.
   B. Southern voters respected his leadership abilities.
   C. the presence of Union troops in the South allowed African Americans to vote.
   D. Southern hero Robert E. Lee endorsed Grant for the presidency.

_____ **20.** The "Whiskey Ring" was
   A. a group of government officials and distillers who filed false tax reports.
   B. an early organized crime ring that broke Prohibition laws.
   C. a group of President Grant's close friends.
   D. a group of distillers that conspired to set high prices for their whiskey.

DIRECTIONS: Essay Answer one of the following questions on a separate sheet of paper. *(20 points)*

21. Describe the Confederacy's financial situation.

22. What were some results of the Civil War, and what two key questions remained unresolved in its aftermath?

The American Republic Since 1877

Chapter 7 Test, Form B

The Civil War and Reconstruction

DIRECTIONS: Matching Match each item in Column A with the items in Column B.
Write the correct letters in the blanks. *(4 points each)*

Column A

_____ **1.** vetoed by Lincoln because he felt that imposing a harsh peace on the South would be counterproductive

_____ **2.** allowed African Americans to own property and to be treated equally in court

_____ **3.** intended to keep African Americans in a condition similar to slavery

_____ **4.** divided the former Confederacy into five military districts

_____ **5.** declared that no state could deny any person "equal protection of the laws"

_____ **6.** required the Senate to approve the president's removal of any government official whose appointment had required the Senate's consent

_____ **7.** intended to combat the activities of the Ku Klux Klan

_____ **8.** suspended for anyone who supported the rebels

_____ **9.** declared that the right to vote "shall not be denied . . . on account of race, color, or previous condition of servitude"

_____ **10.** made more money available for emergency use

Column B

A. Military Reconstruction Act

B. Enforcement Acts

C. black codes

D. Fifteenth Amendment

E. Tenure of Office Act

F. Civil Rights Act of 1866

G. Fourteenth Amendment

H. Wade-Davis Bill

I. Legal Tender Act

J. habeas corpus

DIRECTIONS: Multiple Choice Choose the item that best completes each statement
or answers each question. Write the letter in the blank. *(4 points each)*

_____ **11.** All of the following were Northern advantages over the South EXCEPT
   A. a larger population.
   B. more industry.
   C. greater ability to produce food.
   D. more miles of railroad tracks.

_____ **12.** The North's Anaconda Plan proposed all of the following EXCEPT
   A. a blockade of Confederate ports.
   B. controlling the Mississippi River.
   C. a quick invasion of Richmond.
   D. dividing the Confederacy.

_____ **13.** Hardtack was a
   A. new cone-shaped bullet.
   B. military maneuver.
   C. type of biscuit made of wheat flour.
   D. type of body armor.

_____ **14.** Shortly after McClellan's victory at Antietam, Lincoln fired him because he
   A. disobeyed orders to break off the attack and fall back to regroup.
   B. was becoming more popular than Lincoln.
   C. ignored Lincoln's order to return to Washington, D.C., to defend the capital.
   D. could have destroyed Lee's army, but he let the Confederates slip away.

(continued)

Chapter 7 Test, Form B

Score

_____ 15. Study the map. Capturing Vicksburg was an
important objective for the North because

A. its location made invasion from
there a threat to the North.

B. its capture would give the North
control of the Mississippi River delta.

C. its capture would cut the South in two.

D. its capture would prevent the
South from shipping cotton to Europe.

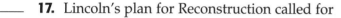

_____ 16. The Amendment to the Constitution that
banned slavery was the

A. Tenth.   **C.** Twelfth.

B. Eleventh.   **D.** Thirteenth.

_____ 17. Lincoln's plan for Reconstruction called for

A. trying Southern leaders for treason.   **C.** revolutionizing Southern habits.

B. punishing Southern armies.   **D.** reconciling with the South.

_____ 18. Under the Republicans' Reconstruction plan, before former Confederate
states could elect people to Congress, they had to

A. ratify the Fourteenth Amendment.

B. redesign their constitutions to deny voting rights to African Americans.

C. redesign their constitutions to deny voting rights to former Confederate leaders.

D. appoint African Americans to at least a fourth of their state government jobs.

_____ 19. Scalawags were

A. wealthy planters who were looking for a way to regain power.

B. white Southerners who supported Reconstruction.

C. Northerners who took positions in the South's new state governments.

D. African Americans who had won office in Southern state governments.

_____ 20. Reconstruction ended when

A. Hayes was elected.   **C.** Hayes pulled troops out of the South.

B. Hayes made plans for the   **D.** industrialization began in the South.
"New South."

DIRECTIONS: Essay Answer one of the following questions on a separate sheet of
paper. *(20 points)*

21. Describe the new styles of fighting introduced in the Civil War, and how new
technology contributed to these changes.

22. Describe some requirements established by black codes in the South.

⭐ **Unit 2 Posttest, Form A**

Score

The Crisis of Union

DIRECTIONS: Matching Match each item in Column A with the items in Column B.
Write the correct letters in the blanks. *(4 points each)*

Column A

_____ **1.** agreement to buy land for the transcontinental railroad from Mexico

_____ **2.** site of the first shots fired in the Civil War

_____ **3.** alleged deal that gave Rutherford B. Hayes the presidency when the election yielded no clear winner

_____ **4.** granted citizenship to all persons born in the United States except Native Americans

_____ **5.** author of *Uncle Tom's Cabin*

_____ **6.** the wearing down of one side by the other through exhaustion of soldiers and resources

_____ **7.** supported war to save the Union, but opposed ending slavery

_____ **8.** site of John Brown's raid

_____ **9.** this battle ended with the South's largest city and center of the cotton trade in Union hands

_____ **10.** asked to command the Union Army but would not fight against his home state

Column B

A. War Democrats

B. Gadsden Purchase

C. Compromise of 1877

D. Fort Sumter

E. Civil Rights Act of 1866

F. New Orleans

G. Harriet Beecher Stowe

H. Robert E. Lee

I. attrition

J. Harpers Ferry

DIRECTIONS: Multiple Choice Choose the item that best completes each statement or answers each question. Write the letter in the blank. *(4 points each)*

_____ **11.** The Wilmot Proviso was intended to
   A. ban slavery in any territory gained from Mexico.
   B. stop Congress from banning slavery in any territory gained from Mexico.
   C. create a compromise by dividing the territories into free and slave states.
   D. make it easier for slaveholders to retrieve an enslaved person who fled to the territories.

_____ **12.** The Kansas-Nebraska Act
   A. destroyed the Free-Soil Party.
   B. helped create the American Party.
   C. destroyed the Know-Nothings and helped create the Whig Party.
   D. destroyed the Whig Party and helped create the Republican Party.

_____ **13.** Charles Sumner was beaten in the Senate because he accused other senators of
   A. voting against slavery.   **C.** inciting border ruffians into Kansas.
   B. taking bribes to vote for slavery.   **D.** forcing Kansas to become a slave state.

(continued)

Unit 2 Posttest, Form A

_____ **14.** According to the Confederate Constitution, each state
    A. could impose its own tariffs.   **C.** was independent.
    B. could decide to accept slavery.   **D.** must obey the Confederacy.

_____ **15.** The Freeport Doctrine held that people in the territories could keep slavery out of their state by
    A. nullifying the *Dred Scott* decision.
    B. refusing to pass laws to regulate and enforce slavery.
    C. voting to enter the Union as a free state.
    D. voting against slavery.

_____ **16.** After the Kansas-Nebraska Act, "border ruffians" crossed into Kansas to
    A. vote for a pro-slavery legislature.   **C.** organize a slave insurrection.
    B. vote for an antislavery legislature.   **D.** attack pro-slavery settlers in Kansas.

_____ **17.** The Legal Tender Act allowed the government to
    A. issue paper money.   **C.** raise tariffs.
    B. issue bonds.   **D.** tax citizens directly.

_____ **18.** The purpose of Grierson's raid was to
    A. disrupt supply lines sustaining the city of Vicksburg.
    B. slow the advance of Grant's troops toward Vicksburg.
    C. buy time for reinforcements to reach the beleaguered defenders of Vicksburg.
    D. distract forces defending Vicksburg so Grant could land south of the city.

_____ **19.** Placed in harbors to blow up ships, Civil War "torpedoes" are now known as
    A. attrition.   **C.** conoidal bullets.
    B. bombs.   **D.** mines.

_____ **20.** Under Johnson's Reconstruction plan, many members of Congress rejected representatives elected by Southern voters because they
    A. were African Americans.
    B. refused to take an oath of loyalty to the Union.
    C. were former Confederate leaders.
    D. did not want to re-admit Southern states to the Union.

DIRECTIONS: Essay Answer one of the following questions on a separate sheet of paper. *(20 points)*

21. What was the Underground Railroad and how did it operate? Name two famous participants and describe what they did.

22. What were some advantages that the North enjoyed over the South in the Civil War?

The American Republic Since 1877

Unit 2 Posttest, Form B

Score

The Crisis of Union

DIRECTIONS: Matching Match each item in Column A with the items in Column B. Write the correct letters in the blanks. *(4 points each)*

Column A

_____ **1.** prison in the South where thousands of prisoners of war died of exposure, lack of food, and disease

_____ **2.** was the subject of sectional conflict over its starting point

_____ **3.** destroyed a Confederate fleet defending Mobile Bay

_____ **4.** Quaker who sheltered escaped African Americans

_____ **5.** declared that no state could deprive any person of life, liberty, or property "without due process of law"

_____ **6.** Union defeat at this early battle made it clear that the North would need a large, well-trained army

_____ **7.** main author of the Compromise of 1850

_____ **8.** nurse who treated the wounded during the Civil War

_____ **9.** the North's victory in this battle convinced Lincoln that the time had come to end slavery in the South

_____ **10.** key border state that stayed in the Union

Column B

A. Maryland

B. Antietam

C. Henry Clay

D. David Farragut

E. Clara Barton

F. First Battle of Bull Run

G. transcontinental railroad

H. Levi Coffin

I. Andersonville

J. Fourteenth Amendment

DIRECTIONS: Multiple Choice Choose the item that best completes each statement or answers each question. Write the letter in the blank. *(4 points each)*

_____ **11.** Most members of the Free-Soil Party
  A. condemned slavery as immoral.
  B. wanted the people of the western territories to make their own decision about slavery in their region.
  C. wanted slavery to expand in order to shift political power to the South.
  D. wanted to preserve the territories in the West for white farmers.

_____ **12.** The Kansas-Nebraska Act made tensions between North and South worse because it
  A. repealed the Missouri Compromise.   **C.** made both states slave states.
  B. repealed the Compromise of 1850.   **D.** forbade slavery in the new territories.

_____ **13.** In his inaugural speech, President Lincoln told the seceding states that he would
  A. declare war if they did not return to the Union.
  B. not interfere with slavery where it already existed.
  C. abolish slavery.
  D. declare war if they did not return the forts and arsenals they had seized.

(continued)

★ Unit 2 Posttest, Form B

Score

_____ **14.** In 1849 thousands of people came to California hoping
   A. to find gold.
   B. it would become a free state.
   C. to purchase the cheap land.
   D. to form a new nation.

_____ **15.** The American Party won many seats in Congress in 1854 by opposing
   A. slavery.
   B. immigration.
   C. the Missouri Compromise.
   D. statehood for Kansas.

_____ **16.** Many African Americans were able to escape from the South because of the
   A. Fugitive Slave Act.
   B. Missouri Compromise.
   C. Underground Railroad.
   D. transcontinental railroad.

_____ **17.** Lincoln fired McClellan because he
   A. disobeyed orders to break off the attack and fall back to regroup.
   B. was becoming more popular than Lincoln.
   C. lost so many soldiers at the battle of Cold Harbor.
   D. let Lee's army slip away at Antietam.

_____ **18.** Which of the following was NOT a disadvantage that the South faced?
   A. lack of railways
   B. size of population
   C. lack of factories
   D. lack of military officers

_____ **19.** As one requirement for receiving a pardon under Lincoln's Reconstruction plan, Southerners had to
   A. promise never to secede from the Union again.
   B. accept the Union's proclamations concerning slavery.
   C. agree to set up schools to educate former slaves.
   D. promise to pay a share of the costs of property damage done to the North.

_____ **20.** The agreement that was thought to have been made between the Democratic and Republican Parties that resulted in Hayes becoming president is known as the
   A. Wade-Davis Compromise.
   B. Reconstruction Compromise.
   C. Compromise of 1877.
   D. Hayes-Tilden Compromise.

DIRECTIONS: Essay Answer one of the following questions on a separate sheet of paper. *(20 points)*

21. Describe the challenges that faced African Americans during Reconstruction.

22. Describe military life during the Civil War.

★ **Unit 3 Pretest, Form A**

Score

The Birth of Modern America

DIRECTIONS: Matching Match each item in Column A with the items in Column B.
Write the correct letters in the blanks. *(4 points each)*

Column A

_____ **1.** wild cattle that roamed the Texas grasslands

_____ **2.** volunteers who enforced laws in the West

_____ **3.** proposed creating two large reservations on the Plains

_____ **4.** leader in the movement to establish African American schools

_____ **5.** Samuel Clemens

_____ **6.** intended to make train service safer and more reliable

_____ **7.** character popularized by a slavery-era blackface stage performer

_____ **8.** journey across the Plains to bring cattle to railroad shipping centers

_____ **9.** often blamed for crime and violence

_____ **10.** corrupt Democratic political machine in New York City

Column B

A. Booker T. Washington

B. long drive

C. Mark Twain

D. time zones

E. vigilance committees

F. Indian Peace Commission

G. immigrants

H. longhorn

I. Tammany Hall

J. Jim Crow

DIRECTIONS: Multiple Choice Choose the item that best completes each statement or answers each question. Write the letter in the blank. *(4 points each)*

_____ **11.** Many of the first Colorado miners did not find gold or silver because
   A. usually the reports of such strikes were false.
   B. the miners could not reach the remote areas where the gold or silver lay.
   C. mining companies had beaten them to the claims.
   D. the gold or silver lay hidden beneath the surface.

_____ **12.** People who would move to an area, hoping to become rich from finding minerals, were known as
   A. settlers.   **C.** frontiersmen.
   B. prospectors.   **D.** ranchers.

_____ **13.** On the Great Plains, wheat had an advantage because
   A. it could withstand drought better than other crops.
   B. it could resist disease better than other crops.
   C. large amounts of it could grow on a relatively small plot of land.
   D. it could bring higher prices than other crops suitable for cultivation there.

(continued)

Unit 3 Pretest, Form A

_____ **14.** Corporations issue stock to
  A. allow them to open factories in rural areas.
  B. allow them to lower prices on their products.
  C. raise large amounts of money and spread financial risk.
  D. create a large business by buying many small businesses.

_____ **15.** Companies during the 1800s generally paid women less than men because they believed women
  A. could not do as much work as men.   **C.** would soon leave to have children.
  B. had men to support them.   **D.** could live on less money than men.

_____ **16.** At the end of a long journey across the sea, most European immigrants to the United States disembarked at
  A. Angel Island.   **C.** Ellis Island.
  B. Manhattan Island.   **D.** Alcatraz Island.

_____ **17.** Often labor unions were not happy about immigration, believing that most immigrants
  A. had no marketable skills.   **C.** would not join a union.
  B. would work for low wages.   **D.** did not understand English.

_____ **18.** The game of football was at first mostly played by
  A. the working classes.   **C.** immigrants.
  B. young children.   **D.** the upper classes.

_____ **19.** With new technology, factories could
  A. produce more goods at lower prices.   **C.** produce fewer goods at lower prices.
  B. produce more goods at higher prices.   **D.** produce fewer goods at higher prices.

_____ **20.** Segregation in the South, unlike the North, was
  A. enforced by law.   **C.** not limited to public places.
  B. enforced by violence.   **D.** not limited to private clubs.

DIRECTIONS: Essay Answer one of the following questions on a separate sheet of paper. *(20 points)*

21. Mark Twain called the period between about 1870 and 1900 the "Gilded Age." Something is "gilded" if it is covered in gold on the outside but made of cheaper material inside. What do you think Twain was trying to say about this era?

22. Mining in the mountainous West in the late 1800s was a story of boomtowns followed by ghost towns. What do you think caused this cycle of boom and bust?

⭐ **Unit 3 Pretest, Form B**

Score

The Birth of Modern America

DIRECTIONS: Matching Match each item in Column A with the items in Column B. Write the correct letters in the blanks. *(4 points each)*

Column A

_____ 1. cycle of many people moving to a town and then leaving it when the mines were played out

_____ 2. stray calves with no identifying brands

_____ 3. relies on supply and demand rather than government to regulate prices and wages

_____ 4. linked distant regions of the United States

_____ 5. combines many firms in the same type of business into one large firm

_____ 6. resulted when sheep herders or farmers blocked cattle trails

_____ 7. disembarkation point for immigrants crossing the Atlantic

_____ 8. place where Louis Sullivan built skyscrapers

_____ 9. offered practical aid and religious counseling to the urban poor

_____ 10. originally organized for social and educational purposes; became a political force

Column B

A. Chicago

B. mavericks

C. laissez-faire

D. boom and bust

E. the Grange

F. Salvation Army

G. horizontal integration

H. Ellis Island

I. range wars

J. transcontinental railroad

DIRECTIONS: Multiple Choice Choose the item that best completes each sentence or answers each question. Write the letter in the blank. *(4 points each)*

_____ 11. Corporations used _____ to find mineral deposits that lay far underground.
A. placer mining
B. quartz mining
C. strip mining
D. diamond mining

_____ 12. George Custer attacked a large group of Lakota and Cheyenne warriors at
A. the Black Hills.
B. Bighorn Mountain.
C. the Little Bighorn River.
D. Wounded Knee.

_____ 13. One reason for America's industrial success is its
A. small workforce.
B. abundant raw materials.
C. wide open spaces.
D. access to oceans.

(continued)

★ Unit 3 Pretest, Form B

Score

_____ **14.** Using information as a business owner to manipulate stock prices and make large gains is known as
  A. information leaks.
  B. stock fraud.
  C. trading on margin.
  D. insider trading.

_____ **15.** According to the concept of laissez-faire, prices and wages are regulated by
  A. businesses.
  B. government.
  C. the GNP.
  D. supply and demand.

_____ **16.** In the late 1800s, _____ became a popular way to sell products to people living in rural areas.
  A. door-to-door salespeople
  B. chain stores
  C. department stores
  D. mail-order catalogs

_____ **17.** Workers were often _____ if they tried to organize a union.
  A. put under contract
  B. sent to another factory
  C. locked out
  D. blacklisted

_____ **18.** What was one of the primary reasons that poor Europeans emigrated to the United States?
  A. to escape persecution
  B. to break away from Europe's class system
  C. to get an education
  D. to gain a sense of individualism

_____ **19.** Popular in Chicago, _____ functioned as community and political centers for men.
  A. Grange halls
  B. amusement parks
  C. saloons
  D. baseball fields

_____ **20.** After the Civil War, the United States had all of the following types of currency in circulation EXCEPT
  A. redbacks.
  B. greenbacks.
  C. gold and silver coins.
  D. national bank notes.

DIRECTIONS: Essay Answer one of the following questions on a separate sheet of paper. *(20 points)*

21. What role did railroads play in settling the Great Plains?

22. What are corporations? Who owns them, and how do they raise money for large projects?

The American Republic Since 1877

⭐ **Chapter 8**

Section Quiz 8-1

DIRECTIONS: Matching Match each item in Column A with the items in Column B. Write the correct letters in the blanks. *(10 points each)*

Column A

_____ **1.** the major route north to Abilene, Kansas

_____ **2.** mining that dug deep beneath the surface

_____ **3.** self-appointed volunteers to track down and punish wrongdoers

_____ **4.** vast areas of grassland owned by the federal government

_____ **5.** process of extracting shallow deposits of ore largely by hand

Column B

A. open range

B. placer mining

C. vigilance committees

D. Chisholm Trail

E. quartz mining

DIRECTIONS: Multiple Choice In the blank at the left, write the letter of the choice that best completes the statement or answers the question. *(10 points each)*

_____ **6.** What brought the first wave of settlers to the West?
  A. ranching
  B. fur trading
  C. farming
  D. mining

_____ **7.** Although only a fraction of the herds survived when ranchers rounded up their cattle in 1866 and drove them to Sedalia, Missouri, it was the first
  A. long drive.
  B. range war.
  C. open range.
  D. wagon train.

_____ **8.** In 1859 when prospector Henry Comstock staked a claim in Six-Mile Canyon, Nevada, the sticky blue-gray mud there turned out to be
  A. iron ore.
  B. fool's gold.
  C. silver ore.
  D. lead.

_____ **9.** Deep deposits of lead that contained large amounts of silver led to the creation of one of the most legendary boomtowns that dotted the mining frontier,
  A. Pike's Peak.
  B. Virginia City.
  C. Comstock.
  D. Leadville.

_____ **10.** Eventually, and after considerable loss of life, the open range was largely fenced off with a new invention called
  A. barbed wire.
  B. lariats.
  C. electric fences.
  D. range barriers.

★ **Chapter 8**

Section Quiz 8-2

DIRECTIONS: Matching Match each item in Column A with the items in Column B. Write the correct letters in the blanks. *(10 points each)*

Column A

_____ **1.** a tract of public land available for settlement

_____ **2.** often brought their owners big profits

_____ **3.** productive farm area that began at the eastern edge of the Great Plains

_____ **4.** explored the Great Plains in 1819

_____ **5.** planting seeds deep in the ground where there was enough moisture for them to grow

Column B

A. bonanza farms

B. Stephen Long

C. Wheat Belt

D. dry farming

E. homestead

DIRECTIONS: Multiple Choice In the blank at the left, write the letter of the choice that best completes the statement or answers the question. *(10 points each)*

_____ **6.** By the 1860s, farmers on the Plains were adopting newly designed steel plows, seed drills, reapers, and
  A. harvesting machines.   **C.** homesteads.
  B. threshing machines.   **D.** irrigation systems.

_____ **7.** Which of the following were NOT hardships that early settlers on the Great Plains faced?
  A. scorching summers   **C.** prairie fires
  B. too many trees   **D.** swarms of grasshoppers

_____ **8.** Settlement in the Great Plains was promoted by the railroads and supported by
  A. the mining industry.   **C.** plow manufacturers.
  B. cattle ranchers.   **D.** the government.

_____ **9.** The Great Plains extends westward to the Rocky Mountains from around the 100th meridian—an imaginary line running north and south from the central Dakotas through
  A. El Paso, Texas.   **C.** Western Texas.
  B. Denver, Colorado.   **D.** St. Louis, Missouri.

_____ **10.** What name did the first explorers of the Great Plains give the area?
  A. Great American Desert   **C.** Unfit Frontier
  B. Wheat Belt   **D.** Indian Territory

★ **Chapter 8**

Section Quiz 8-3

DIRECTIONS: Matching Match each item in Column A with the items in Column B.
Write the correct letters in the blanks. *(10 points each)*

Column A

_____ **1.** leader of the Nez Perce people

_____ **2.** site of a murderous battle between U.S. soldiers and
Lakota men, women, and children

_____ **3.** to be absorbed

_____ **4.** main source of food for many Native Americans

_____ **5.** payments to reservation dwellers

Column B

A. Chief Joseph

B. assimilate

C. annuities

D. Wounded Knee
Creek

E. buffalo

DIRECTIONS: Multiple Choice In the blank at the left, write the letter of the choice
that best completes the statement or answers the question. *(10 points each)*

_____ **6.** The Lakota fought hard to keep control of their hunting grounds, which
extended from the Black Hills westward to the
   A. Pacific coast.   **C.** Gulf of Mexico.
   B. Mississippi River.   **D.** Bighorn Mountains.

_____ **7.** A serious toll was taken on Native Americans from the advancing
American settlers, the loss of hunting grounds, forced movement, and
   A. broken treaties.   **C.** the Civil War.
   B. drought.   **D.** immigration.

_____ **8.** Roaming vast distances, the Sioux and the Dakota were
   A. farmers.   **C.** trappers.
   B. nomads.   **D.** miners.

_____ **9.** Who proposed creating two large reservations on the Plains in 1867, one
for the Sioux and another for southern Plains Indians?
   A. Chief Little Crow   **C.** Indian Peace Commission
   B. George A. Custer   **D.** General Nelson Miles

_____ **10.** Defying the orders of the government agent at the reservation, the
Lakota continued to perform a ritual that was important to them
called the
   A. Buffalo Hunt.   **C.** Bighorn Dance.
   B. Peace Dance.   **D.** Ghost Dance.

⭐ **Chapter 8 Test, Form A**

Settling the West

DIRECTIONS: Matching Match each item in Column A with the items in Column B.
Write the correct letters in the blanks. *(4 points each)*

Column A

_____ **1.** Lakota Sioux chief killed at Wounded Knee

_____ **2.** Lakota Sioux religious leader and war chief who lured an army detachment into an ambush in Wyoming

_____ **3.** commander who battled the Lakota Sioux at Little Bighorn

_____ **4.** chief who led the Dakota Sioux uprising in Minnesota

_____ **5.** leader of the Cheyenne who were massacred at Sand Creek

_____ **6.** leader of an army detachment wiped out by the Lakota Sioux in Wyoming

_____ **7.** commander who attacked the Cheyenne at Sand Creek

_____ **8.** Nez Perce chief who surrendered after losing much of his band in a series of battles

_____ **9.** occurred when farmers blocked cattle trails

_____ **10.** boomtown near the Comstock Lode

Column B

A. Black Kettle

B. John Chivington

C. Little Crow

D. William Fetterman

E. Sitting Bull

F. Crazy Horse

G. George A. Custer

H. Chief Joseph

I. range wars

J. Virginia City

DIRECTIONS: Multiple Choice Choose the item that best completes each statement or answers each question. Write the letter in the blank. *(4 points each)*

_____ **11.** Early prospectors would extract shallow deposits of ore by
    A. quartz mining.
    B. strip mining.
    C. placer mining.
    D. surface mining.

_____ **12.** The Comstock Lode was a rich deposit of
    A. gold.
    B. silver.
    C. copper.
    D. diamonds.

_____ **13.** Many of the first miners in the Colorado mountains did not find minerals because
    A. there were no minerals.
    B. the areas were too remote.
    C. mining companies had claimed them.
    D. the minerals were too deep.

_____ **14.** In the early 1800s, Americans did not think cattle ranches on the Great Plains were practical because
    A. with so little rain, not enough grass could grow to support large herds.
    B. eastern cattle could not survive on the tough prairie grasses.
    C. wagon trains had stripped the land of the resources needed to support ranching.
    D. hostile Native Americans in the area made settlement hazardous.

(continued)

★ **Chapter 8 Test, Form A**

_____ **15.** The Chisholm Trail was a trail that
   A. wagon trains followed west through the Rocky Mountains.
   B. Native Americans traveled on their forced migration to reservations in the West.
   C. cowboys used to drive cattle to a railroad line for sale.
   D. Lewis and Clark mapped on their way to the Pacific coast.

_____ **16.** At first, ranchers saw barbed wire as a threat because it
   A. harmed their cattle.   **C.** required much effort to maintain.
   B. kept their herds from roaming freely.   **D.** kept their herds away from food.

_____ **17.** Under the Homestead Act, homesteaders could gain title to the land by
   A. fencing it within five years.   **C.** living there for five years.
   B. planting it within five years.   **D.** building a home on it.

_____ **18.** One approach to farming the Great Plains was "dry farming," in which farmers
   A. cooperated to build community irrigation ditches from the nearest river.
   B. dug out depressions to catch the precious rain, creating ponds for irrigation.
   C. selected crops that could withstand long periods without rain.
   D. planted seeds deep in the ground where there was enough moisture for them.

_____ **19.** In the 1890s, when a glut of wheat on the world market caused prices to drop, some farmers tried to survive by
   A. planting corn and other crops.   **C.** mortgaging their land.
   B. forming cooperatives.   **D.** buying more land on credit.

_____ **20.** The Dawes Act attempted to help Native Americans by
   A. selling land and building a trust of money for them.   **C.** reintroducing the buffalo to reservation lands.
   B. returning them to their native lands.   **D.** training them to become farmers.

DIRECTIONS: Essay Answer one of the following questions on a separate sheet of paper. *(20 points)*

21. Explain the cycle illustrated in the diagram.

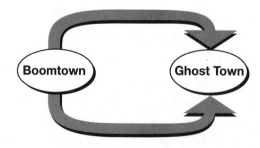

22. How did railroads help to settle the Great Plains?

★ Chapter 8 Test, Form B

Score

Settling the West

DIRECTIONS: Matching Match each item in Column A with the items in Column B. Write the correct letters in the blanks. *(4 points each)*

Column A

_____ **1.** supply point for mining areas in the Rocky Mountains

_____ **2.** closed with the rapid settlement of the West

_____ **3.** prospector who staked a claim in Six-Mile Canyon, Nevada

_____ **4.** destination for those using the Chisholm Trail

_____ **5.** self-appointed law enforcers

_____ **6.** destination for the first cattle drive

_____ **7.** writer who sparked discussion of better treatment for Native Americans

_____ **8.** cattle that roamed wild on the grasslands of Texas

_____ **9.** invention that helped end the cowboy lifestyle

_____ **10.** journey across the Plains to bring cattle to railroad shipping centers

Column B

A. Sedalia

B. barbed wire

C. Henry Comstock

D. Abilene

E. frontier

F. Helen Hunt Jackson

G. vigilance committees

H. long drive

I. Denver

J. longhorn

DIRECTIONS: Multiple Choice Choose the item that best completes each statement or answers each question. Write the letter in the blank. *(4 points each)*

_____ **11.** After ore near the surface dwindled, mining corporations began
   A. quartz mining.
   B. strip mining.
   C. placer mining.
   D. tunnel mining.

_____ **12.** The people who used the phrase "Pikes Peak or Bust" were
   A. mountain climbers in Colorado.
   B. silver miners near Pikes Peak.
   C. gold miners near Pikes Peak.
   D. settlers heading to Colorado.

_____ **13.** The legendary boomtown of Leadville got its name from
   A. rich deposits of lead.
   B. lead deposits that contained large amounts of silver.
   C. lead deposits that contained large amounts of gold.
   D. the town's main industry, which made lead from its rich copper deposits.

_____ **14.** The material for "dime novels" often came from
   A. miners' exaggerated tales of striking it rich.
   B. cowboys' exaggerated tales of daring.
   C. immigrants' exaggerated tales of battles with hostile Native Americans.
   D. explorers' exaggerated tales of adventure and discovery in the wilderness.

(continued)

_____ **15.** The fencing of the open range resulted in all of the following EXCEPT
  A. the end of long cattle drives.
  B. the transition of cowboys to ranch hands.
  C. the replacement of longhorns with new European breeds.
  D. the decline of the cattle industry in favor of sheep ranching.

_____ **16.** Wheat had an advantage on the Great Plains because
  A. it could withstand drought better than other crops.
  B. it could resist disease better than other crops.
  C. large amounts of it could grow on a relatively small plot of land.
  D. it could bring higher prices than other crops suitable for cultivation there.

_____ **17.** Which of the following was a hardship faced by settlers on the Great Plains?
  A. prairie fires   **C.** too many trees
  B. flooding   **D.** loose soil

_____ **18.** Before the Sand Creek Massacre, the Cheyenne had come to Camp Lyon to
  A. negotiate.   **C.** attack.
  B. surrender.   **D.** defend their land.

_____ **19.** The army encouraged white hunters to kill buffalo to
  A. stop buffalo from trampling crops.
  B. starve the Native Americans.
  C. force Native Americans onto reservations.
  D. make way for new railroad lines.

_____ **20.** The confrontation at Wounded Knee occurred because the chief's followers
  A. would not stay on the reservation.   **C.** continued to hunt buffalo.
  B. were raiding nearby farms.   **D.** continued to perform a ritual.

DIRECTIONS: Essay Answer one of the following questions on a separate sheet of paper. *(20 points)*

21. Explain the cause-and-effect diagram about cattle ranching on the Great Plains.

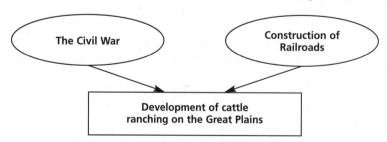

22. Describe the agreement the Dakota Sioux had made with the United States government and the reasons for their uprising.

The American Republic Since 1877

★ **Chapter 9**

Score

Section Quiz 9-1

DIRECTIONS: Matching Match each item in Column A with the items in Column B. Write the correct letters in the blanks. *(10 points each)*

Column A

_____ **1.** people who risk their capital in organizing and running a business

_____ **2.** the total value of all goods and services produced by a country

_____ **3.** act that reversed years of declining tariffs

_____ **4.** "let do," a French phrase meaning "let people do as they choose"

_____ **5.** resource that could be turned into kerosene

Column B

A. Morrill Tariff

B. laissez-faire

C. gross national product

D. petroleum

E. entrepreneurs

DIRECTIONS: Multiple Choice In the blank at the left, write the letter of the choice that best completes the statement or answers the question. *(10 points each)*

_____ **6.** Supporters of laissez-faire generally oppose subsidies and favor
   A. tariffs.
   B. high prices.
   C. free trade.
   D. monopolies.

_____ **7.** By the early 1900s, Americans had transformed the United States into the world's leading
   A. gross national product.
   B. industrial nation.
   C. laissez-faire country.
   D. military establishment.

_____ **8.** Who invented the telephone, which revolutionized both business and personal communication?
   A. Alexander Graham Bell
   B. Thomas Alva Edison
   C. Edwin Drake
   D. George Pullman

_____ **9.** What were equally as important as natural resources in the nation's rapid industrialization?
   A. political systems
   B. tariff laws
   C. new technology
   D. human resources

_____ **10.** The first oil well was drilled near Titusville, Pennsylvania, by
   A. Alexander Graham Bell.
   B. Edwin Drake.
   C. Thomas Alva Edison.
   D. Elisha Otis.

Chapter 9

Section Quiz 9-2

DIRECTIONS: Matching Match each item in Column A with the items in Column B. Write the correct letters in the blanks. *(10 points each)*

Column A

_____ **1.** one of the most famous and successful railroad consolidators

_____ **2.** regions where the same time is kept

_____ **3.** used information he received as a railroad owner to manipulate stock prices to his benefit

_____ **4.** built the Great Northern Railroad

_____ **5.** given to the railroad companies by the government to encourage railroad construction

Column B

A. time zones

B. James J. Hill

C. land grants

D. Cornelius Vanderbilt

E. Jay Gould

DIRECTIONS: Multiple Choice In the blank at the left, write the letter of the choice that best completes the statement or answers the question. *(10 points each)*

_____ **6.** Which transcontinental railroad operated without government subsidies or land grants, became the most successful, and was the only one not forced into bankruptcy?
   A. Central Pacific Railroad   **C.** Pennsylvania Railroad
   B. Great Northern Railroad   **D.** Union Pacific Railroad

_____ **7.** The railroad boom began in 1862 when President Abraham Lincoln signed the
   A. time zone legislation.   **C.** Land Grant Law.
   B. Gettysburg Address.   **D.** Pacific Railway Act.

_____ **8.** By linking the nation, railroads helped increase the size of markets, providing greater opportunities for many
   A. industries.   **C.** Native Americans.
   B. cities.   **D.** insider traders.

_____ **9.** The Central Pacific Railroad began as the dream of engineer
   A. Leland Stanford.   **C.** Theodore Dehone Judah.
   B. Charley Crocker.   **D.** Collis P. Huntington.

_____ **10.** What railroad began pushing westward from Omaha, Nebraska, in 1865 under the direction of engineer Grenville Dodge?
   A. Central Pacific   **C.** Crédit Mobilier
   B. Southern Railway   **D.** Union Pacific

★ **Chapter 9**

Section Quiz 9-3

DIRECTIONS: Matching Match each item in Column A with the items in Column B.
Write the correct letters in the blanks. *(10 points each)*

Column A

_____ **1.** process for making high-quality steel efficiently and
cheaply

_____ **2.** agreements to maintain prices at a certain level

_____ **3.** when a company owns all the different businesses on
which it depends for its operation

_____ **4.** became one of the most successful retail chains in
American history

_____ **5.** when a single company achieves control of an entire
market

Column B

A. Woolworth's

B. pools

C. Bessemer process

D. monopoly

E. vertical
integration

DIRECTIONS: Multiple Choice In the blank at the left, write the letter of the choice
that best completes the statement or answers the question. *(10 points each)*

_____ **6.** What is an organization owned by many people but treated by law as
though it were a single person?
A. a corporation   **C.** a holding company
B. an organized pool   **D.** a trust

_____ **7.** Loans, mortgages, and taxes are examples of a company's
A. stock.   **C.** fixed costs.
B. pools.   **D.** operating costs.

_____ **8.** Combining many firms engaged in the same type of business into one
corporation is called
A. vertical integration.   **C.** horizontal integration.
B. a holding company.   **D.** a monopoly.

_____ **9.** What type of company does not produce anything itself?
A. a corporation   **C.** a monopoly
B. a holding company   **D.** a stock company

_____ **10.** N.W. Ayer and Son of Philadelphia developed bold new formats for
A. chain stores.   **C.** trusts.
B. steel companies.   **D.** advertising.

Chapter 9

Section Quiz 9-4

DIRECTIONS: Matching Match each item in Column A with the items in Column B. Write the correct letters in the blanks. *(10 points each)*

Column A

_____ 1. process whereby an impartial third party helps workers and management reach an agreement

_____ 2. a rise in the value of money

_____ 3. first national association dedicated to promoting women's labor issues

_____ 4. unions limited to people with specific skills

_____ 5. first nationwide industrial union

Column B

A. Knights of Labor

B. Women's Trade Union League

C. arbitration

D. deflation

E. trade unions

DIRECTIONS: Multiple Choice In the blank at the left, write the letter of the choice that best completes the statement or answers the question. *(10 points each)*

_____ 6. What did several railroads announce in July of 1877 that triggered the first nationwide labor protest?

    A. employee layoffs   **C.** blacklists

    B. wage cuts   **D.** sixteen-hour workdays

_____ 7. The first leader of the American Federation of Labor, Samuel Gompers, believed that unions should stay out of

    A. arbitration.   **C.** corporations.

    B. riots.   **D.** politics.

_____ 8. Workers who tried to organize a union or strike were often fired and placed on a list of "troublemakers" called the

    A. union list.   **C.** lockout list.

    B. blacklist.   **D.** strikebreaker list.

_____ 9. Who claimed that after a workers' revolution, the government would seize all private property and create a socialist society where wealth was evenly divided?

    A. the Knights of Labor   **C.** the Marxists

    B. the Pullman Company   **D.** the anarchists

_____ 10. What incident occurred in 1886 that badly hurt the Knights of Labor's reputation?

    A. Haymarket Riot   **C.** Pullman Strike

    B. formation of the American Federation of Labor   **D.** Great Railroad Strike

The American Republic Since 1877

★ Chapter 9 Test, Form A

Industrialization

DIRECTIONS: Matching Match each item in Column A with the items in Column B.
Write the correct letters in the blanks. *(4 points each)*

Column A

_____ **1.** wages, shipping charges, and supplies, for
example

_____ **2.** Iron Molders' International Union, for example

_____ **3.** Knights of Labor, for example

_____ **4.** began the railroad boom

_____ **5.** loans, mortgages, and taxes, for example

_____ **6.** changed bobbins without stopping

_____ **7.** enabled longer and heavier trains

_____ **8.** owns stock of companies that produce goods

_____ **9.** "Let people do as they choose."

_____ **10.** manages property for others

Column B

A. fixed costs

B. holding company

C. industrial union

D. air brakes

E. operating costs

F. trade union

G. Northrop
automatic loom

H. Pacific Railway
Act

I. trust

J. laissez-faire

DIRECTIONS: Multiple Choice Choose the item that best completes each statement
or answers each question. Write the letter in the blank. *(4 points each)*

_____ **11.** Even before the invention of the automobile, petroleum was in high
demand because it could
A. lubricate moving parts in machines.   **C.** be turned into kerosene.
B. be turned into plastics.   **D.** power locomotives.

_____ **12.** Laissez-faire relies on _____ to regulate prices and wages.
A. businesses   **C.** the GNP
B. government   **D.** supply and demand

_____ **13.** During the early days of industrialization, many members of Congress
believed that tariffs were necessary to
A. raise money to operate the government.
B. help new American industries compete with large established European
factories.
C. raise the prices that Europeans would have to pay for American products.
D. entice European consumers to buy American products.

_____ **14.** Economies of scale resulted in
A. a wider variety of products.   **C.** higher costs and higher prices.
B. lower costs and higher prices.   **D.** lower costs and lower prices.

(continued)

Chapter 9 Test, Form A

Score

_____ **15.** The government offered each railroad company building the transcontinental railroad land along its right-of-way to
  A. give railroad workers a place to live.
  B. encourage rapid construction of the tracks.
  C. allow the companies to build stations at important points along the way.
  D. encourage the growth of towns along the tracks.

_____ **16.** Because of the shortage of workers in California, the Central Pacific Railroad hired workers from
  A. China.   **C.** Ireland.
  B. Japan.   **D.** Mexico.

_____ **17.** Railroad companies raised most of the money they needed to build their railroads from
  A. private investors.   **C.** subsidies from tax revenues.
  B. selling government land grants.   **D.** hauling freight to market.

_____ **18.** Corporations can achieve economies of scale by
  A. keeping their fixed costs as low as possible.
  B. keeping their operating costs as low as possible.
  C. investing in more machines and larger manufacturing facilities.
  D. investing in companies in the same business.

_____ **19.** Which of the following choices best describes the diagram?

  A. horizontal integration   **C.** trust company
  B. vertical integration   **D.** holding company

_____ **20.** In the late 1800s, workers' buying power generally increased because
  A. factories often increased wages.
  B. wages increased faster than prices.
  C. prices fell faster than wages.
  D. factories often increased prices.

DIRECTIONS: Essay Answer one of the following questions on a separate sheet of paper. *(20 points)*

21. What causes contributed to the tripling of the American population between 1860 and 1910, and how did this population growth aid industrialization?

22. What is a corporation, who owns it, and how does it raise money?

⭐ **Chapter 9 Test, Form B**

Industrialization

DIRECTIONS: Matching Match each item in Column A with the items in Column B.
Write the correct letters in the blanks. *(4 points each)*

Column A

_____ **1.** set up Menlo Park

_____ **2.** practiced "insider trading"

_____ **3.** "Come here, Watson, I want you."

_____ **4.** "The basic force shaping capitalism is the class struggle between workers and owners."

_____ **5.** began the first direct rail service from New York City to Chicago

_____ **6.** Standard Oil

_____ **7.** drilled the first oil well

_____ **8.** founded a steel company in Pittsburgh

_____ **9.** American Railway Union

_____ **10.** American Federation of Labor

Column B

A. Andrew Carnegie

B. Karl Marx

C. Cornelius Vanderbilt

D. Edwin Drake

E. Samuel Gompers

F. Alexander Graham Bell

G. Jay Gould

H. Thomas Alva Edison

I. Eugene V. Debs

J. John D. Rockefeller

DIRECTIONS: Multiple Choice Choose the item that best completes each statement
or answers each question. Write the letter in the blank. *(4 points each)*

_____ **11.** Supporters of laissez-faire believed the government should interfere in the economy only to
  A. protect property rights and maintain peace.
  B. protect new domestic businesses from foreign competition.
  C. keep prices from rising too high.
  D. bring the country out of an economic crisis.

_____ **12.** Measurements taken of Union soldiers during the Civil War led to the development of
  A. more practical military uniforms.   **C.** rifles made to arm length.
  B. the science of physiology.   **D.** ready-made clothes.

_____ **13.** The two railroads that built the transcontinental railroad were the
  A. Southern Railway and Union Pacific.
  B. Southern Railway and Great Northern.
  C. Union Pacific and Great Northern.
  D. Union Pacific and Central Pacific.

_____ **14.** Construction of the transcontinental railroad pushed west from
  A. St. Louis, Missouri.   **C.** Omaha, Nebraska.
  B. Ogden, Utah.   **D.** Chicago, Illinois.

(continued)

★ **Chapter 9 Test, Form B**

Score

_____ **15.** To make rail service more reliable, in 1883 the American Railway Association
   A. set standards for materials used in the construction of railroad lines.
   B. set a maximum for the number of cars a train could pull.
   C. divided the country into latitude and longitude lines.
   D. divided the country into four time zones.

_____ **16.** In the Crédit Mobilier scandal, Union Pacific investors got rich by
   A. accepting bribes from business owners to route tracks through their towns.
   B. achieving a monopoly in hauling freight along their railroad's tracks.
   C. paying inflated bills from a construction company they controlled.
   D. conspiring with other railroads to set high prices.

_____ **17.** It made sense for big corporations to continue operating during poor economic times because
   A. their operating costs were so small compared to their fixed costs.
   B. their fixed costs were so small compared to their operating costs.
   C. their stock provided a continuous source of income in bad times as well as good.
   D. they could always raise prices to bring in more money.

_____ **18.** Which of the following choices best describes the diagram?

| Oil Co. A | + | Oil Co. B | + | Oil Co. C | = | Mega Oil Co. |

   A. horizontal integration   **C.** trust company
   B. vertical integration   **D.** holding company

_____ **19.** Department stores changed the idea of shopping by
   A. locating in rural areas.
   B. offering low prices instead of elaborate services and decor.
   C. bringing together a huge array of different products in a large elegant building.
   D. coming together to form shopping malls.

_____ **20.** A _____ was a technique for breaking a union in which the company refused to allow the workers on the property and refused to pay them.
   A. blacklist   **C.** shutout
   B. strikebreaker   **D.** lockout

DIRECTIONS: Essay Answer one of the following questions on a separate sheet of paper. *(20 points)*

21. In what ways did the expansion of railroads spur America's industrial growth?

22. What were the basic ideas of Marxism?

⭐ **Chapter 10**

Section Quiz 10-1

DIRECTIONS: Matching Match each item in Column A with the items in Column B.
Write the correct letters in the blanks. *(10 points each)*

Column A

_____ **1.** the most basic and cheapest accommodations on a
steamship

_____ **2.** an anti-immigrant organization

_____ **3.** insurrection against the Chinese government that caused
an increase of Chinese immigrants

_____ **4.** location of a barracks in California to accommodate Asian
immigrants

_____ **5.** a preference for native-born people and a desire to limit
immigration

Column B

A. Angel Island

B. steerage

C. American
Protective
Association

D. nativism

E. Taiping Rebellion

DIRECTIONS: Multiple Choice In the blank at the left, write the letter of the choice
that best completes the statement or answers the question. *(10 points each)*

_____ **6.** Nativism had focused primarily on Irish immigrants but grew to include
Asians, Jews, and
    A. Canadians.
    B. eastern Europeans.
    C. the British.
    D. Scandinavians.

_____ **7.** By the 1890s, immigrants made up significant percentages of some of the
country's largest
    A. plantations.
    B. cities.
    C. farms.
    D. suburbs.

_____ **8.** Where did many Chinese immigrants settle?
    A. western cities
    B. eastern cities
    C. southern plantations
    D. along the New England coast

_____ **9.** What law, passed in 1882, barred Chinese immigration for 10 years and
prevented the Chinese already in the country from becoming citizens?
    A. Workingman's Party of California Act
    B. Chinese Immigration Act
    C. Taiping Act
    D. Chinese Exclusion Act

_____ **10.** The processing center for the vast majority of immigrants arriving on the
East Coast was at
    A. Angel Island.
    B. Staten Island.
    C. Ellis Island.
    D. Long Island.

The American Republic Since 1877

★ **Chapter 10**

Section Quiz 10-2

DIRECTIONS: Matching Match each item in Column A with the items in Column B. Write the correct letters in the blanks. *(10 points each)*

Column A

_____ **1.** an informal political group designed to gain and keep power

_____ **2.** invented the electric trolley car

_____ **3.** documented slum life in the book *How the Other Half Lives*

_____ **4.** a railroad car pulled by horses

_____ **5.** tall steel frame buildings

Column B

A. Jacob Riis

B. skyscrapers

C. Frank J. Sprague

D. horsecar

E. political machine

DIRECTIONS: Multiple Choice In the blank at the left, write the letter of the choice that best completes the statement or answers the question. *(10 points each)*

_____ **6.** What was the famous New York Democratic political machine called?

  A. Tammany Hall

  B. Tammany Tweed

  C. Thomas Pendergast Machine

  D. William M. Tweed Hall

_____ **7.** No one contributed more to the design of skyscrapers than Chicago's

  A. Frank Lloyd Wright.

  B. Potter Palmer.

  C. Louis Sullivan.

  D. Frank J. Sprague.

_____ **8.** America's industrialization not only made some people wealthy; it also helped create a growing

  A. tenement system.

  B. middle class.

  C. agricultural system.

  D. political machine.

_____ **9.** To alleviate congestion in city streets, Chicago built an elevated railroad, and both Boston and New York built America's first

  A. trolley cars.

  B. tunnels.

  C. overpasses.

  D. subway systems.

_____ **10.** Who rose to be one of New York's most powerful party bosses?

  A. Thomas Pendergast

  B. Cornelius Vanderbilt

  C. George Plunkitt

  D. Zalmen Yoffeh

The American Republic Since 1877

⭐ **Chapter 10**

Section Quiz 10-3

DIRECTIONS: Matching Match each item in Column A with the items in Column B. Write the correct letters in the blanks. *(10 points each)*

Column A

_____ 1. entertainment adapted from French theater

_____ 2. belief that a person could rise in society, and go as far as their talents and commitment would take them

_____ 3. realistic writer who wrote *The Age of Innocence*, a stark portrait of upper-class New York society

_____ 4. first salaried baseball team, formed in 1869

_____ 5. wrote "rags-to-riches" novels

Column B

A. Edith Wharton

B. vaudeville

C. Horatio Alger

D. individualism

E. Cincinnati Red Stockings

DIRECTIONS: Multiple Choice In the blank at the left, write the letter of the choice that best completes the statement or answers the question. *(10 points each)*

_____ 6. The ideas of philosopher Herbert Spencer and others applied Charles Darwin's theory of evolution and natural selection to human society and was called
   A. Social Darwinism.
   B. Realism.
   C. Darwin's Followers.
   D. Human Society Theory.

_____ 7. By calling their era the Gilded Age, Mark Twain and Charles Warner were sounding
   A. a plea for individualism.
   B. a warning against realism.
   C. an alarm that beneath the surface lay corruption.
   D. a cry for voter's rights.

_____ 8. The Gospel of Wealth was a philosophy that held that wealthy Americans were responsible for using their great fortunes for social progress, or for engaging in
   A. gentility.
   B. culture.
   C. laissez-faire.
   D. philanthropy.

_____ 9. Just as Darwin had looked at the natural world scientifically, a new movement in art and literature moved away from romanticism and was called
   A. Darwinism.
   B. realism.
   C. modernism.
   D. traditionalism.

_____ 10. Popular culture changed in the late 1800s because industrialization improved the standard of living for many people, enabling them to spend money on
   A. entertainment and recreation.
   B. travel abroad.
   C. clothing.
   D. houses.

★ **Chapter 10**

Section Quiz 10-4

DIRECTIONS: Matching Match each item in Column A with the items in Column B. Write the correct letters in the blanks. *(10 points each)*

Column A

_____ **1.** the idea that people succeed in the world not because of their ability to compete, but because of their ability to cooperate

_____ **2.** Baptist minister and leader in the Social Gospel movement

_____ **3.** prominent naturalist writer

_____ **4.** established in poor neighborhoods where middle-class residents lived and helped the poor residents

_____ **5.** the idea that some people failed in life simply because they were caught up in circumstances they could not control

Column B

A. naturalism

B. Reform Darwinism

C. settlement houses

D. Stephen Crane

E. Walter Rauschenbusch

DIRECTIONS: Multiple Choice In the blank at the left, write the letter of the choice that best completes the statement or answers the question. *(10 points each)*

_____ **6.** Jane Addams, who opened Hull House in Chicago, inspired many more such settlements across the country, including the well-known Henry Street Settlement in New York opened by
  A. Dwight L. Moody.
  B. Booker T. Washington.
  C. Washington Gladden.
  D. Lillian Wald.

_____ **7.** Edward Bellamy published *Looking Backward, 2000–1887*, a novel that depicted ideas opposite of Social Darwinism and laissez-faire, and so were essentially a form of
  A. socialism.
  B. humanism.
  C. progressivism.
  D. naturalism.

_____ **8.** From about 1870 until 1920, reformers worked to better conditions in cities according to biblical ideals of charity and justice in the
  A. Reform Darwinism movement.
  B. Salvation Army.
  C. Social Gospel movement.
  D. Young Men's Christian Association.

_____ **9.** Like the Salvation Army, the Young Men's Christian Association (YMCA) also began in
  A. New York.
  B. England.
  C. Ireland.
  D. Boston.

_____ **10.** What was often crucial to the Americanization of immigrant children?
  A. public schools
  B. ethnic churches
  C. vaudeville
  D. settlement houses

The American Republic Since 1877

★ Chapter 10 Test, Form A

Urban America

DIRECTIONS: Matching Match each item in Column A with the items in Column B. Write the correct letters in the blanks. *(4 points each)*

Column A

_____ 1. developed the theory of evolution and natural selection

_____ 2. argued that society progressed because only the fittest people survived

_____ 3. wrote "rags-to-riches" novels

_____ 4. believed that those who profited from society owed it something in return

_____ 5. with Mark Twain, wrote *The Gilded Age*

_____ 6. Mark Twain's real name

_____ 7. realist painter who even dared to paint President Hayes working in shirtsleeves

_____ 8. wrote the first truly American novel

_____ 9. won the Pulitzer prize for the novel *The Age of Innocence*, a stark portrait of upper-class New York society in the 1870s

_____ 10. the "King of Ragtime"

Column B

A. Horatio Alger

B. Andrew Carnegie

C. Thomas Eakins

D. Mark Twain

E. Edith Wharton

F. Charles Darwin

G. Scott Joplin

H. Herbert Spencer

I. Samuel Clemens

J. Charles Warner

DIRECTIONS: Multiple Choice Choose the item that best completes each statement or answers each question. Write the letter in the blank. *(4 points each)*

_____ 11. By 1900, more than half of all immigrants in the United States were
  A. European Jews.   **C.** Chinese.
  B. eastern and southern Europeans.   **D.** Japanese.

_____ 12. In the early 1860s, Chinese immigrants came to the United States to
  A. escape industrialization in China.   **C.** escape religious persecution.
  B. work in factories in Chicago.   **D.** work on the transcontinental railroad.

_____ 13. Many labor unions opposed immigration, arguing that most immigrants
  A. had no marketable skills.   **C.** would not join a union.
  B. would work for low wages.   **D.** did not understand English.

_____ 14. The Workingman's Party of California was formed to
  A. fight Chinese immigration.
  B. gain better wages and working conditions for factory workers in California.
  C. fight Catholic immigration.
  D. help immigrants find housing and jobs in their new homes.

(continued)

★ **Chapter 10 Test, Form A**

_____ **15.** In the late 1800s, the most common form of mass transit in cities was the
    A. cable car.
    C. horsecar.
    B. trolley car.
    D. subway.

_____ **16.** Most people who lived in "streetcar suburbs" were
    A. high society.
    C. working class.
    B. middle class.
    D. rural gentility.

_____ **17.** William M. Tweed was
    A. the engineer who invented the electric trolley car.
    B. the leader of the Workingman's Party.
    C. the architect who designed America's first skyscraper.
    D. a corrupt party boss in a political machine.

_____ **18.** _____ was the philosophy that wealthy Americans bore the responsibility of using their great fortunes to further social progress.
    A. Social Darwinism
    C. Realism
    B. Gospel of Wealth
    D. Redistribution of Wealth

_____ **19.** In big cities like Chicago in the 1800s, _____ functioned like community centers and political centers for male workers.
    A. churches
    C. saloons
    B. sports clubs
    D. cafes

_____ **20.** For which group has life expectancy increased the most from 1900 to 1997?

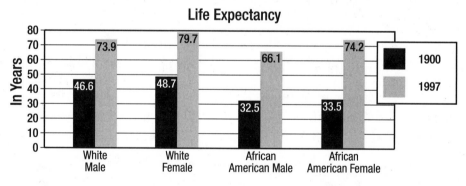

    A. white male
    C. African American male
    B. white female
    D. African American female

DIRECTIONS: Essay Answer one of the following questions on a separate sheet of paper. *(20 points)*

21. Describe several reasons Europeans immigrated to the U.S. in the late 1800s.

22. Explain the meaning of "gilded" and why the period between about 1870 and 1900 was called the "Gilded Age."

⭐ **Chapter 10 Test, Form B**

Score

Urban America

DIRECTIONS: Matching Match each item in Column A with the items in Column B.
Write the correct letters in the blanks. *(4 points each)*

Column A

_____ **1.** early advocate of the Social Gospel

_____ **2.** argued that government could solve society's problems
more efficiently than competition in the marketplace

_____ **3.** revivalist who believed the way to help the poor was by
redeeming their souls and reforming their character

_____ **4.** founder of Tuskegee Institute

_____ **5.** opened Hull House in Chicago

_____ **6.** leader of the Social Gospel movement who believed that
competition was the cause of many social problems

_____ **7.** supported public libraries, believing that access to
knowledge was the key to getting ahead in life

_____ **8.** operated Henry Street Settlement in New York City

_____ **9.** proposed that the government tax the unearned wealth
landowners gained from just waiting for land prices to rise

_____ **10.** published a book describing a perfect society in 2000

Column B

A. Jane Addams

B. Edward Bellamy

C. Booker T.
Washington

D. Henry George

E. Lillian Wald

F. Andrew Carnegie

G. Washington
Gladden

H. Dwight L. Moody

I. Walter
Rauschenbusch

J. Lester Frank
Ward

DIRECTIONS: Multiple Choice Choose the item that best completes each statement
or answers each question. Write the letter in the blank. *(4 points each)*

_____ **11.** Immigrants tended to adjust well to America if they
A. settled in rural areas.
B. settled in cities.
C. settled with their own ethnic group.
D. settled with mixed ethnic groups.

_____ **12.** Which choice below best completes the diagram?

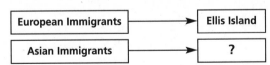

A. Angel Island
B. Manhattan Island
C. Whidbey Island
D. Alcatraz Island

_____ **13.** Nativists wanted to
A. group immigrants into their own sections of the city.
B. assimilate immigrants into American society.
C. limit immigration.
D. convert immigrants to Protestantism.

(continued)

★ **Chapter 10 Test, Form B**

Score

_____ **14.** Subway systems were first developed to
   A. transport people from the suburbs to their jobs in the city.
   B. transport people between cities.
   C. relieve congestion on city streets.
   D. transport farm products to market in cities.

_____ **15.** Tammany Hall was a
   A. saloon.   **C.** dance hall.
   B. theater.   **D.** political machine.

_____ **16.** Political machines provided new city dwellers with necessities such as
   jobs, housing, and police protection in exchange for
   A. kickbacks.   **C.** votes.
   B. graft.   **D.** a portion of their wages.

_____ **17.** The idea of individualism was that
   A. if you want something done right, you should do it yourself.
   B. no matter how humble your origins, you can rise as far as your talents and
   commitment will take you.
   C. you should do your own thing, no matter what other people think.
   D. you make your own happiness—you do not need others to make you happy.

_____ **18.** The first salaried baseball team was the
   A. Boston Red Socks.   **C.** New York Yankees.
   B. Cincinnati Red Stockings.   **D.** Pittsburgh Pirates.

_____ **19.** What philosophy stated that some people failed in life simply because
   they were caught up in circumstances they could not control?
   A. Realism   **C.** Social Darwinism
   B. Naturalism   **D**. Individualism

_____ **20.** What organization offered practical aid and religious counseling to the
   urban poor?
   A. American Protective Association **C.** Tammany Hall
   B. Vaudeville   **D.** Salvation Army

DIRECTIONS: Essay Answer one of the following questions on a separate sheet of
paper. *(20 points)*

21. Describe the problems of urban living in the late 1800s and their causes.

22. Explain the philosophy of Social Darwinism.

★ **Chapter 11**

Score

Section Quiz 11-1

DIRECTIONS: Matching Match each item in Column A with the items in Column B. Write the correct letters in the blanks. *(10 points each)*

Column A

_____ **1.** partial refunds

_____ **2.** when government jobs go to supporters of the winning party in an election

_____ **3.** law that reformed civil service

_____ **4.** renegade reformers who thought of themselves as moral leaders, more concerned with helping the nation than a political party

_____ **5.** declared illegal any, "combination in the form of trust . . . or conspiracy, in restraint of trade or commerce among the several States"

Column B

A. Mugwumps

B. patronage

C. Sherman Antitrust Act

D. rebates

E. Pendleton Act

DIRECTIONS: Multiple Choice In the blank at the left, write the letter of the choice that best completes the statement or answers the question. *(10 points each)*

_____ **6.** From 1877 to 1896, voting patterns in the United States gave the Democrats an edge in the
  A. Senate.
  B. presidential elections.
  C. court systems.
  D. House of Representatives.

_____ **7.** The Republicans and their candidate, Benjamin Harrison, received large contributions for the 1888 campaign from industrialists who benefited from
  A. the patronage system.
  B. the Pendleton Act.
  C. tariff protection.
  D. rebates.

_____ **8.** When Rutherford B. Hayes entered the White House in 1877 and attacked the practice of patronage, New York's Senator Conkling labeled the president and other Republican reformers
  A. Stalwarts.
  B. Mugwumps.
  C. Halfbreeds.
  D. Tammany Hallers.

_____ **9.** In 1884 who was the first elected Democratic president since 1856?
  A. Grover Cleveland
  B. Rutherford B. Hayes
  C. James Garfield
  D. Chester Arthur

_____ **10.** A bill that cut tobacco taxes and tariff rates on raw sugar but raised rates on other goods, such as textiles, to discourage people from buying those imports was the
  A. Sherman Antitrust Act.
  B. McKinley Tariff.
  C. Interstate Commerce Commission.
  D. Pendleton Act.

Chapter 11

Section Quiz 11-2

DIRECTIONS: Matching Match each item in Column A with the items in Column B.
Write the correct letters in the blanks. *(10 points each)*

Column A

_____ **1.** how farmers referred to the decision to stop minting silver

_____ **2.** nation's first national farm organization

_____ **3.** authorized the United States Treasury to purchase 4.5 million ounces of silver per month

_____ **4.** marketing organizations that worked for the benefit of their members

_____ **5.** a movement to increase farmers' political power and to work for legislation in their interest

Column B

A. cooperatives

B. "The Crime of '73"

C. Sherman Silver Purchase Act

D. populism

E. Grange

DIRECTIONS: Multiple Choice In the blank at the left, write the letter of the choice
that best completes the statement or answers the question. *(10 points each)*

_____ **6.** The goldbugs believed the American currency should be based only on gold, while silverites believed coining silver in unlimited quantities would solve the nation's
  A. mining crisis.
  B. economic crisis.
  C. war debts.
  D. political corruption.

_____ **7.** During the late 1880s, members of what organization traveled across the South and West speaking to farmers and organizing local chapters?
  A. the Kansas Alliance
  B. the Grange
  C. the Farmers' Alliance
  D. the subtreasury

_____ **8.** In 1892 the People's Party promised if elected to implement a
  A. graduated income tax.
  B. new tariff law.
  C. gold-based currency.
  D. tax break to big businesses.

_____ **9.** Members of the Kansas Alliance formed the People's Party, also known as the
  A. Goldbugs.
  B. Kansas Grange.
  C. Silverites.
  D. Populists.

_____ **10.** In 1900 the United States officially adopted a gold-based currency when Congress passed the
  A. subtreasury plan.
  B. Gold Standard Act.
  C. Populist Reform Act.
  D. Sherman Silver Purchase Act.

★ **Chapter 11**

Section Quiz 11-3

DIRECTIONS: Matching Match each item in Column A with the items in Column B. Write the correct letters in the blanks. *(10 points each)*

Column A

_____ **1.** separation of the races

_____ **2.** launched a fearless crusade against lynching

_____ **3.** thousands of African Americans who migrated from the rural South to Kansas

_____ **4.** proposed that African Americans concentrate on achieving economic goals rather than legal or political ones

_____ **5.** gave whites a special break by allowing any man to vote if he had an ancestor on the voting rolls in 1867

Column B

A. Ida Wells

B. Booker T. Washington

C. grandfather clause

D. segregation

E. Exodusters

DIRECTIONS: Multiple Choice In the blank at the left, write the letter of the choice that best completes the statement or answers the question. *(10 points each)*

_____ **6.** Between 1890 and 1899, there was an average of 187 lynchings each year carried out by mobs in the
    A. North.
    B. tenements.
    C. South.
    D. New England states.

_____ **7.** In 1886 African American activists gathered in Texas at the home of a white minister named R.M. Humphrey and formed the
    A. Populist Party.
    B. People's Party.
    C. Exodusters.
    D. Colored Farmers' National Alliance.

_____ **8.** Mississippi took the first step to prohibit African Americans from voting when it required that all citizens registering to vote pay a
    A. Jim Crow tax.
    B. poll tax.
    C. head tax.
    D. voting fee.

_____ **9.** To win back the poor white vote, Democratic leaders in the South began appealing to
    A. racism.
    B. Northerners.
    C. Populists.
    D. diversity.

_____ **10.** In 1883 the Supreme Court set the stage for legalized segregation by overturning the
    A. Civil Rights Act of 1875.
    B. Fifteenth Amendment.
    C. Fourteenth Amendment.
    D. *Plessy* v. *Ferguson* decision.

Chapter 11 Test, Form A

Score

Politics and Reform

DIRECTIONS: Matching Match each item in Column A with the items in Column B. Write the correct letters in the blanks. *(4 points each)*

Column A

_____ **1.** pushed through the repeal of the Sherman Silver Purchase Act

_____ **2.** believed that American currency should be based only on gold

_____ **3.** believed that unlimited amounts of silver coins would solve the economic crisis

_____ **4.** executions carried out by a mob without allowing the accused to appear in court

_____ **5.** expressed the ideas that became known as the Atlanta Compromise

_____ **6.** assassinated a few months into his presidency

_____ **7.** a Stalwart who supported the Pendleton Act

_____ **8.** character popularized by a slavery-era stage performer

_____ **9.** established the doctrine of "separate but equal"

_____ **10.** African Americans should pursue economic goals before political goals

Column B

A. Booker T. Washington

B. *Plessy* v. *Ferguson*

C. silverites

D. Chester A. Arthur

E. Atlanta Compromise

F. Jim Crow

G. lynchings

H. goldbugs

I. James A. Garfield

J. Grover Cleveland

DIRECTIONS: Multiple Choice Choose the item that best completes each statement or answers each question. Write the letter in the blank. *(4 points each)*

_____ **11.** Under the Pendleton Act, people would gain government jobs according to
   A. a quota system that balanced the number of jobs going to each party's supporters.
   B. the amount of money they raised for the party's election campaign.
   C. their performance on examinations.
   D. a rotation system that balanced jobs between the parties by setting term limits.

_____ **12.** The Democratic party of the late 1800s was viewed as
   A. the party that preserved the Union.   **C.** the party of personal liberty.
   B. the party of big business.   **D.** the party of reform.

_____ **13.** The Mugwumps were
   A. Republican reformers who supported Cleveland for president.
   B. Democratic reformers who supported Blaine for president.
   C. Republican Stalwarts who supported Cleveland for president.
   D. Republican Halfbreeds who supported Blaine for president.

(continued)

Chapter 11 Test, Form A

_____ **14.** In response to the ruling in *Wabash* v. *Illinois*, Congress created the
   A. McKinley Tariff.
   B. Sherman Antitrust Act.
   C. Pendleton Act.
   D. Interstate Commerce Commission.

_____ **15.** The McKinley Tariff resulted in
   A. a national budget deficit.
   B. a national budget surplus.
   C. sharply increased federal revenue.
   D. revenue for U.S. farmers.

_____ **16.** New technology helped farmers produce more crops, which tended to
   A. lower prices.
   B. raise prices.
   C. decrease demand.
   D. increase demand.

_____ **17.** Many farmers joined the Independent National Party because the party wanted the government to
   A. provide low-cost farm mortgages.
   B. offer price supports for farm products.
   C. increase tariffs.
   D. print more greenbacks.

_____ **18.** The Farmers' Alliance cooperatives failed for all of the following reasons EXCEPT
   A. corruption within them eventually alienated many farmers.
   B. they were too small to dramatically affect world prices for farm products.
   C. they loaned too much money at low interest rates that was never repaid.
   D. many railroads, bankers, and wholesalers discriminated against them.

_____ **19.** The Populists hoped to beat the Democrats in the South by
   A. appealing to white racism.
   B. promising to legalize segregation.
   C. promising government jobs to poor blacks.
   D. appealing to poor whites and poor blacks.

_____ **20.** The Supreme Court set the stage for legalized segregation by overturning the
   A. Civil Rights Act of 1875.
   B. Pendleton Act.
   C. Fourteenth Amendment.
   D. Fifteenth Amendment.

DIRECTIONS: Essay Answer one of the following questions on a separate sheet of paper. *(20 points)*

21. Explain what tariffs do and why many Americans in the 1880s believed that high tariffs were no longer needed.

22. Define "deflation" and explain why it hurt farmers.

⭐ **Chapter 11 Test, Form B**

Politics and Reform

DIRECTIONS: Matching Match each item in Column A with the items in Column B.
Write the correct letters in the blanks. *(4 points each)*

Column A

_____ **1.** used to prevent many African Americans from voting

_____ **2.** referred to the decision to stop minting silver coins

_____ **3.** waged a "front porch campaign" in the 1896 election

_____ **4.** organized the African American mass migration to Kansas

_____ **5.** African American arrested for riding in a "whites-only" railroad car

_____ **6.** particularly concerned with protecting and exercising voting rights for African Americans

_____ **7.** launched a fearless crusade against lynching

_____ **8.** warehouse meant to store crops

_____ **9.** candidate for president in 1896 for the Populists and Democrats

_____ **10.** leader of the Farmers' Alliance

Column B

A. Ida Wells

B. Charles W. Macune

C. grandfather clause

D. Benjamin "Pap" Singleton

E. William Jennings Bryan

F. "The Crime of '73"

G. Homer Plessy

H. W.E.B. Du Bois

I. William McKinley

J. subtreasury

DIRECTIONS: Multiple Choice Choose the item that best completes each statement
or answers each question. Write the letter in the blank. *(4 points each)*

_____ **11.** Republicans of the late 1800s were viewed as
  A. the Catholic party.
  B. the big-city party.
  C. the party of personal liberty.
  D. the party of reform.

_____ **12.** In 1876 and 1888, presidential candidates won the popular vote
  A. and the Electoral College majority.
  B. but still lost the election.
  C. on the Populist Party ticket.
  D. in spite of scandals.

_____ **13.** The Supreme Court case *Wabash* v. *Illinois* established the principle that
  A. only the states can regulate the rates railroads charge for transporting freight.
  B. the federal government may not interfere with corporations' property rights.
  C. only the federal government can regulate interstate commerce.
  D. railroads may set whatever rates they see fit for transporting freight.

_____ **14.** The Sherman Antitrust Act was not very effective initially because
  A. big business was too powerful.
  B. the courts were responsible for enforcement.
  C. graft caused corrupt politicians to look the other way when violations occurred.
  D. enforcers were not sufficiently funded to do their jobs.

(continued)

⭐ **Chapter 11 Test, Form B**

_____ **15.** To get inflation under control after the Civil War, the federal government did all of the following EXCEPT
- **A.** stop making silver into coins.
- **B.** start paying off its bonds.
- **C.** stop printing greenbacks.
- **D.** start exchanging greenbacks for gold coins.

_____ **16.** Passed in several western states, Granger laws
- **A.** required railroads to lay more track.
- **B.** limited railroad rates.
- **C.** allowed greenbacks to be printed.
- **D.** limited bank interest rates.

_____ **17.** Supporters of the subtreasury plan believed that it would
- **A.** increase the money supply.
- **B.** force crop prices up.
- **C.** decrease mortgage interest rates.
- **D.** limit railroad rates.

_____ **18.** Populists in the 1892 elections called for all of the following EXCEPT
- **A.** unlimited coinage of silver.
- **B.** federal ownership of railroads.
- **C.** a graduated income tax.
- **D.** unrestricted immigration.

_____ **19.** Unlike in the North, segregation in the South was
- **A.** enforced by violence.
- **B.** enforced by law.
- **C.** not limited to public places.
- **D.** not limited to private clubs.

_____ **20.** In a newspaper article, Ida Wells reported that three African American grocers in Memphis had been lynched because they had
- **A.** established their store in a "whites-only" neighborhood.
- **B.** competed successfully against white grocers.
- **C.** refused to set their prices at the same level as those of white grocers.
- **D.** refused to serve white patrons.

DIRECTIONS: Essay Answer one of the following questions on a separate sheet of paper. *(20 points)*

21. Use the diagrams to help you explain how forming cooperatives could help farmers.

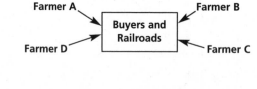

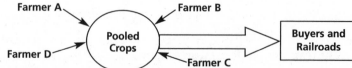

22. Summarize the ideas of Booker T. Washington and W.E.B. Du Bois on how to solve discrimination against African Americans.

The American Republic Since 1877

⭐ **Unit 3 Posttest, Form A**

The Birth of Modern America

DIRECTIONS: Matching Match each item in Column A with the items in Column B.
Write the correct letters in the blanks. *(4 points each)*

Column A

_____ **1.** owning all the different businesses on which the company depends for its operation

_____ **2.** person who cultivated the soil on the Plains

_____ **3.** first leader of the American Federation of Labor

_____ **4.** the spoils system

_____ **5.** called the Plains region the "Great American Desert"

_____ **6.** Lakota Sioux chief killed at Wounded Knee

_____ **7.** built the Great Northern Railroad without any federal land grants or subsidies

_____ **8.** part of the Crédit Mobilier scandal

_____ **9.** a way of merging businesses that did not violate laws against owning other companies

_____ **10.** set up by Colored Farmers' National Alliance to provide economic help to members

Column B

A. Sitting Bull

B. James J. Hill

C. sodbuster

D. Stephen Long

E. patronage

F. trust

G. vertical integration

H. cooperatives

I. Samuel Gompers

J. Oakes Ames

DIRECTIONS: Multiple Choice Choose the item that best completes each statement or answers each question. Write the letter in the blank. *(4 points each)*

_____ **11.** The hand process with which early prospectors would extract the shallow deposits of ore was called
    A. quartz mining.
    B. strip mining.
    C. placer mining.
    D. surface mining.

_____ **12.** The open range was a large area of grassland where
    A. cattle ranchers could claim land within limits set by the government.
    B. cattle ranchers could graze their herds in exchange for a small fee.
    C. cattle ranchers could graze their herds for free.
    D. cattle ranchers could buy land from the government.

_____ **13.** The Homestead Act was ineffective largely because
    A. railroad companies controlled much of the best land.
    B. wealthy European investors quickly bought up much of the best land.
    C. prospective settlers soon learned that life was hard on the arid Great Plains.
    D. few prospective settlers could afford the high price the government set for the land.

(continued)

★ **Unit 3 Posttest, Form A**

_____ **14.** The confrontation at Wounded Knee began because the government agent wanted the Lakota Sioux to stop
    A. hunting outside of the reservation.   **C.** hunting buffalo in violation of a treaty.
    B. raiding nearby farms.   **D.** performing the Ghost Dance.

_____ **15.** As the nation was industrializing, Congress used tariffs to
    A. raise money to operate the government.
    B. help new American industries compete with large established European factories.
    C. raise the prices that Europeans would have to pay for American products.
    D. entice European consumers to buy American products.

_____ **16.** Supporters of free enterprise believed that one reason the United States industrialized so rapidly in the 1800s was because it
    A. used tariffs to protect industries.   **C.** offered high wages.
    B. subsidized new industries.   **D.** offered free trade.

_____ **17.** As city populations grew in the late 1800s, the price of land rose, providing incentive to
    A. move to the suburbs.   **C.** install cable cars.
    B. move from farms to the city.   **D.** build skyscrapers.

_____ **18.** Individualism was the belief that
    A. if you want something done right, you should do it yourself.
    B. no matter how humble your origins, you can rise as far as your talents and commitment will take you.
    C. you should do whatever you want, no matter what other people think.
    D. you make your own happiness—you do not need others to make you happy.

_____ **19.** According to a Supreme Court ruling in 1883, the Fourteenth Amendment did not offer protection from actions by
    A. Congress.   **C.** local government.
    B. state legislatures.   **D.** private businesses.

_____ **20.** Who proposed the Atlanta Compromise?
    A. Ida B. Wells   **C.** Booker T. Washington
    B. Homer Plessy   **D.** W.E.B. Du Bois

DIRECTIONS: Essay Answer one of the following questions on a separate sheet of paper. *(20 points)*

21. How were states able to disfranchise African Americans in the late 1800s, and how did African Americans respond?

22. What were some of the problems of city living in the late 1800s, and what caused these problems?

★ **Unit 3 Posttest, Form B**

Score

The Birth of Modern America

DIRECTIONS: Matching Match each item in Column A with the items in Column B. Write the correct letters in the blanks. *(4 points each)*

Column A

_____ **1.** invention that helped end the cowboy lifestyle

_____ **2.** money that could not be exchanged for gold or silver coins

_____ **3.** refusing to allow workers into the workplace and refusing to pay them

_____ **4.** invented basketball

_____ **5.** separation of races

_____ **6.** closed with the rapid settlement of the West

_____ **7.** invented a process to make high quality steel cheaply and efficiently

_____ **8.** people who own corporations

_____ **9.** doctrine opposed to any government programs that interfered with business

_____ **10.** battled the Lakota Sioux at Little Bighorn

Column B

A. lockout

B. frontier

C. George Custer

D. Henry Bessemer

E. segregation

F. James Naismith

G. stockholders

H. greenbacks

I. barbed wire

J. laissez-faire

DIRECTIONS: Multiple Choice Choose the item that best completes each statement or answers each question. Write the letter in the blank. *(4 points each)*

_____ **11.** At the Comstock Lode, miners found rich deposits of
   A. gold.   **C.** copper.
   B. silver.   **D.** diamonds.

_____ **12.** In 1895 the Supreme Court ruled that the American Sugar Refining Company enjoyed a near monopoly in sugar manufacturing, which
   A. must be broken up to maintain good interstate commerce.
   B. was not a trust in the legal sense.
   C. violated the Sherman Antitrust Act because it was a trust.
   D. did not violate the Sherman Antitrust Act because manufacturing was not interstate commerce.

_____ **13.** To enforce law and order, many boomtowns formed
   A. vigilance committees.
   B. volunteer fire departments.
   C. settlement houses.
   D. commission forms of government.

(continued)

⭐ **Unit 3 Posttest, Form B**

_____ **14.** In the case of *Plessy* v. *Ferguson,* the Supreme Court
   A. overturned Jim Crow laws.
   B. ordered desegregation of schools.
   C. established "one man, one vote" doctrine.
   D. established "separate but equal" doctrine.

_____ **15.** To achieve economies of scale, corporations
   A. kept their fixed costs as low as possible.
   B. kept their operating costs as low as possible.
   C. invested in more machines and larger manufacturing facilities.
   D. invested in companies in the same business.

_____ **16.** The Morrill Land Grant Act led to the spread of
   A. commercial farming.   **C.** segregation.
   B. settlement houses.   **D.** colleges.

_____ **17.** When Mark Twain and Charles Warner called their period the "Gilded Age," they were
   A. celebrating the general wealth of the time.
   B. commenting on the showy mansions built by wealthy entrepreneurs.
   C. sounding an alarm.
   D. inspiring young people to think that they could win success, too.

_____ **18.** "Survival of the fittest" was part of the philosophy of
   A. Social Darwinism.   **C.** Realism.
   B. Gospel of Wealth.   **D.** Individualism.

_____ **19.** The Pendleton Act required government jobs to be distributed according to
   A. a quota system for members of each party.
   B. the spoils system.
   C. the results of civil service examinations.
   D. a rotation system among members of each party.

_____ **20.** The first nationwide labor protest was the
   A. Haymarket Riot.   **C.** Pullman Strike.
   B. Great Railroad Strike of 1877.   **D.** Panic of 1873.

DIRECTIONS: Essay Answer one of the following questions on a separate sheet of paper. *(20 points)*

21. Why do you think large cities grew and flourished after the Civil War?

22. Select one of the themes that was popular in the literature of the late 1800s. Who wrote using that theme, and how did they express that theme?

⭐ **Unit 4 Pretest, Form A**

Score

Imperialism and Progressivism

DIRECTIONS: Matching Match each item in Column A with the items in Column B. Write the correct letters in the blanks. *(4 points each)*

Column A

_____ **1.** yellow journalist

_____ **2.** Communists who overthrew the Russian government

_____ **3.** "fit as a bull moose"

_____ **4.** panic that Communists might seize power in the U.S.

_____ **5.** proposed legislation submitted to the voters for approval

_____ **6.** introduced scientific management

_____ **7.** prohibited materials

_____ **8.** stronger nation defended local rulers from rebellions, but in exchange, local rulers had to accept advice from the stronger nation on how to govern

_____ **9.** region in southeastern Europe that included the Serbs, Bosnians, Croats, and Slovenes

_____ **10.** special election to remove an elected official from office before his or her term had expired

Column B

A. recall

B. protectorate

C. contraband

D. Balkans

E. Theodore Roosevelt

F. Red Scare

G. William Randolph Hearst

H. Bolsheviks

I. referendum

J. Frederick W. Taylor

DIRECTIONS: Multiple Choice Choose the item that best completes each statement or answers each question. Write the letter in the blank. *(4 points each)*

_____ **11.** Hawaii became part of the United States
   A. as part of the treaty ending the Spanish-American War.
   B. because the Hawaiian government applied for statehood.
   C. after a group of planters and U.S. Marines overthrew the Hawaiian queen.
   D. after the United States bought Hawaii from Spain.

_____ **12.** Theodore Roosevelt and the Rough Riders attacked San Juan Hill in
   A. Cuba.   **C.** the Dominican Republic.
   B. Puerto Rico.   **D.** the Philippines.

_____ **13.** Before the United States could build the Panama Canal,
   A. Colombia had to agree to a price for use of the land.
   B. Nicaragua had to agree to a price for use of the land.
   C. Panama had to gain independence from Nicaragua.
   D. Panama had to gain independence from Colombia.

(continued)

_____ **14.** A direct primary is a vote of
   A. all party members for delegates to the party's convention.
   B. the party's state legislators for delegates to the party's convention.
   C. all party members for a candidate to run in the election.
   D. the party's state legislators for a candidate to run in the election.

_____ **15.** Socialists advocate
   A. no government.
   B. no government interference with businesses.
   C. government regulation of businesses.
   D. government ownership of businesses.

_____ **16.** Muckrakers were
   A. politicians who dug up scandals about their political opponents.
   B. journalists who investigated social conditions and political corruption.
   C. rebels in Latin American countries who resisted foreign dominance.
   D. lawyers who used unethical means to win large settlements.

_____ **17.** In World War I, the Central Powers included
   A. Germany and Austria-Hungary.
   B. Germany and Russia.
   C. Britain and France.
   D. Britain and the United States.

_____ **18.** The idea proposed by John Fiske that English-speaking nations would one day dominate the world is known as
   A. imperialism.
   B. Anglo-Saxonism.
   C. nativism.
   D. English protectionism.

_____ **19.** Trench warfare in World War I resulted from the introduction of
   A. tanks.
   B. airplanes.
   C. rapid-fire machine guns.
   D. poison gas.

_____ **20.** In 1898 Germany began to build a navy to challenge _____ undisputed control of the seas.
   A. America's
   B. Great Britain's
   C. France's
   D. Spain's

DIRECTIONS: Essay Answer one of the following questions on a separate sheet of paper. *(20 points)*

21. Referring to his foreign policy, President Theodore Roosevelt once said, "Speak softly and carry a big stick." What do you think he meant by this? Give an example of how this policy might be applied.

22. The Progressive Era was a time of reform in American society. Who do you think the progressives were? What kinds of problems did they see in society?

⭐ **Unit 4 Pretest, Form B**

Imperialism and Progressivism

DIRECTIONS: Matching Match each item in Column A with the items in Column B.
Write the correct letters in the blanks. *(4 points each)*

Column A

_____ **1.** writers who exposed corruption, scandal, and social problems

_____ **2.** headed the Justice Department's General Intelligence Division, which became the FBI

_____ **3.** the U.S. president at the end of World War I

_____ **4.** leader of a naval expedition to Japan

_____ **5.** banned price discrimination

_____ **6.** improving efficiency by managing time, breaking tasks down into small parts, and using standardized tools

_____ **7.** monarch of Hawaii

_____ **8.** ship that exploded in Havana harbor

_____ **9.** famous anti-imperialist

_____ **10.** won World War I

Column B

A. Liliuokalani

B. Allies

C. scientific management

D. J. Edgar Hoover

E. Mark Twain

F. *Maine*

G. Clayton Antitrust Act

H. muckrakers

I. Woodrow Wilson

J. Matthew C. Perry

DIRECTIONS: Multiple Choice Choose the item that best completes each sentence or answers each question. Write the letter in the blank. *(4 points each)*

_____ **11.** The Rough Riders attacked San Juan Hill with the help of
  A. a Cuban rebel unit.
  B. a group of Spanish deserters.
  C. a group of women volunteers.
  D. an African American unit.

_____ **12.** The _____ was built in Central America to save time and money in commercial and military shipping.
  A. Federal Reserve System
  B. Hoover Dam
  C. Suez Canal
  D. Panama Canal

_____ **13.** President _____ was concerned with protecting the environment.
  A. William Taft
  B. Grover Cleveland
  C. Woodrow Wilson
  D. Theodore Roosevelt

_____ **14.** By lowering tariffs, Woodrow Wilson believed that foreign competition would
  A. increase.
  B. turn to other markets.
  C. stay the same.
  D. decrease.

(continued)

⭐ **Unit 4 Pretest, Form B**

_____ **15.** The Constitution originally stated that senators would be selected by
  A. the voters of each state.
  B. the legislature of each state.
  C. a vote of the members of the majority party in each state.
  D. the majority party bosses in each state.

_____ **16.** One function of the Board of Governors of the Federal Reserve system is to
  A. set interest rates that the government charges to its borrowers.
  B. keep the United States from having another depression.
  C. decide all banking regulations for the United States.
  D. set interest rates that the reserve banks could charge other banks.

_____ **17.** Before the Mexican Revolution, most Mexicans
  A. favored entering World War I.
  B. enjoyed a high standard of living.
  C. were unhappy with their democratic government.
  D. were poor and did not own land.

_____ **18.** A region in southeastern Europe ruled at different times by the Ottoman Empire and the Austro-Hungarian Empire is
  A. the Balkans.   **C.** Russia.
  B. Ukraine.   **D.** Greece.

_____ **19.** What did Germans use to get around Britain's naval blockade?
  A. airplanes   **C.** Z-boats
  B. contraband   **D.** U-boats

_____ **20.** During World War I, which of the following groups faced persecution?
  A. Irish Americans   **C.** German Americans
  B. British Americans   **D.** Russian Americans

DIRECTIONS: Essay Answer one of the following questions on a separate sheet of paper. *(20 points)*

21. Describe the role the United States took in Latin American affairs during the late 1800s and early 1900s.

22. How do you think politics has changed since women gained the right to vote?

The American Republic Since 1877

★ **Chapter 12**

Section Quiz 12-1

DIRECTIONS: Matching Match each item in Column A with the items in Column B. Write the correct letters in the blanks. *(10 points each)*

Column A

_____ **1.** wrote a best-selling book that helped to build public support for a big navy

_____ **2.** the economic and political domination of a strong nation over other weaker nations

_____ **3.** idea that Latin America and the United States should work together

_____ **4.** idea that the English-speaking nations were destined to dominate the planet

_____ **5.** took a naval expedition to Japan to negotiate a trade treaty

Column B

A. Pan-Americanism

B. Alfred T. Mahan

C. imperialism

D. Matthew C. Perry

E. Anglo-Saxonism

DIRECTIONS: Multiple Choice In the blank at the left, write the letter of the choice that best completes the statement or answers the question. *(10 points each)*

_____ **6.** What was a territory called when an imperial power allowed local rulers to stay in control and protected them against invasion?
   A. a colony
   B. a protectorate
   C. an unincorporated territory
   D. a state

_____ **7.** When a trade treaty that exempted Hawaiian sugar from tariffs came up for renewal, the Senate insisted that the Hawaiians grant the United States rights to
   A. establish missions.
   B. govern the islands.
   C. increase tourism.
   D. a naval base.

_____ **8.** In the 1880s, American opinion began to shift and more people wanted to make the United States
   A. a world power.
   B. more isolated.
   C. a protectorate.
   D. part of Pan-America.

_____ **9.** When Americans began looking overseas for new markets in the 1800s, they naturally tended to look
   A. eastward.
   B. to Spain.
   C. westward.
   D. to England.

_____ **10.** The Commercial Bureau of the American Republics was an organization that worked to promote cooperation among the nations of the Western Hemisphere and is today called the
   A. Organization of American States.
   B. Pan-American Union.
   C. Western United Nations.
   D. American Republics Organization.

Chapter 12

Score

Section Quiz 12-2

DIRECTIONS: Matching Match each item in Column A with the items in Column B.
Write the correct letters in the blanks. *(10 points each)*

Column A

_____ **1.** governed relations between the United States and Cuba,
effectively making Cuba into an American protectorate

_____ **2.** sensationalist reporting to attract readers

_____ **3.** a volunteer cavalry regiment from the American West

_____ **4.** writer, poet, and exiled leader committed to the cause of
Cuban independence

_____ **5.** an attitude of aggressive nationalism

Column B

A. José Martí

B. jingoism

C. Rough Riders

D. Platt Amendment

E. yellow journalism

DIRECTIONS: Multiple Choice In the blank at the left, write the letter of the choice
that best completes the statement or answers the question. *(10 points each)*

_____ **6.** Shortly after midnight on May 1, 1898, Commodore George Dewey led
his squadron into Manila Bay in

A. Cuba.

B. Hawaii.

C. the Philippines.

D. Spain.

_____ **7.** When the explosion of the *Maine* happened, many Americans blamed it on

A. Cuba.

B. the Foraker Act.

C. the Philippines.

D. Spain.

_____ **8.** Under the Treaty of Paris, Cuba became an independent country, the
United States agreed to pay Spain $20 million for the Philippines, and the
United States acquired Puerto Rico and

A. Guam.

B. Hawaii.

C. the Bahamas.

D. Mexico.

_____ **9.** After much resistance, on April 11, 1898, President McKinley finally
asked Congress to authorize the use of force to end the conflict in

A. Panama.

B. Cuba.

C. Colombia.

D. British Hong Kong.

_____ **10.** Until 1886, about one-third of the Cuban population was

A. from the United States.

B. enslaved.

C. from England.

D. part of the Spanish military.

⭐ **Chapter 12**

Section Quiz 12-3

DIRECTIONS: Matching Match each item in Column A with the items in Column B. Write the correct letters in the blanks. *(10 points each)*

Column A

_____ **1.** United States Navy

_____ **2.** declaration that the United States would intervene in Latin American affairs when necessary to maintain economic and political stability

_____ **3.** said all countries should be allowed to trade with China

_____ **4.** gave the United States the exclusive right to build and control any proposed canal through Central America

_____ **5.** an area where a foreign nation controlled economic development

Column B

A. Hay-Pauncefote Treaty

B. Roosevelt Corollary

C. sphere of influence

D. Open Door policy

E. Great White Fleet

DIRECTIONS: Multiple Choice In the blank at the left, write the letter of the choice that best completes the statement or answers the question. *(10 points each)*

_____ **6.** A group in China besieged foreign embassies in Beijing and killed more than 200 foreigners in what came to be known as the
    A. Boxer Rebellion.   **C.** China War.
    B. Beijing Rebellion.   **D.** Secret Society Rebellion.

_____ **7.** For his efforts in ending the war between Japan and Russia, Teddy Roosevelt won
    A. favor with the Japanese.   **C.** the Nobel Peace Prize.
    B. the presidential election.   **D.** new trade agreements.

_____ **8.** In 1899 the United States was a major power in Asia; however, the nation's primary interest was not conquest but
    A. Anglo-Saxonism.   **C.** an Open Door policy.
    B. commerce.   **D.** imperialism.

_____ **9.** The United States had long considered two possible canal sites, one through Panama and one through
    A. Colombia.   **C.** the Dominican Republic.
    B. El Salvador.   **D.** Nicaragua.

_____ **10.** Who arranged for a small army to stage an uprising in Panama?
    A. Philippe Bunau-Varilla   **C.** John Hay
    B. President Roosevelt   **D.** the Boxers

⭐ Chapter 12 Test, Form A

Score

Becoming a World Power

DIRECTIONS: Matching Match each item in Column A with the items in Column B.
Write the correct letters in the blanks. *(4 points each)*

Column A

_____ **1.** if American business leaders supported Latin American and Asian development, everyone would benefit

_____ **2.** ensured that Cuba would remain tied to the United States

_____ **3.** the United States would intervene in Latin American affairs when necessary

_____ **4.** gave the United States the right to build and control a canal through Central America

_____ **5.** kept Chinese ports open to vessels of all nations

_____ **6.** made Puerto Rico an "unincorporated territory"

_____ **7.** the U.S. had a duty to shape "less civilized" areas

_____ **8.** idea that the U.S. and Latin America should work together

_____ **9.** local rulers had to accept advice from an imperial power

_____ **10.** took a naval expedition to Japan

Column B

A. Open Door Policy

B. Roosevelt Corollary

C. Pan-Americanism

D. Anglo-Saxonism

E. Hay-Pauncefote Treaty

F. Matthew C. Perry

G. Platt Amendment

H. Foraker Act

I. protectorate

J. dollar diplomacy

DIRECTIONS: Multiple Choice Choose the item that best completes each statement
or answers each question. Write the letter in the blank. *(4 points each)*

_____ **11.** In the late 1800s, Europeans were looking overseas for places to sell their products because
    A. they were producing more products than other industrialized countries wanted.
    B. tariffs reduced trade among industrialized countries.
    C. they could sell their products at higher prices in Asia and Africa.
    D. Asia and Africa were producing products that European wanted in exchange for their own.

_____ **12.** President Franklin Pierce sent a naval expedition to Japan to
    A. conquer the islands around Japan.
    B. force Japan to become an American protectorate.
    C. force Japan to trade with the United States.
    D. bring Western civilization to Japan.

_____ **13.** At the First International American Conference, the United States wanted Latin American delegates to agree to a customs union, which would
    A. set up a cultural exchange to learn about each other's customs.
    B. reduce tariffs among American nations.
    C. make Latin American countries protectorates of the United States.
    D. set up an organization among American nations for mutual defense.

(continued)

Chapter 12 Test, Form A

Score

_____ **14.** In the late 1800s, support grew in the U.S. for building a large modern navy to
   A. protect the U.S. from invasion.
   B. conquer Latin American countries.
   C. conquer islands in the Pacific.
   D. avoid being shut out of foreign markets.

_____ **15.** The United States caused an economic crisis in Cuba by
   A. preventing trade with Spain.
   B. blockading the island.
   C. passing a tariff on sugar.
   D. withdrawing American investments.

_____ **16.** According to the treaty that ended the Spanish-American War, the U.S. would
   A. annex Guam, Puerto Rico, and Cuba.
   B. free Cuba, and annex Guam and Puerto Rico.
   C. free Guam and Cuba, and annex Puerto Rico.
   D. free Guam, Puerto Rico, and Cuba.

_____ **17.** The Philippines are now
   A. an American protectorate.
   B. an American commonwealth.
   C. an unincorporated U.S. territory.
   D. an independent country.

_____ **18.** Theodore Roosevelt was chosen as McKinley's running mate in the 1900 election because of his
   A. reform-minded spirit.
   B. skill in foreign policy.
   C. charisma and war fame.
   D. rise from poverty.

_____ **19.** As a result of a war between Japan and China in 1894, Japan acquired
   A. territory in Manchuria.
   B. Korea.
   C. a leasehold in China.
   D. an exclusive right to trade with China.

_____ **20.** When the U.S. assumed the responsibility for collecting customs tariffs in the Dominican Republic, using the Marines as agents, it was applying
   A. the Open Door Policy.
   B. the Roosevelt Corollary.
   C. dollar diplomacy.
   D. the Platt Amendment.

DIRECTIONS: Essay Answer one of the following questions on a separate sheet of paper. *(20 points)*

21. Explain three general factors that were fueling U.S. imperialist policy in the 1880s, as depicted in the diagram.

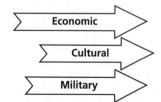

22. What did Puerto Rico's status as an "unincorporated territory" mean?

★ Chapter 12 Test, Form B

Score

Becoming a World Power

DIRECTIONS: Matching Match each item in Column A with the items in Column B. Write the correct letters in the blanks. *(4 points each)*

Column A

_____ **1.** "dollar diplomacy"

_____ **2.** last monarch of Hawaii

_____ **3.** linked Anglo-Saxonism to Christian missionary ideas

_____ **4.** "Speak softly and carry a big stick."

_____ **5.** led revolt in Panama

_____ **6.** negotiated Open Door policy with European powers and Japan

_____ **7.** ambassador whose intercepted letter fueled American feelings toward war with Spain

_____ **8.** naval officer whose book built public support for a large navy

_____ **9.** Filipino revolutionary leader

_____ **10.** invited Latin American nations to attend the First International American Conference

Column B

A. Philippe Bunau-Varilla

B. Theodore Roosevelt

C. Emilio Aguinaldo

D. William Howard Taft

E. Enrique Dupuy de Lôme

F. John Hay

G. James G. Blaine

H. Josiah Strong

I. Liliuokalani

J. Alfred T. Mahan

DIRECTIONS: Multiple Choice Choose the item that best completes each statement or answers each question. Write the letter in the blank. *(4 points each)*

_____ **11.** By the late 1800s, growth of investment opportunities in western Europe had slowed because
   A. most of the industries that Europe's economy needed had been built.
   B. Europe was experiencing an economic depression.
   C. most of Europe's land had been settled.
   D. Europe's factories were making good profits and no longer needed loans.

_____ **12.** The Hawaiian monarchy was overthrown by
   A. a group of Hawaiian peasants, upset over the islands' economic troubles.
   B. an invasion by the United States military.
   C. a group of planters supported by the United States Marines.
   D. a group of Hawaiian peasants supported by the United States Marines.

_____ **13.** The Commercial Bureau of the American Republics, formed to promote cooperation among nations of the Western Hemisphere, is today the
   A. North Atlantic Treaty Organization.   **C.** United Nations.
   B. North American Free Trade Agreement.   **D.** Organization of American States.

(continued)

⭐ **Chapter 12 Test, Form B**

Score

_____ **14.** American support for the rebels in Cuba was fueled by
  A. the desire to protect American sugar interests on the island.
  B. popular interest in starting an American empire by taking control of Cuba.
  C. sensational stories published by rival newspapers.
  D. the fear of having a Spanish colony so close to the United States.

_____ **15.** In 1898 President McKinley sent the battleship *Maine* to Havana to
  A. evacuate Americans if necessary.   **C.** put down the Cuban rebellion.
  B. put down riots by Spanish loyalists.   **D.** negotiate peace with Spain.

_____ **16.** Supporters of annexing the Philippines believed all of the following EXCEPT
  A. the islands would provide the United States with a naval base in Asia.
  B. the United States could profit from the islands' rich mineral resources.
  C. the islands represented a large market for American goods.
  D. America had a duty to teach the "less civilized" peoples how to live properly.

_____ **17.** The Platt Amendment effectively made Cuba into an American
  A. protectorate.   **C.** unincorporated territory.
  B. colony.   **D.** state.

_____ **18.** Theodore Roosevelt became president
  A. by defeating William Jennings Bryan.   **C.** when McKinley died of pneumonia.
  B. by defeating William McKinley.   **D.** when McKinley was assassinated.

_____ **19.** The purpose of the Open Door policy in China was to
  A. end the Boxer Rebellion.   **C.** establish spheres of influence.
  B. gain leaseholds.   **D.** ensure trading rights for all nations.

_____ **20.** Theodore Roosevelt won the Nobel Peace Prize in 1906 for negotiating peace
  A. between Russia and Japan.   **C.** among Russia and European powers.
  B. between China and Japan.   **D.** among factions in Korea.

DIRECTIONS: Essay Answer one of the following questions on a separate sheet of
paper. *(20 points)*

21. The diagram gives the four topics of the Platt Amendment. Explain each provision.

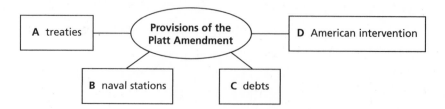

22. Explain Theodore Roosevelt's "big stick" policy and give an example of how it
was applied.

The American Republic Since 1877

★ Chapter 13

Score

Section Quiz 13-1

DIRECTIONS: Matching Match each item in Column A with the items in Column B. Write the correct letters in the blanks. *(10 points each)*

Column A

_____ 1. laws banning the manufacture, sale, and consumption of alcohol

_____ 2. progressives campaigned against this emotional issue

_____ 3. allowed a group of citizens in a state to introduce legislation and required the legislature to vote on it

_____ 4. group of crusading journalists who investigated social conditions and political corruption

_____ 5. right to vote

Column B

A. suffrage

B. prohibition

C. muckrakers

D. child labor

E. initiative

DIRECTIONS: Multiple Choice In the blank at the left, write the letter of the choice that best completes the statement or answers the question. *(10 points each)*

_____ 6. Political reform first came to the state level when Wisconsin voters elected as governor, Republican
   A. Charles Edward Russell.
   B. Frederick W. Taylor.
   C. Jacob Riis.
   D. Robert La Follette.

_____ 7. What did progressives think needed to play a more active role in solving society's problems?
   A. the government
   B. the churches
   C. social welfare organizations
   D. big business

_____ 8. Who formed the National Woman's Party and wanted to use protests to force President Wilson to take action on suffrage?
   A. Lucretia Mott
   B. Carrie Chapman Catt
   C. Lucy Stone
   D. Alice Paul

_____ 9. A law that divides a town or city into areas for commercial, residential, or other development is called a
   A. referendum.
   B. temperance.
   C. zoning law.
   D. recall law.

_____ 10. Efficiency progressives wanted the selection of the heads of city departments to be made by a city manager or
   A. the mayor.
   B. a board of commissioners.
   C. the city council.
   D. a political party.

★ **Chapter 13**

Section Quiz 13-2

DIRECTIONS: Matching Match each item in Column A with the items in Column B.
Write the correct letters in the blanks. *(10 points each)*

Column A

_____ 1. wrote *The Jungle*, a book with appalling descriptions of
conditions in the meatpacking industry

_____ 2. had the authority to investigate corporations and issue
reports on their activities

_____ 3. appointed to head the United States Forest Service

_____ 4. a settlement imposed by an outside party

_____ 5. Roosevelt's reform programs

Column B

A. Gifford Pinchot

B. Square Deal

C. Upton Sinclair

D. arbitration

E. Bureau of
Corporations

DIRECTIONS: Multiple Choice In the blank at the left, write the letter of the choice
that best completes the statement or answers the question. *(10 points each)*

_____ 6. What incident did Roosevelt criticize as an example of groups pursuing
their private interests at the expense of the nation?
A. formation of the Northern Securities   **C.** irrigation in the West
B. coal strike of 1902   **D.** strengthening of the Interstate
Commerce Commission

_____ 7. In early 1902, Roosevelt ordered his attorney general to file a lawsuit
under the Sherman Antitrust Act against
A. the New York Stock Exchange.   **C.** the Burlington Railroad.
B. the Union Pacific Railroad.   **D.** Northern Securities.

_____ 8. Teddy Roosevelt put his stamp on the presidency most clearly in the
area of
A. environmental conservation.   **C.** child labor laws.
B. antitrust legislation.   **D.** arbitration.

_____ 9. The federal government began the large-scale transformation of the
West's landscape and economy with the passage of the
A. Expedition Act.   **C.** Newlands Reclamation Act.
B. Hepburn Act.   **D.** Square Deal.

_____ 10. What gave federal antitrust suits precedence on the dockets of circuit
courts?
A. Expedition Act   **C.** Hepburn Act
B. Department of Commerce and Labor   **D.** Pure Food and Drug Act

★ **Chapter 13**

Section Quiz 13-3

DIRECTIONS: Matching Match each item in Column A with the items in Column B.
Write the correct letters in the blanks. *(10 points each)*

Column A

_____ **1.** disobedience

_____ **2.** senator who wanted to protect high tariffs

_____ **3.** increased the ICC's regulatory powers

_____ **4.** business group

_____ **5.** Speaker of the House who appointed all committees and decided which bills they handled

Column B

A. syndicate

B. Mann-Elkins Act

C. insubordination

D. Nelson Aldrich

E. Joseph G. Cannon

DIRECTIONS: Multiple Choice In the blank at the left, write the letter of the choice
that best completes the statement or answers the question. *(10 points each)*

_____ **6.** Taft gave the impression that he had "sold the Square Deal down the river" by backing speaker Joe Cannon, by supporting Ballinger against Pinchot, and by signing the
   A. Mann-Elkins Act.
   B. Payne-Aldrich Tariff Act.
   C. Ballinger-Pinchot Act.
   D. Sherman Antitrust Act.

_____ **7.** Who was surrounded by suspicion as secretary of the interior because he tried to remove forests and mineral reserves from the public lands and make them available for private development?
   A. Richard A. Ballinger
   B. Gifford Pinchot
   C. James R. Garfield
   D. Nelson Aldrich

_____ **8.** What did Taft establish to investigate and publicize child labor problems?
   A. Bureau of Children Services
   B. Bureau of Children and Family Services
   C. Bureau of Corporations
   D. Children's Bureau

_____ **9.** In October 1911, Taft announced an antitrust lawsuit against
   A. the Tennessee Coal and Iron Company.
   B. the Burlington Railroad.
   C. U.S. Steel.
   D. Standard Oil.

_____ **10.** Taft was a dedicated conservationist and set up the Bureau of Mines to monitor the activities of mining companies, protect waterpower sites from private development, and
   A. create national seashores.
   B. expand the national forests.
   C. encourage hunting laws.
   D. curb industrial pollution.

Name _____ Date _____ Class _____

 Chapter 13

Score

Section Quiz 13-4

DIRECTIONS: Matching Match each item in Column A with the items in Column B. Write the correct letters in the blanks. *(10 points each)*

Column A

_____ **1.** Teddy Roosevelt's program

_____ **2.** direct tax on the earnings of individuals and corporations

_____ **3.** established the eight-hour workday for railroad workers

_____ **4.** created to monitor American business

_____ **5.** Woodrow Wilson's program

Column B

A. Federal Trade Commission

B. New Freedom

C. Adamson Act

D. New Nationalism

E. income tax

DIRECTIONS: Multiple Choice In the blank at the left, write the letter of the choice that best completes the statement or answers the question. *(10 points each)*

_____ **6.** What law reduced the average tariff on imported goods to about 30 percent of the value of the goods, or about half the tariff rate of the 1890s?
  A. Clayton Antitrust Act
  B. Underwood Tariff
  C. Keating-Owen Act
  D. Adamson Act

_____ **7.** The meeting in 1905 that included W.E.B. Du Bois and other African American leaders to demand full political rights and responsibilities for African Americans eventually resulted in the founding of the
  A. Progressive Party.
  B. National Association for the Advancement of Colored People.
  C. Colored Farmers' National Alliance.
  D. Federal Trade Commission.

_____ **8.** To restore public confidence in the banking system, Wilson supported the establishment of a
  A. loan system.
  B. gold-based currency system.
  C. Federal Reserve system.
  D. Federal Trade Commission.

_____ **9.** In the election of 1912, Teddy Roosevelt became the presidential candidate for the newly formed
  A. Progressive Party.
  B. Independent Party.
  C. Libertarian Party.
  D. Populist Party.

_____ **10.** One provision of the Clayton Antitrust Act banned
  A. racial discrimination.
  B. income tax.
  C. child labor.
  D. price discrimination.

★ Chapter 13 Test, Form A

The Progressive Movement

DIRECTIONS: Matching Match each item in Column A with its type of progressivism in the diagram. Write the correct letters in the blanks. *(4 points each)*

Column A

_____ **1.** Interstate Commerce Commission

_____ **2.** referendum

_____ **3.** scientific management

_____ **4.** Women's Christian Temperance Union

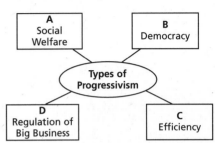

Matching Match the items in Column A with the items in Column B. Write the correct letters in the blanks. *(4 points each)*

Column A

_____ **5.** allowed a group of citizens to introduce legislation and required the legislature to vote on it

_____ **6.** cities run by people who had expertise in city services

_____ **7.** movement for moderation or elimination of alcohol

_____ **8.** allowed proposed legislation to be submitted to the voters for approval

_____ **9.** insurance fund financed by employers

_____ **10.** exposed corruption and scandal

Column B

A. commission plan

B. referendum

C. muckraker

D. workers' compensation

E. initiative

F. temperance

DIRECTIONS: Multiple Choice Choose the item that best completes each statement or answers each question. Write the letter in the blank. *(4 points each)*

_____ **11.** Progressives had a strong faith in
   A. the basic goodness of humanity.   **C.** science and expertise.
   B. politicians to serve the people.   **D.** God.

_____ **12.** Efficiency progressives believed that cities should be run by a
   A. city manager or commissioners.   **C.** mayor appointed by a party.
   B. mayor elected by the people.   **D.** city council elected by the people.

_____ **13.** In the case *Northern Securities* v. *the United States*, the Supreme Court ruled that Northern Securities
   A. violated the Clayton Antitrust Act.
   B. violated the Sherman Antitrust Act.
   C. would be placed under the supervision of the Bureau of Corporations.
   D. would be placed under the supervision of the Interstate Commerce Commission.

(continued)

Chapter 13 Test, Form A

Score

_____ **14.** Wisconsin became known as "the laboratory of democracy" because of its
    A. consumer protection laws.
    B. reforms that broke the power of party bosses.
    C. efforts for woman suffrage.
    D. antitrust laws.

_____ **15.** Alice Paul's strategy alarmed many in the suffrage movement because she wanted to
    A. support Woodrow Wilson.
    B. start a women-only political party.
    C. use protests to force suffrage.
    D. use violence to force suffrage.

_____ **16.** Socialists believe in
    A. no government.
    B. private ownership of business.
    C. government regulation of business.
    D. government ownership of business.

_____ **17.** By 1920 the Interstate Commerce Commission had drifted from its original purpose and had started
    A. raising rates to help ensure railroads' profits.
    B. suing railroads for competing unfairly.
    C. imposing fees on goods transported by rail across state lines.
    D. taking an active role in operating railroads.

_____ **18.** Theodore Roosevelt warned William Howard Taft to stay away from tariff reform because it would
    A. anger powerful business leaders.
    B. anger progressives.
    C. split the Republican Party.
    D. cause House Speaker Joseph Cannon to be removed from power.

_____ **19.** Theodore Roosevelt tried to win the Republican nomination from William Howard Taft in the 1912 election because he believed that Taft
    A. did not deal with trusts aggressively enough.
    B. had failed to live up to progressive ideals.
    C. could not defeat Woodrow Wilson.
    D. was too slow in pushing for tariff reform.

_____ **20.** The Underwood Tariff Act included a provision for
    A. negotiating tariffs with other nations.
    B. levying an income tax.
    C. starting a new national bank.
    D. banning tying agreements.

DIRECTIONS: Essay Answer one of the following questions on a separate sheet of paper. *(20 points)*

21. Describe the situation with patent medicines that led to the passage of the Pure Food and Drug Act, and describe the protections the new law provided.

22. Compare the personalities of Theodore Roosevelt and William Howard Taft.

The American Republic Since 1877

⭐ **Chapter 13 Test, Form B**

Score

The Progressive Movement

DIRECTIONS: Matching Match each item in Column A with the items in Column B.
Write the correct letters in the blanks. *(4 points each)*

Column A

_____ **1.** provided for the direct election of senators

_____ **2.** made it legal for the federal government to tax the income
of individuals directly

_____ **3.** guaranteed women the right to vote

_____ **4.** "laboratory of democracy"

_____ **5.** banned the manufacture, sale, and consumption of alcohol

_____ **6.** tried to open nearly a million acres of public land to
private development

_____ **7.** as governor of New Jersey, he introduced many
progressive reforms

_____ **8.** wrote articles criticizing Standard Oil

_____ **9.** passed in response to *The Jungle*

_____ **10.** investigated and publicized problems with child labor

Column B

A. Richard A.
Ballinger

B. Ida Tarbell

C. Children's Bureau

D. Meat Inspection
Act

E. Sixteenth
Amendment

F. Wisconsin

G. Woodrow Wilson

H. Seventeenth
Amendment

I. prohibition

J. Nineteenth
Amendment

DIRECTIONS: Multiple Choice Choose the item that best completes each statement
or answers each question. Write the letter in the blank. *(4 points each)*

_____ **11.** Through scientific management, a company could become efficient by
  A. keeping staff to a minimum and treating the employees well.
  B. breaking tasks down into small parts and using standardized tools.
  C. keeping staff to a minimum and breaking tasks down into small parts.
  D. using standardized tools and treating employees well.

_____ **12.** In a direct primary,
  A. all party members vote for delegates to the party's convention.
  B. the party's state legislators vote for delegates to the party's convention.
  C. all party members vote for a candidate to run in the general election.
  D. the party's state legislators vote for a candidate to run in the election.

_____ **13.** Theodore Roosevelt viewed the coal miners strike against mine owners
in 1902 as an example of
  A. groups pursuing their private interests at the expense of the nation.
  B. workers pursuing their right to fair wages and safe working conditions.
  C. big business abusing its power by exploiting workers.
  D. big business exercising its right to operate without a union.

(continued)

★ **Chapter 13 Test, Form B**

_____ **14.** The Constitution originally specified that senators would be selected by
  A. the legislature of each state.
  B. the voters of each state.
  C. the majority party in each state.
  D. leaders of the majority party.

_____ **15.** Tragedy at the Triangle Shirtwaist Company led to
  A. child labor laws.
  B. standards for safe use of machines.
  C. laws against harmful fumes.
  D. building codes requiring fire escapes.

_____ **16.** Which of the following choices best completes the diagram?

U.S. Steel would: allow the government to look at its account books and records...	→	The government would: ?

  A. promise not to break up the trust.
  B. promise not to sue the company.
  C. allow the company to correct problems privately without going to court.
  D. allow an arbitrator to rule on whether the company was violating the law.

_____ **17.** The laissez-faire argument for the best way to preserve public land was to
  A. keep it under government control and not allow companies to use it.
  B. keep it under government control, but allow its use for land development projects.
  C. sell it to lumber companies, who would conserve it as a source of profits.
  D. sell it to private individuals, who would conserve it because it belonged to them.

_____ **18.** The Payne-Aldrich Tariff
  A. raised tariffs significantly.
  B. imposed new tariffs.
  C. cut tariffs significantly.
  D. cut tariffs hardly at all.

_____ **19.** Roosevelt believed that Taft's focus on breaking up trusts would
  A. promote competition and lower prices for consumers.
  B. please progressives and help the Republicans stay in power.
  C. destroy the system of cooperation and regulation Roosevelt had arranged.
  D. ruin the efficiency of business and cause prices to rise.

_____ **20.** Wilson believed lower tariff rates would lead American companies to
  A. go out of business.
  B. form trusts.
  C. invest in foreign companies.
  D. improve products and lower prices.

DIRECTIONS: Essay Answer one of the following questions on a separate sheet of paper. *(20 points)*

21. In general, who were the progressives, and what did they believe?

22. Compare the views on trusts expressed by Theodore Roosevelt and Woodrow Wilson during the election campaign of 1912.

⭐ **Chapter 14**

Section Quiz 14-1

DIRECTIONS: Matching Match each item in Column A with the items in Column B.
Write the correct letters in the blanks. *(10 points each)*

Column A

_____ **1.** information designed to influence opinion

_____ **2.** led a group of Mexican guerrillas that burned Columbus, New Mexico

_____ **3.** Germany, Austria-Hungary, Ottoman Empire, and Bulgaria

_____ **4.** German submarines

_____ **5.** Britain, France, and Russia

Column B

A. Central Powers

B. U-boats

C. Pancho Villa

D. propaganda

E. Triple Entente

DIRECTIONS: Multiple Choice In the blank at the left, write the letter of the choice
that best completes the statement or answers the question. *(10 points each)*

_____ **6.** One reason for the tension between the European powers was their intense pride in their homelands called
    A. nationalism.   **C.** imperialism.
    B. socialism.   **D.** progressivism.

_____ **7.** What country made an offer to the Mexican government proposing that Mexico ally itself with them if the United States entered the European war?
    A. Bulgaria   **C.** Germany
    B. France   **D.** Russia

_____ **8.** A major problem in Germany's plan to invade France was that its forces first had to advance through neutral
    A. Amsterdam.   **C.** Switzerland.
    B. Belgium.   **D.** Luxembourg.

_____ **9.** President Wilson used the failure of the Mexicans to apologize for arresting American sailors as an opportunity to overthrow the Mexican leader,
    A. Pancho Villa.   **C.** Francisco Madero.
    B. Porfirio Díaz.   **D.** Victoriano Huerta.

_____ **10.** Since Germany did not want to strengthen the Allies by drawing the United States into war, it agreed with certain conditions to sink no more merchant ships in a promise called the
    A. Zimmermann telegram.   **C.** Sussex Pledge.
    B. Peace Pledge.   **D.** U-boat Pledge.

Chapter 14

Score

Section Quiz 14-2

DIRECTIONS: Matching Match each item in Column A with the items in Column B. Write the correct letters in the blanks. *(10 points each)*

Column A

_____ 1. made any public expression of opposition to the war illegal

_____ 2. created to coordinate the production of war materials

_____ 3. African American unit that won the French decoration, Croix de Guerre, for gallantry

_____ 4. used to raise money to cover the costs of war

_____ 5. when many African Americans left the South to settle in Northern cities

Column B

A. Liberty Bonds and Victory Bonds

B. 369th Infantry

C. Sedition Act of 1918

D. Great Migration

E. War Industries Board

DIRECTIONS: Multiple Choice In the blank at the left, write the letter of the choice that best completes the statement or answers the question. *(10 points each)*

_____ 6. Perhaps the most successful government agency during this time was the Food Administration run by
   A. Bernard Baruch.
   B. George Creel.
   C. Herbert Hoover.
   D. William Howard Taft.

_____ 7. To conserve energy, the Fuel Administration, run by Harry Garfield, shortened workweeks for factories that did not make war materials and introduced
   A. time zones.
   B. daylight savings time.
   C. flexible hours.
   D. conscription.

_____ 8. The fear of spies and emphasis on patriotism quickly led to the mistreatment and persecution of
   A. Irish Americans.
   B. African Americans.
   C. Mexican Americans.
   D. German Americans.

_____ 9. Realizing a draft was necessary, Congress, with Wilson's support, created a new system of conscription called
   A. selective service.
   B. local draft boards.
   C. lotteries.
   D. selective volunteers.

_____ 10. Early in 1917, what division of the military authorized the enlistment of women to meet its clerical needs?
   A. Army
   B. Marines
   C. Air Force
   D. Navy

⭐ **Chapter 14**

Section Quiz 14-3

DIRECTIONS: Matching Match each item in Column A with the items in Column B. Write the correct letters in the blanks. *(10 points each)*

Column A

_____ **1.** supreme commander of the Allied forces

_____ **2.** a group of Communists

_____ **3.** commander of the American troops

_____ **4.** payments for war damages

_____ **5.** the space between opposing trenches

Column B

A. General John J. Pershing

B. Marshall Ferdinand Foch

C. "no-man's land"

D. Bolsheviks

E. reparations

DIRECTIONS: Multiple Choice In the blank at the left, write the letter of the choice that best completes the statement or answers the question. *(10 points each)*

_____ **6.** Who overthrew the Russian government in November of 1917 and established a Communist government there?

    A. Czar Nicholas II

    B. Georges Clemenceau

    C. Vittorio Orlando

    D. Vladimir Lenin

_____ **7.** On November 11, 1918, the fighting stopped and the war ended because Germany had finally signed an armistice, or

    A. cease-fire.

    B. peace treaty.

    C. reparation.

    D. acknowledgment of guilt.

_____ **8.** World War I resulted in the dissolution of four empires: the Austro-Hungarian Empire, the Russian Empire, the German Empire, and the

    A. Chinese Empire.

    B. Slavic Empire.

    C. Yugoslavian Empire.

    D. Ottoman Empire.

_____ **9.** President Wilson called for the creation of a "general association of nations" known as the

    A. United Nations.

    B. League of Nations.

    C. Allies.

    D. Central Powers.

_____ **10.** Where did the Americans shatter German defenses and open a hole in their line with the most massive attack in American history?

    A. Meuse-Argonne

    B. St. Mihiel

    C. Paris

    D. Cantigny

Chapter 14

Section Quiz 14-4

DIRECTIONS: Matching Match each item in Column A with the items in Column B. Write the correct letters in the blanks. *(10 points each)*

Column A

_____ **1.** involves all workers living in a certain location, not just workers in a particular industry

_____ **2.** formed by the Soviet Union to coordinate the activities of Communist parties in other countries

_____ **3.** cost of food, clothing, shelter, and other essentials that people need to survive

_____ **4.** special division within the Justice Department that eventually became the Federal Bureau of Investigation

_____ **5.** expelled from the country

Column B

A. Communist International

B. general strike

C. deported

D. cost of living

E. General Intelligence Division

DIRECTIONS: Multiple Choice In the blank at the left, write the letter of the choice that best completes the statement or answers the question. *(10 points each)*

_____ **6.** One of the largest strikes in American history began when steel workers went on strike for recognition of their union, higher pay, and
    A. medical benefits.
    B. cost of living raises.
    C. shorter hours.
    D. safer working conditions.

_____ **7.** As strikes erupted across the United States in 1919, the fear that Communists, or "reds" as they were called, might seize power led to a nationwide panic known as the
    A. Red Scare.
    B. Red Nativism.
    C. Red Socialism.
    D. Communist Scare.

_____ **8.** Americans often linked radicalism with
    A. nativism.
    B. progressivism.
    C. reform programs.
    D. immigrants.

_____ **9.** Who walked off the job in Boston in what was perhaps the most famous strike of 1919?
    A. shipyard workers
    B. the police force
    C. hospital workers
    D. steel workers

_____ **10.** In addition to the soldiers returning from Europe who needed to find employment, many African Americans who had moved North were competing for jobs and housing, which resulted in
    A. new zoning laws.
    B. race riots.
    C. new industries.
    D. cooperation among races.

The American Republic Since 1877

⭐ **Chapter 14 Test, Form A**

Score

World War I and Its Aftermath

DIRECTIONS: Matching Match each item in Column A with the items in Column B. Write the correct letters in the blanks. *(4 points each)*

Column A

_____ 1. general who failed to capture Pancho Villa

_____ 2. Mexican guerrilla leader who conducted raids into the U.S.

_____ 3. promise not to sink more merchant ships without warning

_____ 4. gave patriotic speeches urging support of war effort

_____ 5. Serbian nationalist group behind assassination of Archduke Ferdinand

_____ 6. method of loaning money to the government to pay for war

_____ 7. spying to acquire government secrets

_____ 8. supreme commander of the Allied forces

_____ 9. Bolshevik leader

_____ 10. stockbroker who led the War Industries Board

Column B

A. Sussex Pledge

B. Black Hand

C. Bernard Baruch

D. John Pershing

E. Ferdinand Foch

F. Pancho Villa

G. espionage

H. Vladimir Lenin

I. Liberty Bonds

J. Four-Minute Men

DIRECTIONS: Multiple Choice Choose the item that best completes each statement or answers each question. Write the letter in the blank. *(4 points each)*

_____ 11. Woodrow Wilson sent marines into several Latin American countries to
   A. protect the southwestern border of the United States from attack.
   B. preserve trading rights for American companies in Latin America.
   C. protect United States citizens living in Latin America when civil wars broke out there.
   D. set up stable democratic governments in Latin America.

_____ 12. President Wilson's invasion of Veracruz was
   A. opposed in Europe and Latin America.   **C.** applauded by Europeans.
   B. supported by Britain and Germany.   **D.** welcomed by Latin Americans.

_____ 13. The Triple Entente included
   A. Germany, Bulgaria, and Italy.   **C.** Britain, France, and Russia.
   B. Germany, Turkey, and Russia.   **D.** Britain, France, and the U.S.

_____ 14. In the case *Schenck* v. *the United States*, the Supreme Court ruled that
   A. immigrants from countries at war with the United States could be excluded from positions of power.
   B. freedom of speech could be curbed in wartime.
   C. the right to bear arms could be limited for immigrants.
   D. the Sedition Act was unconstitutional.

(continued)

⭐ **Chapter 14 Test, Form A**

_____ **15.** The event that touched off the first declaration of war in World War I was
    A. the assassination of the archduke of Germany.
    B. the assassination of the heir to the throne of Austria-Hungary.
    C. the German invasion of Belgium.
    D. the German invasion of Russia.

_____ **16.** World War I was the first war in which
    A. African American soldiers were not segregated from white soldiers.
    B. women officially served in the armed forces.
    C. the government officially imposed conscription.
    D. the military drafted African American men.

_____ **17.** To conserve energy during World War I, the Fuel Administration introduced
    A. longer workdays.
    B. daylight savings time.
    C. Hooverizing.
    D. corn-based fuels.

_____ **18.** The Great Migration during World War I was a flow of
    A. European immigrants fleeing to the United States to escape the war in Europe.
    B. French refugees fleeing to Britain ahead of the German onslaught.
    C. Mexicans fleeing to the American Southwest to escape political turmoil.
    D. African Americans moving from the South to Northern cities.

_____ **19.** Which of the following innovations best completes the diagram?

    A. tanks
    B. airplanes
    C. rapid-fire machine guns
    D. poison gas

_____ **20.** The "Big Four" who attended the peace conference at the end of World War I were the leaders from the United States, Britain, France, and
    A. Russia.
    B. Germany.
    C. Italy.
    D. Austria-Hungary.

DIRECTIONS: Essay Answer one of the following questions on a separate sheet of paper. *(20 points)*

21. Describe two events that pushed the United States toward entering World War I.

22. Describe Woodrow Wilson's Fourteen Points plan by summarizing the main purpose of the first five points, then the next eight points, and finally the fourteenth point.

The American Republic Since 1877

★ Chapter 14 Test, Form B

Score

World War I and Its Aftermath

DIRECTIONS: Matching For each country or region numbered on the map, identify its status during World War I. Match the choices in Column A to the appropriate numbers on the map. Write the letter of each choice in the blanks provided. Letters will be used more than once. *(4 points each)*

Column A

_____ **1.** area #1

_____ **2.** area #2

_____ **3.** area #3

_____ **4.** area #4

_____ **5.** area #5

_____ **6.** area #6

_____ **7.** area #7

_____ **8.** area #8

_____ **9.** area #9

_____ **10.** area #10

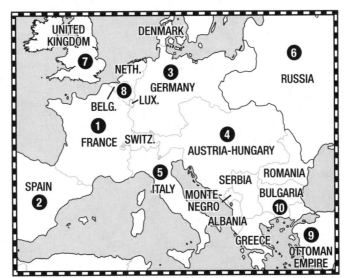

Status

A. Allied power

B. Central power

C. Neutral nation

DIRECTIONS: Multiple Choice Choose the item that best completes each statement or answers each question. Write the letter in the blank. *(4 points each)*

_____ **11.** Woodrow Wilson used Mexico's refusal to apologize for arresting American sailors in Tampico as an excuse to
   A. arrest Mexican sailors currently in United States ports.
   B. deport Mexican citizens in the United States back to Mexico.
   C. attempt to overthrow the Mexican government.
   D. conduct a series of raids across the border into Mexico.

_____ **12.** The Triple Alliance included
   A. Germany, Austria-Hungary, and Italy.
   B. Germany, Austria-Hungary, and Russia.
   C. Britain, France, and Russia.
   D. Britain, France, and the United States.

_____ **13.** In 1908 the Serbs became furious when
   A. the Ottoman Empire refused them independence.
   B. Austria-Hungary refused them independence.
   C. a Slav assassinated their leader.
   D. Austria-Hungary annexed Bosnia.

(continued)

⭐ **Chapter 14 Test, Form B**

_____ **14.** According to the Zimmermann telegram, if Mexico allied with Germany, Germany would
  A. send troops to support the Huerta government.
  B. prevent the United States from taking control of Mexico.
  C. help Mexico regain Texas, New Mexico, and Arizona.
  D. help Mexico take control of Central America.

_____ **15.** According to the Selective Service Act, the order in which men were called to service would be determined by
  A. local draft boards.
  B. military headquarters in Washington, D.C.
  C. age, drafting 21-year-olds first and 30-year-olds last.
  D. lottery.

_____ **16.** During World War I, Americans were encouraged to "Hooverize" by
  A. observing Wheatless Mondays.   **C.** buying Liberty Bonds.
  B. observing Heatless Mondays.   **D.** buying only products necessary to live.

_____ **17.** "Selling" the war to the American people was the task of
  A. J. Edgar Hoover.   **C.** the War Industries Board.
  B. the War Propaganda Board.   **D.** the Committee on Public Information.

_____ **18.** Criticism of the war at home was effectively silenced by
  A. the Committee on Public Information. **C.** the Red Scare.
  B. the Espionage and Sedition Acts.   **D.** the Palmer raids.

_____ **19.** In World War I, airplanes were first used to
  A. transport troops to the front.   **C.** bomb enemy trenches.
  B. observe enemy activities.   **D.** bring supplies to the troops.

_____ **20.** The organization that eventually became the Federal Bureau of Investigation was originally formed to
  A. uncover German spies during World War I.
  B. spread propaganda within the United States in support of the war.
  C. infiltrate unions to head off strikes.
  D. raid radical headquarters looking for evidence of a Communist conspiracy.

DIRECTIONS: Essay Answer one of the following questions on a separate sheet of paper. *(20 points)*

21. Explain the purpose of the War Industries Board and the National War Labor Board, and describe their activities.

22. What caused inflation after World War I, and how did inflation help cause the wave of strikes in the United States?

⭐ **Unit 4 Posttest, Form A**

Imperialism and Progressivism

DIRECTIONS: Matching Match each item in Column A with the items in Column B. Write the correct letters in the blanks. *(4 points each)*

Column A

_____ **1.** placed less emphasis on military force and more on helping Latin American industry

_____ **2.** kept Cuba tied to the United States

_____ **3.** powerful senator who pushed for construction of a new navy

_____ **4.** gave the United States the right to build and control a canal through Central America

_____ **5.** writers who exposed corruption

_____ **6.** a collection of views about how to fix the problems in American society

_____ **7.** the United States would intervene in Latin American affairs when necessary to maintain economic and political stability in the Western Hemisphere

_____ **8.** formed initially from the members of the Triple Entente

_____ **9.** conscription system created during Wilson's administration

_____ **10.** an imperial power defends local rulers from rebellions and invasion in return for political influence

Column B

A. selective service

B. Hay-Pauncefote Treaty

C. dollar diplomacy

D. Allies

E. progressivism

F. protectorate

G. muckrakers

H. Henry Cabot Lodge

I. Platt Amendment

J. Roosevelt Corollary

DIRECTIONS: Multiple Choice Choose the item that best completes each statement or answers each question. Write the letter in the blank. *(4 points each)*

_____ **11.** President Franklin Pierce ordered Commodore Perry to Japan to
 A. conquer it.
 B. force it to become a protectorate.
 C. force it to trade with the U.S.
 D. bring Western civilization to Japan.

_____ **12.** In the Boxer Rebellion, the Boxers were trying to
 A. win Korean independence.
 B. win Manchurian independence.
 C. expel the Japanese.
 D. expel foreign influences.

_____ **13.** The Open Door policy in China was intended to
 A. end the Boxer Rebellion.
 B. distribute leaseholds.
 C. establish spheres of influence.
 D. allow trade with China for all nations.

_____ **14.** In 1907 the "Great White Fleet" went to Japan to
 A. force Japan to give up its claims in China.
 B. demonstrate to Japan that the United States could uphold its interests in Asia.
 C. help defend Japan from Russian aggression.
 D. demonstrate to Russia that the United States would defend Japan.

(continued)

★ **Unit 4 Posttest, Form A**

_____ **15.** When the United States assumed the responsibility for collecting customs tariffs in the Dominican Republic, it was applying
   A. the Roosevelt Corollary.   **C.** dollar diplomacy.
   B. the Open Door policy.   **D.** the Platt Amendment.

_____ **16.** The Bureau of Corporations was created to
   A. settle disputes between corporations and their workers.
   B. investigate unsafe working conditions and force corporations to improve.
   C. oversee land development projects and manage natural resources.
   D. investigate corporations and issue reports on their activities.

_____ **17.** Supporters of laissez-faire believed that the best way to preserve public land was to
   A. keep it under government control and not allow companies to use it.
   B. keep it under government control, but allow its use for land development projects.
   C. sell it to private individuals, who would conserve it because it belonged to them.
   D. sell it to lumber companies, who would conserve it because it was a source of their profits.

_____ **18.** Samuel Gompers called the Clayton Antitrust Act the worker's "Magna Carta" because it
   A. declared that unions were not unlawful combinations in restraint of trade.
   B. banned lockouts and other strikebreaking practices.
   C. legalized strikes.
   D. allowed unions to require all workers at a company to join the union.

_____ **19.** In World War I, American soldiers were nicknamed
   A. Rebels.   **C.** Liberators.
   B. GIs.   **D.** doughboys.

_____ **20.** After the Bolsheviks took power, Russia
   A. declared war on Austria-Hungary.
   B. joined the Allies.
   C. began to win the war on the eastern front.
   D. pulled out of the war.

DIRECTIONS: Essay Answer one of the following questions on a separate sheet of paper. *(20 points)*

21. What arguments did supporters make for annexing the Philippines?

22. Describe the proposal contained in the Zimmermann telegram and its intent. Also explain how the United States learned about it and reacted to it.

★ **Unit 4 Posttest, Form B**

Imperialism and Progressivism

DIRECTIONS: Matching Match each item in Column A with the items in Column B. Write the correct letters in the blanks. *(4 points each)*

Column A

_____ 1. the United States had a duty to shape the "less civilized" corners of the earth

_____ 2. destroyed several Spanish warships in Manila Bay

_____ 3. group that included Germany and Austria-Hungary

_____ 4. a Quaker social worker who wanted to use protests to force action on suffrage

_____ 5. battles in the air between aircraft with attached machine guns

_____ 6. authorized federal funds to pay for irrigation and land development projects

_____ 7. speakers who urged audiences to support the war through various activities

_____ 8. the idea that the United States and Latin America should work together

_____ 9. original position of the United States in World War I

_____ 10. organization proposed to preserve peace and prevent future wars

Column B

A. neutrality

B. Newlands Reclamation Act

C. George Dewey

D. Pan-Americanism

E. Four-Minute Men

F. Central Powers

G. Anglo-Saxonism

H. Alice Paul

I. League of Nations

J. dogfights

DIRECTIONS: Multiple Choice Choose the item that best completes each statement or answers each question. Write the letter in the blank. *(4 points each)*

_____ 11. In the late 1800s, many people believed that the United States should build a large modern navy to
   A. protect the United States from invasion.
   B. conquer Latin American countries.
   C. conquer islands in the Pacific.
   D. avoid being shut out of foreign markets.

_____ 12. As a result of the Platt Amendment, Cuba had effectively become an American
   A. state.   **C.** protectorate.
   B. colony.   **D.** unincorporated territory.

_____ 13. The Boxer Rebellion was an attempt to
   A. win independence for Manchuria.   **C.** force the Japanese out of China.
   B. win independence for Korea.   **D.** force foreign influences out of China.

(continued)

⭐ **Unit 4 Posttest, Form B**

_____ **14.** According to efficiency progressives, cities should be run by a
  A. city manager or commissioners.
  C. mayor appointed by the majority party.
  B. mayor directly elected by the people.
  D. city council directly elected by the people.

_____ **15.** Theodore Roosevelt believed that trusts were
  A. efficient, and government should leave them alone.
  B. illegal, and government should break them up.
  C. inefficient, and government should disband them.
  D. efficient, but needed government supervision.

_____ **16.** Drifting away from its original purpose, the Interstate Commerce Commission had started to
  A. raise rates to help ensure railroads' profits.
  B. sue railroads for competing unfairly.
  C. charge fees for goods transported by rail across state lines.
  D. operate railroads directly.

_____ **17.** No American troop ships were sunk on their way to Europe during World War I, largely due to
  A. radar.
  C. anti-submarine mines.
  B. steel-hulled ships.
  D. the convoy system.

_____ **18.** The first declaration of war in World War I came after
  A. the assassination of Archduke Ferdinand.
  B. Russia signed a treaty to support Austria.
  C. Germany invaded Belgium.
  D. Germany invaded Russia.

_____ **19.** Criticism of World War I at home was effectively silenced by
  A. the Propaganda Commission.
  C. the Red Scare.
  B. the Espionage and Sedition Acts.
  D. the Palmer raids.

_____ **20.** Republicans chose Calvin Coolidge as their vice-presidential candidate in the 1920 election largely because of his handling of the
  A. Chicago race riots.
  C. Boston Police Strike.
  B. Red Scare.
  D. Seattle General Strike.

DIRECTIONS: Essay Answer one of the following questions on a separate sheet of paper. *(20 points)*

21. Explain how the Federal Reserve system operates to support the banking system and regulate the economy.

22. Describe some ways in which the Food Administration helped to ensure that the nation and troops would have enough food during World War I.

⭐ **Unit 5 Pretest, Form A**

Boom and Bust

DIRECTIONS: Matching Match each item in Column A with the items in Column B.
Write the correct letters in the blanks. *(4 points each)*

Column A

_____ **1.** buy now, pay later

_____ **2.** women who symbolized the new morality of the 1920s

_____ **3.** offered jobs to unemployed young men during the Depression

_____ **4.** built a powerful and corrupt political machine

_____ **5.** introduced an early form of jazz

_____ **6.** desire to avoid entanglements in European affairs

_____ **7.** created to regulate the stock market and prevent fraud

_____ **8.** Franklin Roosevelt's program for ending the Depression

_____ **9.** believed in creationism instead of evolution

_____ **10.** wrote *A Farewell to Arms*

Column B

A. Fundamentalists

B. Ernest Hemingway

C. New Deal

D. flappers

E. Securities and Exchange Commission

F. isolationism

G. Louis Armstrong

H. Civilian Conservation Corps

I. installment plan

J. Huey Long

DIRECTIONS: Multiple Choice Choose the item that best completes each sentence
or answers each question. Write the letter in the blank. *(4 points each)*

_____ **11.** The new morality of the 1920s placed a high value on
    A. work.
    B. religion.
    C. personal freedom.
    D. wealth.

_____ **12.** The Scopes trial was about
    A. enforcing Prohibition.
    B. curbing the Ku Klux Klan.
    C. controlling immigration.
    D. teaching evolution.

_____ **13.** A center of creativity and freedom where many artists, writers, and
intellectuals of the 1920s gathered was
    A. Boston.
    B. Greenwich Village.
    C. Charlestown.
    D. Haight-Ashbury.

_____ **14.** African American arts flourished in the 1920s in what became known
as the
    A. Great Transformation.
    B. Great Awakening.
    C. South Side Renaissance.
    D. Harlem Renaissance.

(continued)

Unit 5 Pretest, Form A

_____ **15.** Henry Ford dramatically increased efficiency in car manufacturing by
   A. reducing the number of separate parts required for each car.
   B. installing a moving assembly line.
   C. training workers to do every task required to make a car.
   D. paying workers a bonus when they exceeded their production quota.

_____ **16.** All of these were products of the Prohibition movement EXCEPT
   A. the Volstead Act.   **C.** the Eighteenth Amendment.
   B. secret speakeasy bars.   **D.** the Seventeenth Amendment.

_____ **17.** What was a major characteristic of Coolidge's administration?
   A. efforts to reduce corruption in government
   B. strict government oversight of private business
   C. a return to the values of rural America
   D. entrance into a war with Spain concerning Cuba

_____ **18.** To solve the banking crisis during the Great Depression, the Roosevelt administration
   A. put all banks under government operation.
   B. printed more money.
   C. closed the banks, reopening only those that examiners found to be sound.
   D. made loans to failing banks out of Federal Reserve funds.

_____ **19.** What occurred during the Great Crash of 1929?
   A. a run on banks by depositors   **C.** a steady decline in stock prices
   B. a strengthening of the nation's banks **D.** a city-wide fire in San Francisco

_____ **20.** To pay for programs to fight the Depression, the Roosevelt administration
   A. raised taxes.   **C.** printed money.
   B. borrowed money.   **D.** used gold reserves.

DIRECTIONS: Essay Answer one of the following questions on a separate sheet of paper. *(20 points)*

21. In the 1920s, a new law made it a crime to manufacture, transport, or sell alcohol. Why do you think supporters wanted this law? How do you think Americans reacted to the law?

22. In the 1920s, automobiles became affordable for the majority of Americans. How do you think automobiles affected life in America in the 1920s?

★ Unit 5 Pretest, Form B

Boom and Bust

DIRECTIONS: Matching Match each item in Column A with the items in Column B.
Write the correct letters in the blanks. *(4 points each)*

Column A

_____ **1.** established limits on immigration

_____ **2.** famous Harlem nightspot

_____ **3.** Harding's secretary of the treasury

_____ **4.** allowed workers to participate in corporate profit sharing

_____ **5.** when creditors take possession of property

_____ **6.** controlled flooding through the use of dams

_____ **7.** desire to stay out of European politics

_____ **8.** wrote *The Grapes of Wrath*

_____ **9.** established an arbitration process for resolving complaints brought by union members

_____ **10.** Henry Ford's Model T

Column B

A. isolationism

B. foreclose

C. Wagner Act

D. John Steinbeck

E. Tennessee Valley Authority

F. Andrew Mellon

G. Cotton Club

H. Flivver

I. welfare capitalism

J. Emergency Quota Act

DIRECTIONS: Multiple Choice Choose the item that best completes each sentence
or answers each question. Write the letter in the blank. *(4 points each)*

_____ **11.** Which of these terms is NOT associated with the worsening Depression?
A. shantytowns   **C.** hobos
B. Bohemian   **D.** breadlines

_____ **12.** All of the following are examples of discontent in the early 1930s
EXCEPT
A. Communist Party hunger marches.   **C.** an increase in strikes by union workers.
B. the destruction of crops by farmers.   **D.** the bonus marches of veterans.

_____ **13.** What was a major development in popular culture during the 1920s?
A. a strong interest in Hollywood and "talking" pictures
B. a preference for watching television over listening to the radio
C. an increase in regional interests and a decline in mass media
D. a declining interest in sports and sports heroes

_____ **14.** Some Americans criticized the New Deal because it
A. supported deficit spending.   **C.** imposed fewer taxes on the wealthy.
B. lacked business regulation.   **D.** imposed a mandatory retirement age.

(continued)

★ **Unit 5 Pretest, Form B**

Score

_____ **15.** The nation's banks were weakened by the stock market crash because
  A. banks had invested their deposits in the stock market.
  B. banks obtained much of their operating funds from the sale of their stock.
  C. people no longer had money to deposit in banks.
  D. people could no longer afford to take out loans from banks.

_____ **16.** Which of the following statements about Franklin Roosevelt is true?
  A. He set up an agency for the unemployed in New York.
  B. He was elected governor of New Jersey.
  C. He said, "The only thing we have to fear is war."
  D. He was unpopular because of his misuse of government power.

_____ **17.** In 1934 Roosevelt closed the Civil Works Administration because
  A. it had accomplished its goal.
  B. it was failing to accomplish its goal.
  C. jobs in private business were starting to open up for these workers.
  D. he did not want people to depend on the federal government to give them jobs.

_____ **18.** How did President Hoover try to promote economic recovery?
  A. by stepping up public works projects
  B. by announcing concern that the crash was coming
  C. by increasing taxes to pay for projects
  D. by legislating a stop to wage-slashing

_____ **19.** Deficit spending was advocated by
  A. Keynesian economists.   **C.** laissez-faire economists.
  B. monetarists.   **D.** balanced-budget economists.

_____ **20.** In the end, the New Deal had
  A. successfully ended the Depression.
  B. solved the unemployment problem but did not end the Depression.
  C. limited success in ending the Depression, although recovery was not complete until after World War II.
  D. left Americans with a strong sense of insecurity and fear for the future.

DIRECTIONS: Essay Answer one of the following questions on a separate sheet of paper. *(20 points)*

21. What was the major cause of the Great Depression?

22. Describe the goals of the Social Security Act.

★ **Chapter 15**

Score

Section Quiz 15-1

DIRECTIONS: Matching Match each item in Column A with the items in Column B.
Write the correct letters in the blanks. *(10 points each)*

Column A

_____ **1.** evangelical preacher who conducted revivals and faith healings in Los Angeles

_____ **2.** established a temporary quota system, limiting immigration

_____ **3.** founded the American Birth Control League

_____ **4.** opposed all forms of government

_____ **5.** published *Coming of Age in Samoa*

Column B

A. Margaret Sanger

B. anarchists

C. Emergency Quota Act

D. Aimee Semple McPherson

E. Margaret Mead

DIRECTIONS: Multiple Choice In the blank at the left, write the letter of the choice
that best completes the statement or answers the question. *(10 points each)*

_____ **6.** Many Americans feared that the country was losing its traditional values
and responded by joining a religious movement known as
  A. Fundamentalism.
  B. Quakerism.
  C. Protestantism.
  D. Catholicism.

_____ **7.** What was the name of the science that lent authority to racist theories
and reinvigorated the nativist argument for strict immigration control?
  A. nativism
  B. creationism
  C. evolution
  D. eugenics

_____ **8.** The National Origins Act of 1924 and the demand for cheap farm labor in
California and the Southwest contributed to the large wave of
immigration from
  A. China.
  B. South America.
  C. Mexico.
  D. Canada.

_____ **9.** What did many of the groups who wanted to restrict immigration and
preserve what they considered traditional values fear was taking over
the nation?
  A. Communists
  B. anarchists
  C. a "new morality"
  D. a new religion

_____ **10.** Where did the debate over science and religion and their place in
education take place during the summer of 1925?
  A. at Billy Sunday's revivals
  B. in the Scopes trial
  C. in Florence Sabin's research
  D. in Lyman Stewart's book, *The Fundamentals*

Chapter 15

Section Quiz 15-2

DIRECTIONS: Matching Match each item in Column A with the items in Column B. Write the correct letters in the blanks. *(10 points each)*

Column A

_____ **1.** a film star

_____ **2.** Chicago poet who used common speech to glorify the Midwest

_____ **3.** part of Manhattan where many artists, writers, and intellectuals flocked

_____ **4.** famous writer who created colorful, glamorous characters who chased futile dreams in *The Great Gatsby*

_____ **5.** Realist painter who conveyed disenchantment and isolation

Column B

A. F. Scott Fitzgerald

B. Edward Hopper

C. Mary Pickford

D. Greenwich Village

E. Carl Sandburg

DIRECTIONS: Multiple Choice In the blank at the left, write the letter of the choice that best completes the statement or answers the question. *(10 points each)*

_____ **6.** Many novelists of the 1920s created characters who were flawed individuals but still had heroic qualities of mind and spirit. These characters were called

A. "heroic antiheroes."   **C.** "Hollow Men."

B. Bohemians.   **D.** "Galloping Ghosts."

_____ **7.** Although sports became increasingly popular in the 1920s, nothing quite matched the allure of

A. poetry.   **C.** motion pictures.

B. theater.   **D.** radio.

_____ **8.** What sports star was nicknamed the "Sultan of Swat" and became a national hero?

A. Jack Dempsey   **C.** Red Grange

B. Babe Ruth   **D.** Bill Tilden

_____ **9.** American artists and writers experimented with how to express the challenges faced by individuals in the modern world as they searched for

A. modernism.   **C.** popular culture.

B. styles.   **D.** meaning.

_____ **10.** What artist applied the influence of photography and the geometric forms of Cubism to his paintings of urban and rural American landscapes?

A. John Marin   **C.** Eugene O'Neill

B. Paul Cézanne   **D.** Charles Scheeler

The American Republic Since 1877

★ Chapter 15

Section Quiz 15-3

DIRECTIONS: Matching Match each item in Column A with the items in Column B. Write the correct letters in the blanks. *(10 points each)*

Column A

_____ **1.** first important writer of the Harlem Renaissance

_____ **2.** "the Empress of the Blues"

_____ **3.** the first musical written, produced, and performed by African Americans

_____ **4.** flowering of African American arts

_____ **5.** author whose work influenced contemporary writers Ralph Ellison and Toni Morrison

Column B

A. Zora Neale Hurston

B. Claude McKay

C. *Shuffle Along*

D. Bessie Smith

E. Harlem Renaissance

DIRECTIONS: Multiple Choice In the blank at the left, write the letter of the choice that best completes the statement or answers the question. *(10 points each)*

_____ **6.** What music with its bold solos and improvisational freedom is recognized around the world as the distinctive American contribution to music?

    A. ragtime   **C.** country

    B. jazz   **D.** classical

_____ **7.** The Great Migration had a significant impact on the political power of African Americans in the

    A. presidential election.   **C.** South.

    B. Democratic Party.   **D.** North.

_____ **8.** Two striking characteristics of Harlem Renaissance writing found in the poetry of Claude McKay are an expression of proud defiance and a bitter contempt of

    A. nationalism.   **C.** racism.

    B. anarchists.   **D.** Communists.

_____ **9.** One of the NAACP's greatest political triumphs occurred in 1930 with the defeat of Judge John J. Parker's nomination to the

    A. U.S. Supreme Court.   **C.** Senate.

    B. House of Representatives.   **D.** Circuit Court.

_____ **10.** The Universal Negro Improvement Association was founded by a dynamic black leader from Jamaica,

    A. Langston Hughes.   **C.** Duke Ellington.

    B. Paul Robeson.   **D.** Marcus Garvey.

★ **Chapter 15 Test, Form A**

Score

The Jazz Age

DIRECTIONS: Matching Match each item in Column A with the items in Column B.
Write the correct letters in the blanks. *(4 points each)*

Column A

_____ 1. writer who became a leading voice of the African American experience in the United States

_____ 2. prosecutor at the Scopes trial

_____ 3. leader of the "back to Africa" movement

_____ 4. pilot of the first solo nonstop transatlantic flight

_____ 5. composer, pianist, and bandleader whose sound was a blend of improvisation and orchestration

_____ 6. gangster in Chicago during Prohibition

_____ 7. first African American representative elected to Congress from a Northern state

_____ 8. one of the first woman anthropologists

_____ 9. former major league baseball player turned evangelical fundamentalist preacher

_____ 10. singer who seemed to symbolize soul

Column B

A. Bessie Smith

B. Marcus Garvey

C. Charles Lindbergh

D. Oscar DePriest

E. William Jennings Bryan

F. Langston Hughes

G. Billy Sunday

H. Duke Ellington

I. Margaret Mead

J. Al Capone

DIRECTIONS: Multiple Choice Choose the item that best completes each sentence or answers each question. Write the letter in the blank. *(4 points each)*

_____ 11. Many people viewed Sacco and Vanzetti with suspicion because they were
  A. German immigrants and anarchists.   **C.** Italian immigrants and anarchists.
  B. German immigrants and socialists.   **D.** Italian immigrants and socialists.

_____ 12. In the early 1920s, the Ku Klux Klan added to its membership by
  A. hiring public relations people to promote the Klan.
  B. holding rallies open to everyone.
  C. opening membership to all whites, regardless of religion.
  D. publicizing their support of legitimate political goals.

_____ 13. After the Emergency Quota Act was passed, admission to the United States was based on immigrants'
  A. literacy test scores.   **C.** wealth.
  B. job skills.   **D.** ethnic identity and national origin.

_____ 14. The new morality of the 1920s glorified
  A. work.   **C.** personal freedom.
  B. promiscuity.   **D.** wealth.

(continued)

⭐ **Chapter 15 Test, Form A**

_____ **15.** John T. Scopes was put on trial for
  A. violating Prohibition laws.   **C.** teaching creationism.
  B. being a leader of the Ku Klux Klan.   **D.** teaching evolution.

_____ **16.** The Butler Act
  A. outlawed the teaching of creationism.
  B. outlawed the teaching of evolution.
  C. banned the making and sale of liquor.
  D. enforced the Eighteenth Amendment.

_____ **17.** The Twenty-first Amendment
  A. established Prohibition.   **C.** guaranteed women the right to vote.
  B. repealed Prohibition.   **D.** guaranteed African Americans the right to vote.

_____ **18.** The "Sultan of Swat" was the nickname for
  A. Jack Dempsey.   **C.** Babe Ruth.
  B. Red Grange.   **D.** Bill Tilden.

_____ **19.** The flowering of African American arts in the 1920s became known as the
  A. Great Migration.   **C.** South Side Renaissance.
  B. Great Awakening.   **D.** Harlem Renaissance.

_____ **20.** The Universal Negro Improvement Association was formed to
  A. promote black pride and unity.   **C.** elect African Americans to Congress.
  B. promote integration.   **D.** protest the horrors of lynching.

DIRECTIONS: Essay Answer one of the following questions on a separate sheet of paper. *(20 points)*

21. According to the National Origins Act of 1924, the United States would accept the most new immigrants from which nation shown in the graph? From which nation would the least new immigrants be accepted? Explain how the National Origins Act favored immigrants from some regions of Europe over others.

22. Describe how the automobile played a role in encouraging the new morality of the 1920s.

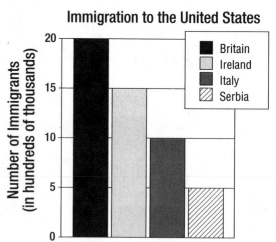

Immigration to the United States

Number of Immigrants (in hundreds of thousands)

Legend: Britain, Ireland, Italy, Serbia

The American Republic Since 1877

★ Chapter 15 Test, Form B

The Jazz Age

DIRECTIONS: Matching Match each item in Column A with the items in Column B. Write the correct letters in the blanks. *(4 points each)*

Column A

_____ **1.** artistic and unconventional lifestyle in the 1920s

_____ **2.** helped spread the new ideas and attitudes of the 1920s

_____ **3.** God created the world as described in the Bible

_____ **4.** created powerful African American voting blocs in Northern cities

_____ **5.** a government's right to control people and property in the interest of public safety, health, welfare, and morals

_____ **6.** dramatic dual between fundamentalism and modernism

_____ **7.** illegal production and distribution of liquor

_____ **8.** warned against breeding the "unfit" or "inferior"

_____ **9.** human beings developed from lower forms of life

_____ **10.** bobbed their hair and drank prohibited liquor

Column B

A. bootlegging

B. evolution

C. Great Migration

D. flappers

E. police powers

F. mass media

G. eugenics

H. Scopes trial

I. Bohemian

J. creationism

DIRECTIONS: Multiple Choice Choose the item that best completes each sentence or answers each question. Write the letter in the blank. *(4 points each)*

_____ **11.** The Ku Klux Klan began to decline in the late 1920s, largely as a result of
  A. the arrest of key Klan leaders.   **C.** scandals involving Klan leaders.
  B. their violent tactics.   **D.** the shift away from nativism.

_____ **12.** The National Origins Act of 1924
  A. banned Mexican immigrants from entering the United States.
  B. allotted a small portion of the quota to immigrants from Mexico.
  C. allotted a large portion of the quota to immigrants from Mexico.
  D. exempted Mexicans from the quota system.

_____ **13.** The purpose of the Volstead Act was to
  A. limit immigration.   **C.** ban the teaching of evolution.
  B. enforce Prohibition.   **D.** prohibit lynching.

_____ **14.** One effect of the Eighteenth Amendment was
  A. a decrease in immigration.   **C.** an increase in federal police powers.
  B. an increase in immigration.   **D.** the decline of Fundamentalism as a national political force.

(continued)

⭐ **Chapter 15 Test, Form B**

Score

_____ **15.** Ernest Hemingway's *A Farewell to Arms*
    A. portrayed war's meaningless violence.
    B. glorified war.
    C. exposed the emptiness and superficiality of much of modern society.
    D. portrayed the vitality and freedom of the new morality.

_____ **16.** The golden age of Hollywood began in 1927 with the release of
    A. the first motion picture.   **C.** the first animated film.
    B. the first feature-length film.   **D.** the first motion picture with sound.

_____ **17.** In 1920 in one of the first commercial radio broadcasts in history, listeners of station KDKA in Pittsburgh heard the
    A. Dempsey-Tunney title fight.
    B. *Amos 'n' Andy* show.
    C. news of Warren G. Harding's victory in the presidential election.
    D. news of the first successful transatlantic flight.

_____ **18.** The Cotton Club was
    A. a Chicago speakeasy where gangsters congregated.
    B. a Harlem nightspot where many African American entertainers got their start.
    C. a Hollywood nightspot frequented by the stars of the silver screen.
    D. a fictitious Chicago nightclub featured in the famous picture *The Jazz Singer*.

_____ **19.** The NAACP's lobbying efforts influenced the House of Representatives to pass, in 1922,
    A. anti-lynching legislation.   **C.** legislation supporting African American voting rights.
    B. anti-segregation legislation.   **D.** equal opportunity legislation.

_____ **20.** One of the NAACP's greatest political triumphs occurred in 1930 with the
    A. signing of a law against lynching.
    B. signing of a law banning discrimination in federal jobs.
    C. defeat of a racist judge nominated for the Supreme Court.
    D. appointment of an African American to the Supreme Court.

DIRECTIONS: Essay Answer one of the following questions on a separate sheet of paper. *(20 points)*

21. Explain the relationship depicted in the diagram.

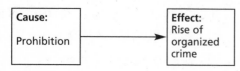

22. Describe the changes in women's lives in the 1920s.

The American Republic Since 1877

Copyright © by The McGraw-Hill Companies, Inc.

★ **Chapter 16**

Section Quiz 16-1

DIRECTIONS: Matching Match each item in Column A with the items in Column B.
Write the correct letters in the blanks. *(10 points each)*

Column A

_____ **1.** Wisconsin senator who ran against the Democratic and
Republican nominees for president in 1924

_____ **2.** friends of President Harding

_____ **3.** President Harding's campaign slogan

_____ **4.** freedom from prosecution

_____ **5.** dean of the Columbia Law School chosen as attorney
general by President Coolidge

Column B

A. immunity

B. Ohio Gang

C. Harlan Fiske
Stone

D. return to normalcy

E. Robert M.
La Follette

DIRECTIONS: Multiple Choice In the blank at the left, write the letter of the choice
that best completes the statement or answers the question. *(10 points each)*

_____ **6.** Although many of President Harding's appointments were disastrous, he
did appoint several distinguished cabinet members including the
secretary of commerce,
   A. Andrew Mellon.   **C.** Harry Daugherty.
   B. Herbert Hoover.   **D.** John W. Davis.

_____ **7.** President Coolidge's philosophy of government was that government
should interfere with business and industry as little as possible and that
prosperity rested on the shoulders of
   A. business leadership.   **C.** a strong military.
   B. educational institutions.   **D.** church leaders.

_____ **8.** President Harding fit in comfortably with the powerful Ohio Republican
   A. House of Representatives.   **C.** political machine.
   B. reform issues.   **D.** progressive ideas.

_____ **9.** President Coolidge's simple and frugal manner contrasted not only with
Harding but also with the spirit of the time—the booming, materialistic
era of the
   A. Progressive Party.   **C.** Ohio Gang.
   B. Roaring Twenties.   **D.** Fourteen Points.

_____ **10.** President Harding's secretary of the interior, Albert B. Fall, secretly
allowed private interests to lease lands containing U.S. Navy oil reserves,
causing a scandal that came to be known as the
   A. Teapot Dome scandal.   **C.** Fall scandal.
   B. Forbes scandal.   **D.** Daugherty scandal.

Chapter 16

Score

Section Quiz 16-2

DIRECTIONS: Matching Match each item in Column A with the items in Column B.
Write the correct letters in the blanks. *(10 points each)*

Column A

_____ 1. set requirements that workers employed by Henry Ford had to meet

_____ 2. authorized postal officials to contract with private airplane operators to carry mail

_____ 3. established a permanent network of radio stations to distribute daily programs

_____ 4. raised tariffs in an effort to protect American industry from foreign competition

_____ 5. large-scale product manufacturing usually by machinery

Column B

A. National Broadcasting Company

B. mass production

C. Kelly Act

D. Sociological Department

E. Fordney-McCumber Act

DIRECTIONS: Multiple Choice In the blank at the left, write the letter of the choice
that best completes the statement or answers the question. *(10 points each)*

_____ 6. What system of manufacturing adopted by Henry Ford divided operations into simple tasks that unskilled workers could do and cut unnecessary motion to a minimum?
    A. assembly line   **C.** Flivver
    B. mass production   **D.** apprentice system

_____ 7. To create consumers for their new products, manufacturers turned to
    A. television.   **C.** advertising.
    B. mass production.   **D.** newspaper and magazine articles.

_____ 8. Henry Ford almost single-handedly changed the auto from a toy of the wealthy to an affordable necessity for the
    A. delivery industry.   **C.** farmers.
    B. middle class.   **D.** city dwellers.

_____ 9. In 1926 the aviation industry received federal aid for building airports with the passage of the
    A. Air Commerce Act.   **C.** Airmail Act.
    B. Lindbergh Air Act.   **D.** Kelly Act.

_____ 10. The consumer goods industry created many new products for
    A. factories.   **C.** businesses.
    B. the airline industry.   **D.** the home.

★ **Chapter 16**

Section Quiz 16-3

DIRECTIONS: Matching Match each item in Column A with the items in Column B.
Write the correct letters in the blanks. *(10 points each)*

Column A

_____ 1. when the United States invited representatives from eight
countries to discuss disarmament

_____ 2. outlawed war

_____ 3. a national policy of avoiding involvement in world
affairs

_____ 4. guaranteed China's independence

_____ 5. a pause

Column B

A. isolationism

B. Nine-Power
Treaty

C. Kellogg-Briand
Pact

D. moratorium

E. Washington
Conference

DIRECTIONS: Multiple Choice In the blank at the left, write the letter of the choice
that best completes the statement or answers the question. *(10 points each)*

_____ 6. The General Accounting Office was set up in 1921 to
  A. prepare a federal budget.
  B. track government spending.
  C. regulate radio frequencies.
  D. regulate Prohibition.

_____ 7. The Four-Power Treaty between the United States, Japan, France, and
Britain recognized each country's island possessions in the
  A. Northern Hemisphere.
  B. Caribbean Sea.
  C. Atlantic.
  D. Pacific.

_____ 8. The chief architect of economic policy in the United States during the
1920s was
  A. Andrew Mellon.
  B. President Harding.
  C. Herbert Hoover.
  D. Charles Evan Hughes.

_____ 9. What crippled the German economy?
  A. isolationists
  B. moratoriums
  C. reparation payments
  D. supply-side economists

_____ 10. Herbert Hoover sought to provide economic stability in various
industries by trying to balance government regulation with his own
philosophy of
  A. welfare capitalism.
  B. cooperative individualism.
  C. supply-side economics.
  D. open shops.

⭐ **Chapter 16 Test, Form A**

Normalcy and Good Times

DIRECTIONS: Matching Match each item in Column A with the items in Column B. Write the correct letters in the blanks. *(4 points each)*

Column A

_____ **1.** profit sharing, medical care benefits, and pensions

_____ **2.** form trade associations and share information with the federal government

_____ **3.** recognized each country's island possessions in the Pacific

_____ **4.** payments Germany was required to make as punishment for starting the war

_____ **5.** Henry Ford's Model T car

_____ **6.** pause in doing something, such as constructing new warships

_____ **7.** attempted to outlaw war

_____ **8.** made possible by affordable cars

_____ **9.** growth through lower taxes

_____ **10.** enormously increased manufacturing efficiency

Column B

A. Kellogg-Briand Pact

B. assembly line

C. supply-side economics

D. welfare capitalism

E. reparations

F. cooperative individualism

G. "Tin Lizzie"

H. Four-Power Treaty

I. moratorium

J. commuters

DIRECTIONS: Multiple Choice Choose the item that best completes each sentence or answers each question. Write the letter in the blank. *(4 points each)*

_____ **11.** Warren G. Harding won the presidency by appealing to Americans' desire to
  A. reform society.
  B. become a world power.
  C. return to normal life after the war.
  D. repeal Prohibition.

_____ **12.** Calvin Coolidge became president when
  A. he defeated Warren G. Harding.
  B. he defeated Robert La Follette.
  C. Warren G. Harding was assassinated.
  D. Warren G. Harding died in office.

_____ **13.** Attorney General Harry Daugherty resigned in disgrace after being investigated for taking bribes in exchange for allowing
  A. a private company to drill for oil on public lands.
  B. someone to acquire a valuable German-owned company seized during the war.
  C. immunity to wealthy businessmen accused of insider trading.
  D. two powerful corporations to merge.

_____ **14.** Coolidge believed that government should
  A. regulate business.
  B. not interfere with business.
  C. break up trusts.
  D. become involved in social reform.

(continued)

Copyright © by The McGraw-Hill Companies, Inc.

★ Chapter 16 Test, Form A

Score

_____ **15.** Ford's system for making cars increased efficiency by
  A. reducing the number of car parts.   **C.** training workers to do every task.
  B. dividing the job into simple tasks.   **D.** assigning a team to each car.

_____ **16.** The purpose of Henry Ford's Sociological Department was to
  A. set requirements workers had to meet. **C.** negotiate with the union.
  B. improve employee relations.   **D.** provide a channel for communication.

_____ **17.** Commercial radio began its rise in November 1920, with the news that
  A. World War I was over.   **C.** Coolidge had won the election.
  B. an American had flown over the   **D.** Harding had won the election.
  Atlantic.

_____ **18.** In the 1920s, young people began to look for careers as
  A. entrepreneurs.   **C.** business owners.
  B. stockholders.   **D.** managers in a corporate bureaucracy.

_____ **19.** Some members of Congress tried to help farmers by proposing the
  McNary-Haugen Bill, which called for the government to
  A. place tariffs on foreign agricultural products to protect American farmers from
  foreign competition.
  B. set higher prices for agricultural products sold in the United States.
  C. buy American crop surpluses and use them to feed the military.
  D. buy American crop surpluses and sell them abroad.

_____ **20.** Unions declined during the 1920s in part because many corporations instituted
  A. cooperative individualism.   **C.** Sociological Departments.
  B. supply-side economics.   **D.** welfare capitalism.

DIRECTIONS: Essay Answer one of the following questions on a separate sheet of
paper. (*20 points*)

21. Describe the factors that prevented farmers from sharing in the prosperity of the
1920s.

22. Use the diagram to help you explain how supporters of supply-side economics
believed that lower tax rates would actually result in more tax money collected.

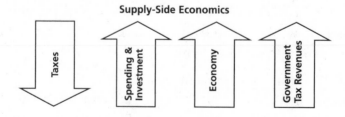

Supply-Side Economics

Taxes   Spending & Investment   Economy   Government Tax Revenues

★ **Chapter 16 Test, Form B**

Score

Normalcy and Good Times

DIRECTIONS: Matching Put the choices in column A in the proper sequence in the diagram. Write the letters from the diagram in the blanks provided. *(4 points each)*

Column A

_____ **1.** lower car prices for consumers

_____ **2.** less time required to build cars

_____ **3.** adoption of the assembly line at Ford

_____ **4.** lower production costs

A → B → C → D

DIRECTIONS: Matching Match each item in Column A with the items in Column B. Write the correct letters in the blanks. *(4 points each)*

Column A

_____ **5.** installed the first moving assembly line in 1914

_____ **6.** first cabinet officer in history to go to prison

_____ **7.** presidential nominee of the Progressive Party in 1924

_____ **8.** made first solo transatlantic flight

_____ **9.** sold medical supplies from veterans' hospitals

_____ **10.** "Four-fifths of all our troubles in this life would disappear if we would only sit down and keep still."

Column B

A. Calvin Coolidge

B. Albert B. Fall

C. Henry Ford

D. Charles Lindbergh

E. Charles R. Forbes

F. Robert La Follette

DIRECTIONS: Multiple Choice Choose the item that best completes each sentence or answers each question. Write the letter in the blank. *(4 points each)*

_____ **11.** The Ohio Gang was
   A. a powerful crime syndicate.
   B. a group of notorious bank robbers.
   C. a group of Coolidge's friends.
   D. a group of Harding's friends.

_____ **12.** In the Teapot Dome scandal, a government official received bribes for
   A. allowing private interests to lease lands containing U.S. Navy oil reserves.
   B. allowing private interests to drill for oil in a national park.
   C. allowing lumber companies to cut trees in national forests.
   D. promising immunity for businessmen who overcharged the U.S. Navy.

_____ **13.** Calvin Coolidge grew up
   A. on a Midwestern farm.
   B. on a Vermont farm.
   C. in a wealthy section of Boston.
   D. on a ranch in Wyoming.

_____ **14.** An innovation instituted by International Harvester in 1926 was
   A. a 5-day workweek.
   B. mass production.
   C. an annual 2-week paid vacation.
   D. an 8-hour workday.

(continued)

The American Republic Since 1877

⭐ **Chapter 16 Test, Form B**

Score

_____ **15.** Henry Ford's business philosophy was to increase sales by
  A. providing consumers with a variety of styles and colors.
  B. advertising.
  C. lowering the cost per car.
  D. constantly improving his cars' mechanical reliability.

_____ **16.** The federal government began to support the airline industry after
  A. the Wright brothers' successful flight at Kitty Hawk.
  B. entrepreneurs such as Glenn Curtiss started building practical aircraft.
  C. World War II.
  D. Alexander Graham Bell invented ailerons.

_____ **17.** An unintended affect of the Fordney-McCumber Act was
  A. an increase in prices of foreign goods for American consumers.
  B. a decrease in prices of foreign goods for American consumers.
  C. a reaction in foreign markets against American agricultural products.
  D. an increase in demand in foreign markets for American agricultural products.

_____ **18.** Secretary of Commerce Herbert Hoover believed that waste could be reduced and costs lowered if trade associations would
  A. voluntarily share information with one another.
  B. voluntarily share information with the Bureau of Standards.
  C. collaborate to set reasonable wage rates for workers in similar jobs.
  D. collaborate to set reasonable prices for similar products.

_____ **19.** After World War I, most Americans wanted to avoid future wars by
  A. joining the League of Nations.
  B. excluding Germany from the League of Nations.
  C. avoiding involvement in European affairs.
  D. forbidding Germany to rebuild its armed forces.

_____ **20.** The result of the Dawes Plan was
  A. Europe's deeper descent into debt.
  B. Europe's gradual economic recovery.
  C. lower prices for European products sold in the United States.
  D. higher prices for European products sold in the United States.

DIRECTIONS: Essay Answer one of the following questions on a separate sheet of paper. *(20 points)*

21. Compare the personalities of Calvin Coolidge and Warren G. Harding.

22. How did the automobile affect American business and society in the 1920s?

⭐ **Chapter 17**

Section Quiz 17-1

DIRECTIONS: Matching Match each item in Column A with the items in Column B.
Write the correct letters in the blanks. *(10 points each)*

Column A

_____ **1.** buying and selling ownership shares of companies

_____ **2.** a key cause of the Depression

_____ **3.** takes place when many depositors decide to withdraw their money at one time

_____ **4.** making a down payment and paying the rest of the price in monthly installments

_____ **5.** when stock prices continue to rise

Column B

A. bank run

B. stock market

C. installment plan

D. bull market

E. overproduction

DIRECTIONS: Multiple Choice In the blank at the left, write the letter of the choice
that best completes the statement or answers the question. *(10 points each)*

_____ **6.** In order to protect loans made by stockbrokers to investors who bought stocks on margin, brokers could issue a
    A. collateral.
    B. speculation call.
    C. margin call.
    D. foreclosure.

_____ **7.** What severely dampened commerce on both sides of the Atlantic and intensified the Depression in the United States?
    A. the bull market
    B. the Federal Reserve
    C. Black Tuesday
    D. the Hawley-Smoot Tariff

_____ **8.** In 1929 the top 5 percent of all American households earned 30 percent of the nation's income, which is
    A. an uneven distribution of wealth.
    B. supply-side economics.
    C. a bull market.
    D. a recession.

_____ **9.** October 29, 1929, the day when stock prices took the steepest dive of that time, is known as
    A. Black Thursday.
    B. Black Tuesday.
    C. Bloody Monday.
    D. Panic Tuesday.

_____ **10.** For some banks, the losses they suffered in the crash were more than they could absorb and they were forced to
    A. increase interest rates.
    B. approve more loans.
    C. attract more depositors.
    D. close.

⭐ **Chapter 17**

Section Quiz 17-2

DIRECTIONS: Matching Match each item in Column A with the items in Column B.
Write the correct letters in the blanks. *(10 points each)*

Column A

_____ **1.** places where newly homeless people put up shacks on unused or public lands

_____ **2.** unemployed Americans who wandered around the country, walking, hitchhiking, or "riding the rails"

_____ **3.** a famous film of the Depression era

_____ **4.** court officers

_____ **5.** private charities set up to give poor people a meal

Column B

A. hobos

B. *Gone with the Wind*

C. bailiffs

D. shantytowns

E. soup kitchens

DIRECTIONS: Multiple Choice In the blank at the left, write the letter of the choice that best completes the statement or answers the question. *(10 points each)*

_____ **6.** Beginning in 1932, America's pastures and wheat fields from the Dakotas to Texas became a vast
    A. "Bread Basket."
    B. "Dust Bowl."
    C. mud basin.
    D. prairie.

_____ **7.** Many families on the Great Plains packed their belongings into old cars or trucks and headed west, hoping for a better life in
    A. the cities.
    B. the mountains.
    C. California.
    D. New Mexico.

_____ **8.** Most people during the Depression were able to enjoy two popular forms of entertainment: the movies and
    A. sailing.
    B. television.
    C. travel.
    D. radio.

_____ **9.** Daytime radio dramas were sponsored by makers of laundry soap and nicknamed
    A. soap operas.
    B. laundry stories.
    C. guiding lights.
    D. detergent dramas.

_____ **10.** The Dust Bowl occurred because plowed land was left uncultivated and there was a terrible
    A. insect infestation.
    B. drought.
    C. winter.
    D. increase of wild grasses.

★ **Chapter 17**

Section Quiz 17-3

DIRECTIONS: Matching Match each item in Column A with the items in Column B.
Write the correct letters in the blanks. *(10 points each)*

Column A

_____ **1.** held rallies and "hunger marches" during the Depression

_____ **2.** World War I veterans who marched to Washington, D.C.

_____ **3.** created when the government spends more money than it collects in taxes

_____ **4.** created a pool of money to rescue troubled banks

_____ **5.** government-financed building projects

Column B

A. National Credit Corporation

B. budget deficit

C. American Communist Party

D. public works

E. Bonus Army

DIRECTIONS: Multiple Choice In the blank at the left, write the letter of the choice
that best completes the statement or answers the question. *(10 points each)*

_____ **6.** By 1932 Hoover concluded that the only way to provide funding for borrowers was for the government to do the lending, so he requested that Congress set up the

    A. Reconstruction Finance Corporation.

    B. Federal Reserve Board.

    C. Emergency Relief and Construction Act.

    D. National Credit Corporation.

_____ **7.** Hoover did not want the government to create many new jobs because that would mean increased government

    A. involvement in business.

    B. taxes.

    C. regulation.

    D. spending.

_____ **8.** Between 1930 and 1934, creditors foreclosed on nearly one million farms, and farmers retaliated in all of the following ways EXCEPT by

    A. destroying their crops to reduce the supply and raise prices.

    B. blocking milk trucks and emptying milk cans into ditches.

    C. preventing the delivery of vegetables to distributors.

    D. marching to Washington, D.C., in protest.

_____ **9.** The public's perception of President Hoover was shaped by the image of the routed Bonus Marchers and the

    A. lingering Depression.

    B. hunger marches.

    C. public works.

    D. National Credit Corporation.

_____ **10.** Hoover believed that only state and city governments should dole out

    A. loans.

    B. relief.

    C. work programs.

    D. soup kitchens.

⭐ **Chapter 17 Test, Form A**

The Great Depression Begins

DIRECTIONS: Matching Match each item in Column A with the items in Column B.
Write the correct letters in the blanks. *(4 points each)*

Column A

_____ **1.** fictitious heroine in *Gone with the Wind*

_____ **2.** comic star of stage and screen who was one of the many people wiped out financially in the stock market crash

_____ **3.** led the troops that dispersed the Bonus Army

_____ **4.** wrote *The Grapes of Wrath*, about a family fleeing the Dust Bowl

_____ **5.** fictitious companion of the Lone Ranger

_____ **6.** many depositors withdrawing money at once

_____ **7.** investing in the stock market hoping for a quick profit

_____ **8.** homeless wanderers who often rode the rails

_____ **9.** spending more than is collected in taxes

_____ **10.** stock market crash

Column B

A. hobos

B. Black Tuesday

C. bank run

D. Tonto

E. Groucho Marx

F. Douglas MacArthur

G. Scarlett O'Hara

H. John Steinbeck

I. speculation

J. budget deficit

DIRECTIONS: Multiple Choice Choose the item that best completes each sentence
or answers each question. Write the letter in the blank. *(4 points each)*

_____ **11.** A major campaign issue in the 1928 election was
    A. economic recovery.   **C.** Depression relief.
    B. Prohibition.   **D.** social reform.

_____ **12.** Alfred E. Smith endured a smear campaign in the 1928 election because
    A. he was a Quaker.   **C.** he was Catholic.
    B. he was a Mormon.   **D.** he was Jewish.

_____ **13.** Stock prices first began to decline in late 1929 because
    A. stockbrokers stopped margin loans.   **C.** several companies went bankrupt.
    B. company earnings declined.   **D.** investors began to sell their stock.

_____ **14.** During the Great Depression, when a bank collapsed,
    A. the government stepped in to run the bank.
    B. the government covered the bank's debts.
    C. the government repaid deposits on insured accounts only.
    D. depositors lost their savings.

_____ **15.** The Federal Reserve contributed to the Depression by
    A. lowering loan rates.   **C.** loaning to foreign companies.
    B. raising loan rates.   **D.** loaning to speculators.

(continued)

Chapter 17 Test, Form A

_____ **16.** In 1932 farmers on the Great Plains began to lose their crops because
    A. the soil lost its fertility.   **C.** a wheat fungus devastated the fields.
    B. frequent rains eroded the soil.   **D.** the soil dried up.

_____ **17.** President Hoover hoped that public works would
    A. solve the budget deficit.   **C.** provide jobs lost in the private sector.
    B. spur the construction industry.   **D.** spur industry to create more jobs.

_____ **18.** The National Credit Corporation tried to rescue troubled banks using
    A. tax money.   **C.** deficit spending.
    B. money from New York bankers.   **D.** money borrowed from foreign banks.

_____ **19.** President Hoover opposed direct federal relief to the unemployed because
he believed that
    A. only state and city governments should dole out relief.
    B. the Depression would end soon.
    C. charities could provide sufficient relief until the economy improved.
    D. individuals should be responsible for taking care of themselves.

_____ **20.** Thousands of World War I veterans came to Washington in 1932 to lobby
Congress to
    A. enact a bonus for war veterans.
    B. pass legislation giving veterans their promised bonus early.
    C. provide public works jobs for unemployed veterans.
    D. provide military jobs for unemployed veterans.

DIRECTIONS: Essay Answer one of the following questions on a separate sheet of
paper. *(20 points)*

21. Use the example depicted in the diagram to explain how buying on margin
works, and its risks and rewards.

22. Discuss three major causes of the Great Depression.

★ **Chapter 17 Test, Form B**

The Great Depression Begins

DIRECTIONS: Matching Match each item in Column A with the items in Column B.
Write the correct letters in the blanks. *(4 points each)*

Column A

_____ **1.** "wet" candidate in the 1928 election

_____ **2.** film superstar who fled to Hollywood to escape hardship in Europe

_____ **3.** successful engineer and former head of the Food Administration during World War I

_____ **4.** loss of property due to nonpayment of the mortgage

_____ **5.** buying now and making payments each month

_____ **6.** communities of makeshift shacks on public lands

_____ **7.** system for buying and selling shares of companies

_____ **8.** drought-related conditions in the Great Plains

_____ **9.** money that went directly to impoverished families

_____ **10.** stockbroker's demand for immediate repayment of a loan

Column B

A. shantytowns

B. Alfred E. Smith

C. Marlene Dietrich

D. stock market

E. relief

F. foreclosed

G. installment plan

H. margin call

I. Dust Bowl

J. Herbert Hoover

DIRECTIONS: Multiple Choice Choose the item that best completes each sentence
or answers each question. Write the letter in the blank. *(4 points each)*

_____ **11.** A major reason for Herbert Hoover's landslide victory in the 1928 election was
A. the prosperity of the 1920s.
B. his tax relief plan.
C. his promise to end Prohibition.
D. his plan to support farm prices.

_____ **12.** Before the late 1920s, stock prices
A. did not change much.
B. generally reflected the stocks' true value.
C. generally did not reflect the stocks' true value.
D. were too high for most people to afford.

_____ **13.** The stock market crash weakened the nation's banks because
A. banks had invested their deposits in the stock market.
B. banks depended on income from the sale of their stock for operating funds.
C. investors no longer had money to deposit in banks.
D. investors could no longer afford to take out loans from banks.

_____ **14.** Most economists agree that a key cause of the Depression was
A. overconsumption.
B. overproduction.
C. inflation.
D. deflation.

(continued)

⭐ **Chapter 17 Test, Form B**

_____ **15.** During the Depression, many unemployed people
   A. destroyed "Hoovervilles."   **C.** collected unemployment.
   B. lived in federal housing.   **D.** rode the rails.

_____ **16.** The first feature-length animated film was
   A. *Animal Crackers.*   **C.** *Snow White and the Seven Dwarfs.*
   B. *The Wizard of Oz.*   **D.** *Mr. Smith Goes to Washington.*

_____ **17.** To pay for public works, the government would have to raise taxes or
   A. print money.   **C.** borrow from foreign governments.
   B. reduce inflation.   **D.** borrow from banks.

_____ **18.** The purpose of the Reconstruction Finance Corporation was to
   A. regulate the stock market.
   B. manage public works projects.
   C. make loans to banks, railroads, and agricultural institutions.
   D. administer public assistance programs for the unemployed and the homeless.

_____ **19.** The Emergency Relief and Construction Act provided
   A. direct federal relief.
   B. loans to the states for direct relief.
   C. loans to businesses willing to create jobs by constructing new facilities.
   D. loans to banks so that they could make home construction loans.

_____ **20.** When the Senate voted the new bonus bill down, many veterans waiting outside the capitol building
   A. rioted and burned several public buildings.
   B. fixed bayonets on their service rifles and prepared to fight.
   C. left peacefully.
   D. refused to leave, remaining on the capitol steps until they were evicted by force.

DIRECTIONS: Essay Answer one of the following questions on a separate sheet of paper. *(20 points)*

21. Use the diagram to help you explain how banks operate and why runs on banks can result in bank failure.

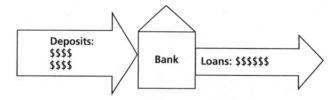

22. Describe Herbert Hoover's dilemma in considering whether to greatly increase public works projects to spur economic recovery.

★ **Chapter 18**

Section Quiz 18-1

DIRECTIONS: Matching Match each item in Column A with the items in Column B.
Write the correct letters in the blanks. *(10 points each)*

Column A

_____ **1.** closing banks before bank runs could put them out of business

_____ **2.** Roosevelt succeeded this New York governor when the governor ran for president

_____ **3.** a monetary standard in which one ounce of gold equaled a set number of dollars

_____ **4.** a paralyzing disease

_____ **5.** Roosevelt's policies during the Great Depression

Column B

A. Alfred E. Smith

B. bank holidays

C. New Deal

D. polio

E. gold standard

DIRECTIONS: Multiple Choice In the blank at the left, write the letter of the choice
that best completes the statement or answers the question. *(10 points each)*

_____ **6.** While recovering from polio, who did Roosevelt depend on to keep his name prominent in the New York Democratic Party?
    A. his cousin Theodore   **C.** Albert E. Smith
    B. his wife Eleanor   **D.** Woodrow Wilson

_____ **7.** Franklin Roosevelt was born in 1882 to a wealthy family from
    A. Philadelphia.   **C.** New York.
    B. Denver.   **D.** Boston.

_____ **8.** Bank runs increased before Roosevelt's inauguration because some people thought he would abandon the gold standard and reduce the value of
    A. the dollar.   **C.** farm crops.
    B. silver.   **D.** mortgages.

_____ **9.** While in the New York State Senate, Roosevelt won a reputation as a
    A. party boss.   **C.** Republican.
    B. progressive reformer.   **D.** conservative.

_____ **10.** What position, appointed by Woodrow Wilson, did Roosevelt hold through World War I?
    A. attorney general   **C.** ambassador to Mexico
    B. secretary of agriculture   **D.** assistant secretary of the navy

Chapter 18

Section Quiz 18-2

DIRECTIONS: Matching Match each item in Column A with the items in Column B. Write the correct letters in the blanks. *(10 points each)*

Column A

_____ **1.** provides government insurance for bank deposits up to a certain amount

_____ **2.** channeled money to state and local agencies to fund their relief projects

_____ **3.** suspended the antitrust laws

_____ **4.** direct talks via radio that FDR held with the American people

_____ **5.** most highly praised New Deal work relief program

Column B

A. Civilian Conservation Corps

B. fireside chats

C. National Industrial Recovery Act

D. Federal Emergency Relief Administration

E. Federal Deposit Insurance Corporation

DIRECTIONS: Multiple Choice In the blank at the left, write the letter of the choice that best completes the statement or answers the question. *(10 points each)*

_____ **6.** To regulate the stock market and prevent fraud, Congress created an independent agency called the
    A. Securities Act.
    B. Federal Deposit Insurance Corporation.
    C. Securities and Exchange Commission.
    D. Emergency Banking Relief Act.

_____ **7.** Perhaps no group of Americans had been as badly hurt by the Depression as had the nation's
    A. farmers.
    B. miners.
    C. factory workers.
    D. wealthy.

_____ **8.** The Glass-Steagall Act separated commercial banking from
    A. the Securities and Exchange Commission.
    B. the Treasury Department.
    C. investment banking.
    D. bank holidays.

_____ **9.** What was the period called between March 9 and June 16, 1933, when Congress passed 15 major acts to meet the economic crisis?
    A. the First New Deal
    B. the New Nationalism
    C. the New Freedom
    D. the Hundred Days

_____ **10.** The Public Works Administration was created as a federal relief agency to put back to work the unemployed in the
    A. arts and entertainment industry.
    B. mining industry.
    C. fishing industry.
    D. construction industry.

★ **Chapter 18**

Section Quiz 18-3

DIRECTIONS: Matching Match each item in Column A with the items in Column B. Write the correct letters in the blanks. *(10 points each)*

Column A

_____ **1.** a new federal agency created "for work relief and to increase employment by providing useful projects"

_____ **2.** government practice of spending borrowed money to pay for programs without regard to a balanced budget

_____ **3.** law providing some security for the elderly

_____ **4.** guaranteed workers the right to organize unions without interference from employers and to bargain collectively

_____ **5.** Supreme Court case that struck down the National Industrial Recovery Act

Column B

A. National Labor Relations Act

B. deficit spending

C. Social Security Act

D. Works Progress Administration

E. *Schechter* v. *United States*

DIRECTIONS: Multiple Choice In the blank at the left, write the letter of the choice that best completes the statement or answers the question. *(10 points each)*

_____ **6.** A process whereby dissatisfied union members could take their complaints to a neutral party who would listen to both sides and decide the issue is called
   A. sit-down strikes.
   B. labor relations.
   C. union activism.
   D. binding arbitration.

_____ **7.** In August 1934, business leaders and anti-New Deal politicians from both parties joined together to create the
   A. "Share Our Wealth" clubs.
   B. American Liberty League.
   C. National Union for Social Justice.
   D. Townshend Plan.

_____ **8.** In what became known as the "sick chicken case," the Court ruled that the Constitution did not allow Congress to delegate its powers to
   A. the executive branch.
   B. state governments.
   C. the court system.
   D. individual politicians.

_____ **9.** What did the series of programs and reforms that Roosevelt launched in 1935 come to be called?
   A. the Second New Deal
   B. the Committee for Industrial Organization
   C. the American Liberty League
   D. the Townshend Plan

_____ **10.** Perhaps the most serious threat to President Roosevelt from the left came from Democratic senator
   A. Huey Long.
   B. Francis Townshend.
   C. Charles Coughlin.
   D. Harry Hopkins.

★ **Chapter 18**

Section Quiz 18-4

DIRECTIONS: Matching Match each item in Column A with the items in Column B.
Write the correct letters in the blanks. *(10 points each)*

Column A

_____ 1. head of the Public Works Administration who pushed for
more government spending

_____ 2. mediating role of the government to work out conflicts
among competing interest groups

_____ 3. head of the Works Progress Administration

_____ 4. British economist who argued that the government should
spend heavily during a recession

_____ 5. first woman to hold a cabinet post as Secretary of Labor

Column B

A. Harry Hopkins

B. Frances Perkins

C. Harold Ickes

D. broker state

E. John Maynard
Keynes

DIRECTIONS: Multiple Choice In the blank at the left, write the letter of the choice
that best completes the statement or answers the question. *(10 points each)*

_____ 6. Who helped bring about the change in the African American and
women's vote?
A. Frances Perkins
B. First Lady Eleanor Roosevelt
C. Alfred Landon
D. Huey Long

_____ 7. According to Keynesian economics, Roosevelt had done exactly the
wrong thing in 1937 when he
A. cut back programs.
B. approved more government
spending.
C. increased the scope of programs.
D. encouraged new businesses.

_____ 8. The Fair Labor Standards Act of 1935 provided more protection for
workers, the abolition of child labor, and
A. the right to join a union.
B. a 40-hour workweek.
C. a labor relations mediator.
D. a fair-hiring provision.

_____ 9. What created the impression that Roosevelt was trying to interfere with
the Constitution's separation of powers and undermine the Court's
independence?
A. cutting federal programs
B. the recession of 1937
C. the court-packing plan
D. the broker state plan

_____ 10. Two important Supreme Court decisions resulted in the ability of the
federal government to mediate between competing groups and increased
federal power over
A. the military.
B. international relations.
C. the states.
D. the economy.

The American Republic Since 1877

⭐ **Chapter 18 Test, Form A**

Roosevelt and the New Deal

DIRECTIONS: Matching Match each item in Column A with the items in Column B.
Write the correct letters in the blanks. *(4 points each)*

Column A

_____ 1. hired workers directly, including thousands of women, to build or improve airports, roads, and playgrounds

_____ 2. established a 40-hour workweek for many workers

_____ 3. established to provide some security for unemployed workers

_____ 4. required companies that sold stocks and bonds to provide complete and truthful information to investors

_____ 5. awarded contracts to construction companies to build highways, dams, schools, and other facilities

_____ 6. subsidized loans for builders willing to buy blocks of slums and build low-cost housing

_____ 7. prohibited commercial banks from speculating on the stock market

_____ 8. formed to oppose the New Deal

_____ 9. sponsored the controversial "Federal Number One" program

_____ 10. covered people's savings in banks against loss

Column B

A. Glass-Steagall Act

B. Fair Labor Standards Act

C. National Housing Act

D. Works Progress Administration

E. Public Works Administration

F. American Liberty League

G. Securities Act

H. Civil Works Administration

I. Social Security Act

J. Federal Deposit Insurance Corporation

DIRECTIONS: Multiple Choice Choose the item that best completes each sentence or answers each question. Write the letter in the blank. *(4 points each)*

_____ 11. As governor of New York, Franklin Roosevelt won popularity by
    A. siding with unions.
    B. giving frequent radio addresses.
    C. helping people economically.
    D. cutting income taxes statewide.

_____ 12. During the Depression, many state governors declared "bank holidays" to
    A. give bank employees a break.
    B. prevent bank runs.
    C. reduce the value of the dollar.
    D. help the Federal Reserve.

_____ 13. Roosevelt's advisers who supported "New Nationalism" wanted government
    A. to work with business.
    B. to run key parts of the economy.
    C. to break up big companies.
    D. to set up welfare programs.

_____ 14. To fight the Depression, Roosevelt believed the first thing to do was to
    A. provide direct relief to people.
    B. set up public works programs.
    C. restore confidence in the banks.
    D. provide relief for farmers.

(continued)

_____ **15.** To regulate the stock market, the Roosevelt Administration created the
  A. Federal Trade Commission.
  B. Securities and Exchange Commission.
  C. National Recovery Administration.
  D. Social Security Administration.

_____ **16.** The National Industrial Recovery Act set up
  A. trusts to promote competition.
  B. codes of fair competition.
  C. three work shifts per day.
  D. laws banning unions.

_____ **17.** One main purpose of the Townsend plan was to
  A. free up jobs for the unemployed.
  B. redistribute wealth.
  C. nationalize the banking system.
  D. end public works programs.

_____ **18.** In the case *Schechter* v. *United States*, the Supreme Court
  A. struck down the first New Deal.
  B. struck down the NIRA.
  C. struck down deficit spending.
  D. struck down the Glass-Steagall Act.

_____ **19.** Framers of the Social Security Act saw it primarily as
  A. an insurance bill.
  B. a welfare bill.
  C. a retirement pension bill.
  D. a relief bill.

_____ **20.** Franklin Roosevelt's "court-packing plan" was a serious mistake because
  A. many Americans opposed the idea of forced retirement.
  B. the angry judges reacted by striking down much of the New Deal legislation.
  C. it appeared to interfere with the Constitution's separation of powers.
  D. the angry judges struck down the plan as unconstitutional.

DIRECTIONS: Essay Answer one of the following questions on a separate sheet of paper. *(20 points)*

21. Describe Franklin Roosevelt's personality and approach to the nation's problems.

22. Fill in the diagram about the Social Security system. Then write an essay describing how it initially worked, who benefited, and who did not.

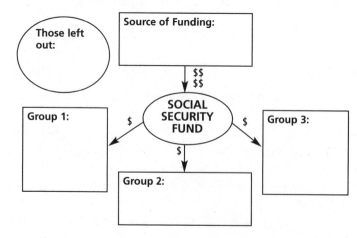

Name _____ Date _____ Class _____

Roosevelt and the New Deal

DIRECTIONS: Matching Match each item in Column A with the items in Column B.
Write the correct letters in the blanks. *(4 points each)*

Column A

_____ **1.** started the United Steelworkers of America

_____ **2.** offered unemployed young men work planting trees,
fighting forest fires, and building reservoirs

_____ **3.** set up a process whereby dissatisfied union members
could take their complaints to binding arbitration

_____ **4.** urged consumers to buy goods only from companies that
displayed its blue eagle symbol

_____ **5.** promoted codes of fair competition

_____ **6.** Louisiana senator who championed the downtrodden and
built a powerful and corrupt political machine

_____ **7.** leader of the United Mine Workers

_____ **8.** treasury secretary who favored balancing the budget

_____ **9.** head of the Federal Emergency Relief Administration and
one of the most influential people in Roosevelt's
administration

_____ **10.** proposed a monthly government pension for citizens over
age 60 to be entirely spent each month

Column B

A. Civilian
Conservation
Corps

B. Wagner Act

C. National
Industrial
Recovery Act

D. Committee for
Industrial
Organization

E. Huey Long

F. Harry Hopkins

G. John L. Lewis

H. National Recovery
Administration

I. Henry
Morgenthau

J. Francis Townsend

DIRECTIONS: Multiple Choice Choose the item that best completes each sentence
or answers each question. Write the letter in the blank. *(4 points each)*

_____ **11.** Although they disagreed on specifics, Roosevelt's advisers favored government
  A. promoting competition.   **C.** laissez faire.
  B. breaking up trusts.   **D.** intervention in the economy.

_____ **12.** Roosevelt's advisers who supported "New Freedom" wanted government
  A. to work together with business.   **C.** to break up big companies.
  B. to run key parts of the economy.   **D.** to set up welfare programs.

_____ **13.** The Emergency Banking Relief Act helped solve the banking crisis by
  A. putting all banks under government operation.
  B. declaring that the gold standard would not be abandoned.
  C. issuing licenses to banks that federal examiners found to be financially sound.
  D. closing the banks long enough for the Federal Reserve to replenish their
    gold reserves.

(continued)

Chapter 18 Test, Form B

_____ **14.** The Agricultural Adjustment Administration tried to help farmers by
   A. paying them to grow more crops.   **C.** buying farm surpluses.
   B. paying them not to grow crops.   **D.** making land available for farming.

_____ **15.** The Home Owners' Loan Corporation
   A. provided money to help the unemployed pay their mortgages.
   B. lowered mortgage rates when people lost their jobs and could no longer pay.
   C. lengthened the mortgage repayment term and lowered rates for the employed.
   D. provided low-cost loans to help homeless people buy a home.

_____ **16.** Senator Huey Long wanted the government to
   A. share the wealth of the rich.   **C.** pay citizens over 60 a monthly pension.
   B. balance the budget.   **D.** stop interfering with business.

_____ **17.** The Federal Number One program employed
   A. young men ages 18 to 25.   **C.** displaced tenant farmers.
   B. workers in the construction industry.   **D.** people in the arts.

_____ **18.** The Committee for Industrial Organization set out to organize
   A. all workers in Michigan.
   B. all workers in GM's Flint, Michigan, plant.
   C. all unskilled workers in the automobile industry.
   D. all skilled and unskilled workers in the automobile industry.

_____ **19.** Which of the following choices best completes the diagram about the
   historic political realignment triggered by the New Deal?
   A. white Southerners
   B. African Americans
   C. business leaders
   D. progressives

_____ **20.** Roosevelt triggered a new economic downturn in 1937 by
   A. increasing government spending.   **C.** increasing taxes.
   B. decreasing government spending.   **D.** decreasing taxes.

DIRECTIONS: Essay Answer one of the following questions on a separate sheet of
paper. *(20 points)*

21. Describe the provisions of the National Labor Relations Act and the work of the
   board it created.

22. Discuss the New Deal's legacy, including its effectiveness in dealing with the
   Depression and its lasting effects on the role of government.

The American Republic Since 1877

Unit 5 Posttest, Form A

Boom and Bust

DIRECTIONS: Matching Match each item in Column A with the items in Column B.
Write the correct letters in the blanks. *(4 points each)*

Column A

_____ **1.** homeless people who wandered the country

_____ **2.** money provided directly to people in need

_____ **3.** Roosevelt's attempt to appoint new Supreme Court justices

_____ **4.** awarded contracts to construction companies to build highways, dams, and schools

_____ **5.** made illegal liquor readily available in rural America

_____ **6.** paid farmers to take land out of production

_____ **7.** paying with borrowed money

_____ **8.** argued that government should spend heavily during a recession

_____ **9.** promoting economic growth through lower taxes

_____ **10.** investors trying to make a quick profit on the stock market

Column B

A. supply-side economics

B. Agricultural Adjustment Administration

C. bootlegging

D. hobos

E. deficit spending

F. John Maynard Keynes

G. relief

H. court-packing plan

I. Public Works Administration

J. speculators

DIRECTIONS: Multiple Choice Choose the item that best completes each sentence
or answers each question. Write the letter in the blank. *(4 points each)*

_____ **11.** Eugenics fueled arguments against
  A. immigration.
  B. evolution.
  C. Prohibition.
  D. lynching.

_____ **12.** The Scopes trial tested a law that banned the
  A. manufacture, transport, and sale of liquor.
  B. Ku Klux Klan.
  C. teaching of creationism.
  D. teaching of evolution.

_____ **13.** A major element of the new morality was
  A. an increase in stay-at-home mothers.
  B. an increase in women going to college.
  C. a decrease in the use of automobiles.
  D. an increase in traditional values in marriage.

_____ **14.** Which of these is an example of the 1920s rise of nativist ideas?
  A. the growing support for the eugenics movement
  B. the strong support for Sacco and Vanzetti
  C. the formation of a Catholic Boys Club by William J. Simmons
  D. the belief that new-stock Americans should replace old-stock Americans

(continued)

★ **Unit 5 Posttest, Form A**   Score

_____ 15. Most Americans of the 1920s wanted to avoid future wars by
    A. joining the League of Nations.
    B. dividing Germany among the Allies.
    C. avoiding involvement in European affairs.
    D. forbidding Germany to rebuild its armed forces.

_____ 16. Representatives of eight countries gathered at the Washington
    Conference in 1921 to discuss
    A. economic aid to Europe.   **C.** the League of Nations.
    B. reparations.   **D.** disarmament.

_____ 17. Which of the following statements about Andrew Mellon is true?
    A. He believed in applying business principles to government.
    B. He was the secretary of the treasury under Wilson.
    C. He increased government spending.
    D. He advocated an increase in income tax rates.

_____ 18. Roosevelt's program to restore confidence in the banking system
    included the
    A. Securities and Change Act.   **C.** Insecurities Commission.
    B. Emergency Banking Relief Act.   **D.** Federal Deposit Authority.

_____ 19. To prevent fraud in the stock market, Congress created the
    A. Federal Trade Commission.   **C.** National Recovery Administration.
    B. Securities and Exchange Commission.   **D.** Social Security Administration.

_____ 20. Framers of the Social Security Act saw it primarily as an insurance bill
    because
    A. workers paid premiums.
    B. it provided welfare benefits.
    C. it provided aid to poor families with young children.
    D. it made relief payments directly to needy families.

DIRECTIONS: Essay Answer one of the following questions on a separate sheet of
paper. *(20 points)*

21. Explain how the Volstead Act contributed to a rise in organized crime.

22. Explain how overproduction helped cause the Great Depression.

The American Republic Since 1877

⭐ **Unit 5 Posttest, Form B**

Boom and Bust

DIRECTIONS: Matching Match each item in Column A with the items in Column B.
Write the correct letters in the blanks. *(4 points each)*

Column A

_____ 1. secret bars

_____ 2. human beings developed from lower forms of life over
millions of years

_____ 3. world heavyweight boxing champion from 1919 to 1926

_____ 4. narrow focus on local interests

_____ 5. payments required as punishment for starting a war

_____ 6. God made the world according to the Bible

_____ 7. bandleader during the Harlem Renaissance

_____ 8. rising stock prices over a long period

_____ 9. president who could be "silent in five languages"

_____ 10. employees are not required to join a union

Column B

A. reparations

B. Jack Dempsey

C. bull market

D. Calvin Coolidge

E. Duke Ellington

F. open shop

G. creationism

H. provincialism

I. evolution

J. speakeasies

DIRECTIONS: Multiple Choice Choose the item that best completes each sentence
or answers each question. Write the letter in the blank. *(4 points each)*

_____ 11. The Emergency Quota Act admitted immigrants to the United States
based on
   A. sponsorship by an American citizen.   **C.** wealth.
   B. job skills.   **D.** ethnic identity and national origin.

_____ 12. Which amendment repealed Prohibition?
   A. Twenty-second Amendment   **C.** Nineteenth Amendment
   B. Twenty-first Amendment   **D.** Eighteenth Amendment

_____ 13. Claude McKay, Langston Hughes, and the Cotton Club were all part of the
   A. Black Nationalist Movement.   **C.** South Side Renaissance.
   B. Great Awakening.   **D.** Harlem Renaissance.

_____ 14. What major effect did the new automobile industry of the 1920s have on
American society?
   A. Workers did not have to commute any more.
   B. The mail delivery system expanded across the country.
   C. Ownership of cars by the wealthy caused resentment in the lower classes.
   D. Car costs were reduced by the mass production system.

(continued)

_____ **15.** During the 1920s, unions declined in part because many corporations instituted
  A. cooperative individualism.   **C.** Sociological Departments.
  B. reparations.   **D.** welfare capitalism.

_____ **16.** All of the following characterized the consumer society of the 1920s EXCEPT
  A. there was less borrowing of money for fear of being in debt.
  B. advertisers developed messages for mass audiences.
  C. welfare capitalism provided workers with improved benefits.
  D. products focused on Americans' concerns with fashion and success.

_____ **17.** Which of the following was a likely cause of the Great Depression?
  A. decreasing purchasing power of Americans in debt
  B. low tariffs restricting the sale of goods
  C. an increase in major cash purchases by consumers
  D. the sale of too many automobiles in a flooded market

_____ **18.** Which of the following statements about Roosevelt's election to a second term is true?
  A. Roosevelt won in a very close electoral count.
  B. Changes in African American voting patterns helped elect him.
  C. It followed the Supreme Court-packing move.
  D. The upper classes continued to strongly support Roosevelt.

_____ **19.** What was the goal of the 1937 National Housing Act?
  A. to restrict the practice of tenant farming
  B. to restrict the amount by which landlords could raise rents
  C. to subsidize the building of low-cost housing
  D. to subsidize the building of slums in several cities

_____ **20.** To pull the economy out of a recession, Keynesian economists advocated
  A. deficit spending.   **C.** raising taxes.
  B. balancing the budget.   **D.** raising interest rates.

DIRECTIONS: Essay Answer one of the following questions on a separate sheet of paper. *(20 points)*

21. Explain how Henry Ford was able to make automobiles affordable for the majority of Americans.

22. Describe the main provisions of the Social Security Act.

⭐ **Unit 6 Pretest, Form A**

Global Struggles

DIRECTIONS: Matching Match each item in Column A with the items in Column B. Write the correct letters in the blanks. *(4 points each)*

Column A

_____ 1. imaginary line between Communist Eastern Europe and the West

_____ 2. murder of millions of European Jews by the Nazis

_____ 3. deadly radiation created by a nuclear blast

_____ 4. period of rapidly increasing birthrates between 1945 and 1961

_____ 5. leader of the Nazi Party

_____ 6. period of confrontation and competition between the United States and the Soviet Union

_____ 7. Hitler's imagined "master race"

_____ 8. a cultural distance between children and their parents in the 1950s

_____ 9. wrote a diary of her family's life in hiding after the Nazis overran the Netherlands

_____ 10. Japanese pilots who intentionally crashed their planes into American ships

Column B

A. Cold War

B. Aryans

C. kamikazes

D. iron curtain

E. Adolf Hitler

F. Anne Frank

G. generation gap

H. "final solution"

I. baby boom

J. fallout

DIRECTIONS: Multiple Choice Choose the item that best completes each sentence or answers each question. Write the letter in the blank. *(4 points each)*

_____ 11. The Nazi Party in Germany was similar to Italy's
  A. Communist Party.
  B. Socialist Party.
  C. Fascist Party.
  D. Anarchist Party.

_____ 12. The British Royal Air Force's attempt to save Britain from German invasion is known as the
  A. Storm the Beaches Campaign.
  B. English Channel Defense.
  C. Churchill Plan.
  D. Battle of Britain.

_____ 13. What is the major tenet of fascism?
  A. that individuals and nations should work together to be great
  B. that government-run collective businesses are best
  C. that a nation is more important than an individual
  D. that individuals should elect government officials

(continued)

Unit 6 Pretest, Form A

_____ **14.** In their major offensive to liberate Europe, the Allies landed their invasion forces in
  - **A.** Calais, France.
  - **B.** Normandy, France.
  - **C.** Hamburg, Germany.
  - **D.** Warsaw, Poland.

_____ **15.** The American program to build an atomic bomb was called
  - **A.** the Manhattan Project.
  - **B.** Operation Overlord.
  - **C.** D-Day.
  - **D.** Operation Liberty.

_____ **16.** The day after Germany surrendered was proclaimed
  - **A.** D-Day.
  - **B.** V-J Day.
  - **C.** V-G Day.
  - **D.** V-E Day.

_____ **17.** A United States bomber dropped the first atomic bomb on
  - **A.** Hiroshima.
  - **B.** Nagasaki.
  - **C.** Tokyo.
  - **D.** Iwo Jima.

_____ **18.** In the Korean War, the opposing forces were
  - **A.** the United States against North Korea.
  - **B.** the United States against North Korea and the Soviet Union.
  - **C.** the United Nations against North Korea.
  - **D.** the United Nations against North Korea and China.

_____ **19.** A fanatical witch hunt in the 1950s for Communist influences in the United States was called
  - **A.** Bolshevism.
  - **B.** the Marshall Plan.
  - **C.** McCarthyism.
  - **D.** Fascism.

_____ **20.** The GI Bill enabled many returning soldiers to
  - **A.** find jobs in business.
  - **B.** deal with their war experiences.
  - **C.** attend college.
  - **D.** make a career in military service.

DIRECTIONS: Essay Answer one of the following questions on a separate sheet of paper. *(20 points)*

21. During World War II, American decision-makers knew the terrible destructive power of the atomic bomb the United States was developing. Successful testing of the bomb set off a debate about whether to use it against Japan. Describe what you think might have been the arguments on each side of the debate. Why do you think President Truman finally decided to use it?

22. Television became more affordable for Americans during World War II. In the years following the war, television ownership soared. How do you think the rise of television affected the Hollywood movie industry? What kinds of things do you think Hollywood might have done in response?

⭐ **Unit 6 Pretest, Form B**

Global Struggles

DIRECTIONS: Matching Match each item in Column A with the items in Column B.
Write the correct letters in the blanks. *(4 points each)*

Column A

_____ **1.** led a revolt in Spain in 1936

_____ **2.** prime minister of Britain during World War II

_____ **3.** president of the United States during World War II

_____ **4.** leader of Italy during World War II

_____ **5.** leader of Germany during World War II

_____ **6.** emperor of Japan during World War II

_____ **7.** took over the Soviet Union after Lenin's death in 1924

_____ **8.** group of cargo ships escorted by navy warships

_____ **9.** a provision for American economic aid to Europe

_____ **10.** became president after Roosevelt's death

Column B

A. convoy

B. Harry S Truman

C. Hirohito

D. Franklin Roosevelt

E. Marshall Plan

F. Adolf Hitler

G. Winston Churchill

H. Joseph Stalin

I. Benito Mussolini

J. Francisco Franco

DIRECTIONS: Multiple Choice Choose the item that best completes each sentence
or answers each question. Write the letter in the blank. *(4 points each)*

_____ **11.** Germany, Japan, and Italy were known as the
  A. Allies.   **C.** Axis Powers.
  B. Triple Entente.   **D.** Central Powers.

_____ **12.** Many Jews were killed in a night of anti-Jewish violence throughout
  Germany and Austria called
  A. blitzkrieg.   **C.** *Kristallnacht*.
  B. *Anschluss*.   **D.** Gestapo.

_____ **13.** What happened on December 7, 1941?
  A. A German U-boat sank the American passenger liner *Lusitania*.
  B. Germany invaded America's ally, Great Britain.
  C. Japan declared war on the United States.
  D. Japan attacked Pearl Harbor.

_____ **14.** Before September 1, 1939, Hitler's aggressive actions included
  A. claiming the Austrian-speaking area of Czechoslovakia.
  B. the forcible unification of Germany and Austria.
  C. giving up Danzig to obtain other territory.
  D. the massive preparation to invade Russia.

(continued)

★ **Unit 6 Pretest, Form B**

_____ **15.** How was Roosevelt able to help Britain before the United States joined World War II?
- **A.** by exchanging port rights for old American destroyers
- **B.** by declaring the Neutrality Act null and void
- **C.** by selling arms without telling Congress
- **D.** by getting Congress to nullify the Neutrality Act

_____ **16.** How did the Allies drive back the Japanese in the Pacific?
- **A.** by focusing on the Japanese amphtracs
- **B.** by bombing the islands but never going ashore
- **C.** with kamikaze pilots
- **D.** with an island-hopping campaign

_____ **17.** Which of the following occurred during the Korean War?
- **A.** The Soviet Union helped South Korea build up an army.
- **B.** President Truman backed the battle plans of General MacArthur.
- **C.** Chinese cities were bombed with atomic weapons.
- **D.** China entered the war and fought UN troops.

_____ **18.** Which of the following occurred in the United States during the Cold War?
- **A.** *Sputnik* was launched right after NASA was created.
- **B.** President Eisenhower reduced the nuclear arsenal.
- **C.** Hollywood ignored the Cold War hoopla.
- **D.** People practiced duck-and-cover drills in schools.

_____ **19.** The GI Bill was designed to
- **A.** help veterans find jobs in business.
- **B.** provide loans to help veterans start businesses, buy homes, and attend college.
- **C.** attract veterans to a career in military service.
- **D.** provide bonuses, health care, and government jobs for veterans.

_____ **20.** Jonas Salk made a major breakthrough by developing
- **A.** the transistor.
- **B.** ENIAC.
- **C.** cinemascope.
- **D.** a vaccine against polio.

DIRECTIONS: Essay Answer one of the following questions on a separate sheet of paper. *(20 points)*

21. How did the Great Depression lead to World War II?

22. How were American women's roles different in World War II than they had been in World War I?

Chapter 19

Section Quiz 19-1

DIRECTIONS: Matching Match each item in Column A with the items in Column B.
Write the correct letters in the blanks. *(10 points each)*

Column A

_____ **1.** Germany, Italy, and Japan

_____ **2.** idea that a country should focus on its own problems and
avoid international commitments

_____ **3.** Adolf Hitler's autobiography written while he was in
prison

_____ **4.** a kind of aggressive nationalism

_____ **5.** resource-rich province of China invaded by the Japanese
army

Column B

A. isolationism

B. Axis Powers

C. fascism

D. *Mein Kampf*

E. Manchuria

DIRECTIONS: Multiple Choice In the blank at the left, write the letter of the choice
that best completes the statement or answers the question. *(10 points each)*

_____ **6.** Who was a fervent anti-Communist and a great admirer of Benito
Mussolini's leadership style?
A. Adolf Hitler   **C.** Francisco Franco
B. Joseph Stalin   **D.** Vladimir Lenin

_____ **7.** Many military officers in Japan were strong nationalists and believed
Japan was destined to dominate
A. North America.   **C.** East Asia.
B. South America.   **D.** Europe.

_____ **8.** In 1927 the Soviet dictator Joseph Stalin began a massive effort to
A. overthrow communism.   **C.** educate the peasants.
B. industrialize his country.   **D.** increase trade.

_____ **9.** One of the new political parties to rise during the political and economic
chaos in Germany after World War I was the National Socialist German
Workers' Party, also known as the
A. Socialist Party.   **C.** Fascist Party.
B. Nazi Party.   **D.** Bolshevik Party.

_____ **10.** Who was the leader of the 1936 rebellion in Spain that quickly became a
civil war?
A. Benito Mussolini   **C.** Francisco Franco
B. Vladimir Lenin   **D.** Gerald M. Nye

Chapter 19

Section Quiz 19-2

DIRECTIONS: Matching Match each item in Column A with the items in Column B. Write the correct letters in the blanks. *(10 points each)*

Column A

_____ **1.** lightning war

_____ **2.** unification

_____ **3.** a line of concrete bunkers and fortifications built by the French along the German border

_____ **4.** the policy of giving concessions in exchange for peace

_____ **5.** a Polish port with strong German roots

Column B

A. blitzkrieg

B. Danzig

C. Maginot Line

D. appeasement

E. *Anschluss*

DIRECTIONS: Multiple Choice In the blank at the left, write the letter of the choice that best completes the statement or answers the question. *(10 points each)*

_____ **6.** The Nazi-Soviet nonaggression pact contained a secret deal between Germany and the Soviet Union to divide

    A. Czechoslovakia.   **C.** Austria.

    B. Belgium.   **D.** Poland.

_____ **7.** The air battle between the German *Luftwaffe* and the British air force that began in June 1940 and lasted into the fall of 1940 became known as

    A. *sitzkrieg*.   **C.** the Munich Crisis.

    B. the Battle of Britain.   **D.** the "Miracle at Dunkirk."

_____ **8.** In late 1937, Hitler concluded that Germany would gain supplies of food, defensible frontiers, and soldiers by seizing Austria and

    A. Czechoslovakia.   **C.** Belgium.

    B. Poland.   **D.** France.

_____ **9.** After the fall of Poland, Hitler and his generals decided to attack

    A. Belgium and Luxembourg.   **C.** Norway and Denmark.

    B. Japan and China.   **D.** France and England.

_____ **10.** After being trapped by the Germans in Belgium, the only port remaining open for Britain and France to evacuate their surviving troops was at

    A. Antwerp.   **C.** Dunkirk.

    B. Brussels.   **D.** Danzig.

The American Republic Since 1877

★ Chapter 19

Score

Section Quiz 19-3

DIRECTIONS: Matching Match each item in Column A with the items in Column B.
Write the correct letters in the blanks. *(10 points each)*

Column A

_____ **1.** Hebrew for "catastrophe" and used specifically to refer to the Holocaust

_____ **2.** girl who kept a diary of her life in hiding from the Nazis

_____ **3.** extermination camp where 1,600,000 people died

_____ **4.** German government's secret police

_____ **5.** took citizenship away from Jewish Germans and banned marriage between Jews and other Germans

Column B

A. Nuremberg Laws

B. Auschwitz

C. Anne Frank

D. Shoah

E. Gestapo

DIRECTIONS: Multiple Choice In the blank at the left, write the letter of the choice
that best completes the statement or answers the question. *(10 points each)*

_____ **6.** What event in 1938 marked a significant escalation in the Nazi policy of persecution against the Jews?

    A. *Kristallnacht*

    B. Nuremberg Laws

    C. Wannsee Conference

    D. Battle of Britain

_____ **7.** Few Americans wanted to raise immigration quotas, even to accommodate European

    A. leaders.

    B. trade.

    C. peace.

    D. refugees.

_____ **8.** What was the name of one of the first and largest concentration camps built near the town of Weimar in 1937?

    A. Wannsee

    B. Buchenwald

    C. Treblinka

    D. *Kristallnacht*

_____ **9.** The Nazis reserved their strongest hatred for Jews, although they also held other groups in contempt including homosexuals, the disabled, Gypsies, and

    A. brown-eyed people.

    B. Scandinavians.

    C. Slavic peoples.

    D. the Japanese.

_____ **10.** In 1942 Nazi leaders met to make plans for exterminating Europe's Jews more quickly and efficiently at

    A. the Wannsee Conference.

    B. the Munich Conference.

    C. Nuremberg.

    D. the Berlin Meetings.

Chapter 19

Score

Section Quiz 19-4

DIRECTIONS: Matching Match each item in Column A with the items in Column B. Write the correct letters in the blanks. *(10 points each)*

Column A

_____ **1.** materials important for fighting a war

_____ **2.** revised to allow warring countries to buy arms from the United States on a cash-and-carry basis

_____ **3.** American destroyer torpedoed and sunk by a German submarine

_____ **4.** stated the United States could lend or lease arms to any country considered "vital to the defense of the United States"

_____ **5.** the entire western half of the Atlantic Ocean that Roosevelt declared as neutral territory

Column B

A. Lend-Lease Act

B. hemispheric defense zone

C. Neutrality Act of 1939

D. strategic materials

E. *Reuben James*

DIRECTIONS: Multiple Choice In the blank at the left, write the letter of the choice that best completes the statement or answers the question. *(10 points each)*

_____ **6.** In June 1941, in violation of the Nazi-Soviet pact, Hitler launched a massive invasion of
   A. Norway.
   B. Bulgaria.
   C. the Soviet Union.
   D. Czechoslovakia.

_____ **7.** In 1941 President Roosevelt began sending lend-lease aid to
   A. China.
   B. Britain.
   C. the Philippines.
   D. France.

_____ **8.** Roosevelt and Churchill met near Newfoundland in 1941 and agreed on the text of the
   A. Export Control Act.
   B. Neutrality Act.
   C. Lend-Lease Act.
   D. Atlantic Charter.

_____ **9.** What did Roosevelt want to build on British-controlled land that compelled him to bypass the provisions of the Neutrality Act and trade 50 old destroyers with Britain?
   A. new industries
   B. military bases
   C. research centers
   D. schools

_____ **10.** What finally brought the United States into World War II?
   A. sinking of the *Reuben James*
   B. Americans' horror at the persecution of people by Nazis
   C. Japanese attack on Pearl Harbor
   D. the Atlantic Charter

⭐ **Chapter 19 Test, Form A**

Score

A World in Flames

DIRECTIONS: Matching Match each item in Column A with the items in Column B.
Write the correct letters in the blanks. *(4 points each)*

Column A

_____ **1.** unification

_____ **2.** Nazi extermination camp

_____ **3.** Fuhrer

_____ **4.** period when Britain and France waited for the Germans to attack

_____ **5.** Nazi government secret police

_____ **6.** *Il Duce*

_____ **7.** mass killing of millions of European Jews by the Nazis

_____ **8.** requirement imposed by the first two Neutrality Acts for the purchase of nonmilitary supplies from the U. S.

_____ **9.** depended on radios to coordinate the large number of tanks and aircraft

_____ **10.** French fortifications along the German border

Column B

A. blitzkrieg

B. Benito Mussolini

C. Maginot Line

D. Holocaust

E. Auschwitz

F. Adolf Hitler

G. *Anschluss*

H. cash and carry

I. Gestapo

J. *sitzkrieg*

DIRECTIONS: Multiple Choice Choose the item that best completes each sentence
or answers each question. Write the letter in the blank. *(4 points each)*

_____ **11.** Two causes of the rise of dictatorships after World War I were
   A. the peace treaty and economic depression.
   B. new political ideas and economic depression.
   C. the peace treaty and lack of strong leadership after the war.
   D. new political ideas and lack of strong leadership after the war.

_____ **12.** Adolf Hitler blamed Germany's defeat in World War I on the
   A. weak German ruler.   **C.** Jews.
   B. democratic form of government.   **D.** Slavs.

_____ **13.** The Nye Committee report created the impression that America's entry into World War I was influenced by
   A. attacks on American merchant ships.   **C.** American arms manufacturers.
   B. militarism in Europe.   **D.** the American Communist Party.

_____ **14.** Claiming part of Czechoslovakia posed a problem for Hitler for all of the following reasons EXCEPT
   A. the Czechs spoke several different languages.
   B. Czechoslovakia was a democracy.
   C. the Czechs had a strong military.
   D. Czechoslovakia was allied with France and the Soviet Union.

(continued)

_____ **15.** Which choice best completes the diagram?

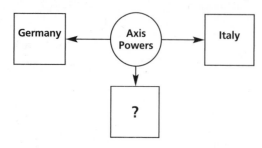

A. Spain   **C.** Japan
B. USSR   **D.** Austria

_____ **16.** The British and French realized that appeasement had failed when Hitler
  A. invaded Czechoslovakia.   **C.** invaded Poland.
  B. invaded Austria.   **D.** made demands for territory in Poland.

_____ **17.** The Nuremberg Laws
  A. took citizenship away from Jewish Germans.
  B. required all Jewish Germans to move to concentration camps.
  C. required all Jewish Germans to leave the country.
  D. authorized German police to shoot Jewish Germans.

_____ **18.** Most of the Jewish refugees aboard the SS *St. Louis*
  A. immigrated to the U.S.   **C.** were given refuge in Mexico.
  B. disembarked in Cuba.   **D.** died in the Nazis' "final solution."

_____ **19.** The Nazis' "final solution" referred to their plans to
  A. defeat France.   **C.** exterminate Europe's Jews.
  B. conquer Britain.   **D.** rule Europe after conquering it.

_____ **20.** In presenting his "Four Freedoms," Roosevelt was trying to
  A. justify America's neutrality.
  B. justify his call for speeding up America's military build-up.
  C. shift public opinion toward entering the war.
  D. shift public opinion toward helping Britain.

DIRECTIONS: Essay Answer one of the following questions on a separate sheet of paper. *(20 points)*

21. Describe fascism and the beliefs of its followers.

22. Describe the "Miracle at Dunkirk" and Hitler's surprising order that helped make it possible.

Chapter 19 Test, Form B

Score

A World in Flames

DIRECTIONS: Matching Match the countries in the map with their World War II leaders. Write the letters from the map in the blanks provided. *(4 points each)*

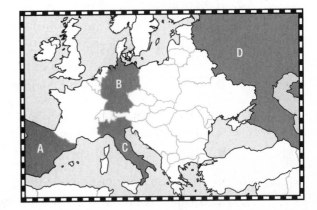

Column A

_____ **1.** Joseph Stalin

_____ **2.** Francisco Franco

_____ **3.** Adolf Hitler

_____ **4.** Benito Mussolini

DIRECTIONS: Matching Match each item in Column A with the items in Column B. Write the correct letters in the blanks. *(4 points each)*

Column A

_____ **5.** believed by Hitler to be a "master race" destined to rule the world

_____ **6.** one of the first and largest Nazi concentration camps

_____ **7.** idea that trade between nations helps to prevent war

_____ **8.** living space

_____ **9.** Hitler's autobiography

_____ **10.** German air force

Column B

A. Aryans

B. internationalism

C. Buchenwald

D. *Luftwaffe*

E. *Mein Kampf*

F. lebensraum

DIRECTIONS: Multiple Choice Choose the item that best completes each sentence or answers each question. Write the letter in the blank. *(4 points each)*

_____ **11.** To get resources, the Japanese military invaded
    A. Taiwan.
    B. Korea.
    C. Tibet.
    D. Manchuria.

_____ **12.** The Neutrality Act of 1935 made it illegal for
    A. American citizens to join another country's military.
    B. Americans to sell arms to any country at war.
    C. Congress to declare war on any country.
    D. Americans to join the Communist or Fascist Party.

_____ **13.** The first area that Hitler "unified" with Germany was
    A. the Sudetenland.
    B. Czechoslovakia.
    C. Poland.
    D. Austria.

(continued)

★ Chapter 19 Test, Form B

_____ **14.** In the Munich Conference, Britain and France
   A. told Hitler that they would declare war if he invaded Czechoslovakia.
   B. gave in to Hitler's demands for the Sudetenland.
   C. allowed Czechoslovakia to become a German protectorate.
   D. told Hitler they would declare war if he invaded Poland.

_____ **15.** The Nazi-Soviet nonaggression treaty contained a secret deal to
   A. divide Poland between them.   **C.** not fight each other.
   B. divide France between them.   **D.** fight France and Britain.

_____ **16.** In the Battle of Britain,
   A. British troops defeated the German ground invasion.
   B. the British sunk most of the German ships that crossed the English Channel.
   C. the German air force destroyed the Royal Air Force.
   D. the Royal Air Force saved Britain from invasion.

_____ **17.** A night of anti-Jewish violence became known as
   A. blitzkrieg.   **C.** *Kristallnacht*.
   B. *Anschluss*.   **D.** Gestapo.

_____ **18.** In the Wannsee Conference, Nazi leaders
   A. planned the invasion of Poland.   **C.** planned the "final solution."
   B. negotiated with Britain and France   **D.** negotiated a nonaggression treaty
       for the Sudetenland.   with the Soviet Union.

_____ **19.** Roosevelt sent destroyers to Britain in exchange for
   A. cash.   **C.** U.S. bases on British-held territory.
   B. a promise to pay at war's end.   **D.** manufactured British goods.

_____ **20.** The Lend-Lease Act was Roosevelt's way of getting arms to Britain
       without Britain having to
   A. pick them up.   **C.** take out loans to pay for them.
   B. return them after the war.   **D.** pay cash.

DIRECTIONS: Essay Answer one of the following questions on a separate sheet of
paper. *(20 points)*

21. Describe Adolf Hitler's beliefs, including his views on different races.

22. Although no consensus has been reached for why an event so horrifying as the
   Holocaust could have occurred, give five factors that most historians think could
   have contributed.

The American Republic Since 1877

★ **Chapter 20**

Section Quiz 20-1

DIRECTIONS: Matching Match each item in Column A with the items in Column B.
Write the correct letters in the blanks. *(10 points each)*

Column A

_____ **1.** government agreed to pay a company whatever it cost to make a product plus a guaranteed percentage of the costs as profit

_____ **2.** an African American unit, the 99th Pursuit Squadron, that played an important role during the Battle of Anzio

_____ **3.** nickname for American soldiers because their clothing was labeled "Government Issue"

_____ **4.** first regular army corps for women

_____ **5.** basic cargo ship used during the war

Column B

A. Women's Army Corps

B. cost-plus contracts

C. GIs

D. Liberty ship

E. Tuskegee Airmen

DIRECTIONS: Multiple Choice In the blank at the left, write the letter of the choice
that best completes the statement or answers the question. *(10 points each)*

_____ **6.** The *Pittsburgh Courier* argued that African Americans should join the war effort in order to achieve a double victory over Hitler's racism and racism at home in a campaign called
   A. "Double V."
   B. "Tuskegee Airmen."
   C. "Fight for Right."
   D. "Two V."

_____ **7.** The automobile industry was uniquely suited to the mass production of
   A. "Government Issue" clothing.
   B. ships.
   C. military equipment.
   D. buildings to house soldiers.

_____ **8.** After France surrendered to Germany in June 1940, two members of Congress introduced the
   A. War Production Board.
   B. Women's Army Auxiliary Corps.
   C. Reconstruction Finance Corporation.
   D. Selective Service and Training Act.

_____ **9.** During World War II, the Army enlisted women for the first time, although they were barred from
   A. combat.
   B. basic training.
   C. the barracks.
   D. clerical positions.

_____ **10.** What did Roosevelt establish in 1943 to settle arguments between different agencies concerning production of goods for the war?
   A. War Production Board
   B. Selective Service
   C. Reconstruction Finance Corporation
   D. Office of War Mobilization

Chapter 20

Section Quiz 20-2

DIRECTIONS: Matching Match each item in Column A with the items in Column B.
Write the correct letters in the blanks. *(10 points each)*

Column A

_____ **1.** cargo ships traveled in groups and were escorted by navy warships

_____ **2.** turning point in the war that put the Germans on the offensive

_____ **3.** edges

_____ **4.** turning point in the war that stopped the Japanese advance in the Pacific

_____ **5.** when 78,000 prisoners of war were forced to march 65 miles to a Japanese prison camp

Column B

A. Battle of Midway

B. Battle of Stalingrad

C. Bataan Death March

D. convoy system

E. periphery

DIRECTIONS: Multiple Choice In the blank at the left, write the letter of the choice
that best completes the statement or answers the question. *(10 points each)*

_____ **6.** On April 18, 1942, American bombs fell on Japan for the first time when the carriers' usual short-ranged bombers were replaced with long-range
  A. paratroopers.
  B. code breakers.
  C. radar.
  D. B-25 bombers.

_____ **7.** If British and American troops opened a second front by attacking Germany from the west, it would take pressure off the
  A. Pacific war.
  B. Soviet Union.
  C. Italians.
  D. French.

_____ **8.** On November 8, 1942, the American invasion of North Africa began under the command of General
  A. Dwight D. Eisenhower.
  B. George Patton.
  C. Douglas MacArthur.
  D. Ernest King.

_____ **9.** In June 1942, decoded Japanese messages alerted the United States to the Japanese attack on
  A. Hawaii.
  B. Midway.
  C. New Guinea.
  D. Manchuria.

_____ **10.** The Battle of the Atlantic slowly turned in favor of the Allies, in part due to new technology, including depth charges, sonar, and
  A. B-25 bombers.
  B. mass production.
  C. convoy systems.
  D. radar.

The American Republic Since 1877

★ **Chapter 20**

Section Quiz 20-3

DIRECTIONS: Matching Match each item in Column A with the items in Column B.
Write the correct letters in the blanks. *(10 points each)*

Column A

_____ **1.** first civil rights agency established by the federal
government since the Reconstruction era

_____ **2.** gardens planted to produce more food for the war effort

_____ **3.** tried to help Japanese Americans who had lost property
during the relocation

_____ **4.** created to stabilize both wages and prices

_____ **5.** symbol of the campaign to hire women during the wartime
labor shortage

Column B

A. Japanese American
Citizens League

B. victory gardens

C. "Rosie the
Riveter"

D. Office of Price
Administration

E. Fair Employment
Practices
Commission

DIRECTIONS: Multiple Choice In the blank at the left, write the letter of the choice
that best completes the statement or answers the question. *(10 points each)*

_____ **6.** In order to save fabric for the war, most men wore a
  A. sport coat.
  B. shirt with no jacket.
  C. "victory suit."
  D. "zoot suit."

_____ **7.** The Office of Price Administration began rationing, or limiting the
availability of, many consumer products to make sure enough were
available for
  A. military use.
  B. the elderly.
  C. children.
  D. schools.

_____ **8.** To help farmers in the Southwest overcome the labor shortage, the
government introduced the
  A. Migrant Worker Program.
  B. Relocation Program.
  C. Rosie the Riveter Program.
  D. Bracero Program.

_____ **9.** In 1942 Secretary of War Henry Stimson declared most of the West Coast
a military zone and ordered all people of Japanese ancestry to evacuate to
  A. Japan.
  B. internment camps.
  C. concentration camps.
  D. the East Coast.

_____ **10.** Taken together, the growth of southern California and the expansion of
cities in the Deep South created a new industrial region—
  A. the Sunbelt.
  B. the Southwest Corridor.
  C. the Southbelt.
  D. Sun City.

★ **Chapter 20**

Section Quiz 20-4

DIRECTIONS: Matching Match each item in Column A with the items in Column B.
Write the correct letters in the blanks. *(10 points each)*

Column A

_____ **1.** an amphibious tractor invented in the late 1930s to rescue
people in Florida swamps

_____ **2.** when Japanese pilots would deliberately crash their planes
into American ships, killing themselves but also inflicting
severe damage

_____ **3.** an amphibious truck

_____ **4.** code name for the invasion of France

_____ **5.** the day of the invasion of France

Column B

A. D-Day

B. amphtrac

C. kamikaze attacks

D. DUKW

E. Operation
Overlord

DIRECTIONS: Multiple Choice In the blank at the left, write the letter of the choice
that best completes the statement or answers the question. *(10 points each)*

_____ **6.** It took the Allies five months to break through the German lines at
Cassino and
  A. Pas-de-Calais.   **C.** Salerno.
  B. Anzio.   **D.** Guadalcanal.

_____ **7.** One part of the American plan for the defeat of Japan called for General
MacArthur's troops to advance through the Solomon Islands, capture the
north coast of New Guinea, and then retake
  A. the Philippines.   **C.** Indonesia.
  B. Manchuria.   **D.** Australia.

_____ **8.** The bombing campaign between January 1943 and May 1945 did not
destroy Germany's economy or undermine German morale, but it did
destroy many aircraft factories, wrecked the railroad system, and caused
a severe
  A. water shortage.   **C.** oil shortage.
  B. ecological crisis.   **D.** political scandal.

_____ **9.** On June 6, 1944, nearly 7,000 ships carrying more than 100,000 soldiers
set sail for the coast of
  A. Northern Africa.   **C.** Japan.
  B. the Philippines.   **D.** Normandy.

_____ **10.** General MacArthur's campaign in the southwest Pacific began with the
invasion of
  A. Australia.   **C.** Guadalcanal.
  B. Vietnam.   **D.** Normandy.

Chapter 20

Section Quiz 20-5

DIRECTIONS: Matching Match each item in Column A with the items in Column B.
Write the correct letters in the blanks. *(10 points each)*

Column A

_____ 1. code-name for the American program to build an atomic bomb

_____ 2. where the International Military Tribunal tried German leaders suspected of committing war crimes

_____ 3. dirt walls, several feet thick, that were covered in shrubbery and surrounded many fields in Normandy

_____ 4. the day after the unconditional surrender by Germany on May 7, 1945

_____ 5. code-name for the atomic bomb dropped on Hiroshima

Column B

A. V-E Day

B. hedgerows

C. Manhattan Project

D. "Little Boy"

E. Nuremburg

DIRECTIONS: Multiple Choice In the blank at the left, write the letter of the choice
that best completes the statement or answers the question. *(10 points each)*

_____ 6. In 1944, at the Dumbarton Oaks Estate in Washington, D.C., delegates from 39 countries met to discuss a new international organization, which was to be called the
   A. League of Nations.
   B. United Nations.
   C. Allies.
   D. International Military Tribunal.

_____ 7. The German's goal for the Battle of the Bulge was to cut off Allied supplies coming through the port of
   A. Antwerp, Belgium.
   B. Odense, Denmark.
   C. Helsinki, Finland.
   D. Nice, France.

_____ 8. Where did American military planners choose to invade in order to stockpile supplies and build up troops for an invasion of Japan?
   A. Hiroshima
   B. Nagasaki
   C. Iwo Jima
   D. Okinawa

_____ 9. Faced with the massive destruction caused by atomic bombs and the shock of the Soviets joining the war, the Japanese emperor ordered his government to surrender on August 15, 1945—
   A. Armistice Day.
   B. V-E Day.
   C. V-J Day.
   D. Veterans Day.

_____ 10. Where did American military planners decide to invade so B-29s could be refueled?
   A. Iwo Jima
   B. Okinawa
   C. Tokyo
   D. the Mariana Islands

⭐ **Chapter 20 Test, Form A**

Score

America and World War II

DIRECTIONS: Matching Match each item in Column A with the items in Column B. Write the correct letters in the blanks. *(4 points each)*

Column A

_____ **1.** in overall command of the invasion of France

_____ **2.** "I felt like the moon, the stars, and all the planets had fallen on me."

_____ **3.** commander of the United States Navy in the Pacific

_____ **4.** head of the Brotherhood of Sleeping Car Porters who pressured Roosevelt to provide jobs for African Americans in defense factories

_____ **5.** led the American team of engineers and scientists building the atomic bomb

_____ **6.** highest-ranking African American officer in the U.S. Army

_____ **7.** signed a letter to Roosevelt, warning that powerful bombs may be constructed using uranium

_____ **8.** director of the WAC

_____ **9.** upon evacuating the Philippines, said "I shall return"

_____ **10.** led the troops that rescued the Americans trapped at Bastogne

Column B

A. A. Philip Randolph

B. Benjamin O. Davis

C. Chester Nimitz

D. Robert Oppenheimer

E. George Patton

F. Harry S Truman

G. Oveta Culp Hobby

H. Albert Einstein

I. Douglas MacArthur

J. Dwight D. Eisenhower

DIRECTIONS: Multiple Choice Choose the item that best completes each sentence or answers each question. Write the letter in the blank. *(4 points each)*

_____ **11.** The cost-plus system sped up war production by
  A. imposing penalties on companies that did not meet their production quotas.
  B. providing larger profits for companies that worked fast and produced a lot.
  C. allowing previously competing companies to work together.
  D. providing bonuses for superior workmanship in war production.

_____ **12.** Most Liberty ships were hard to sink because they were
  A. made of steel rather than iron.
  B. made with thick hulls.
  C. faster than other ships.
  D. welded rather than riveted.

_____ **13.** During World War II, women were recruited into the military to
  A. serve in light combat.
  B. serve as cooks and nurses.
  C. release men for combat.
  D. entertain the troops.

_____ **14.** Japan's goal in attacking Midway Island was to
  A. gain a base from which to attack Hawaii.
  B. cut American supply lines to Australia.
  C. destroy the American fleet.
  D. gain control of resources on Midway.

(continued)

★ **Chapter 20 Test, Form A**

_____ **15.** Roosevelt created the Fair Employment Practices Commission to
   A. mediate disputes between labor and management to avoid strikes.
   B. enforce nondiscrimination in hiring workers in defense industries.
   C. control wages and prices.
   D. recruit women and minorities to work in defense factories.

_____ **16.** As a result of a presidential order allowing the military to declare any part of the United States to be a military zone,
   A. many areas of the West became off-limits to civilians.
   B. many Japanese Americans were moved to internment camps.
   C. much of the Nevada desert became a weapons testing ground.
   D. many military installations sprang up along the West Coast.

_____ **17.** Blue points and red points were a system for
   A. rewarding American civilians.   **C.** prioritizing targets for attack.
   B. rationing goods.   **D.** mapping opposing forces.

_____ **18.** The Allies placed inflated rubber tanks, empty tents, and dummy landing craft along the coast of Britain to convince the Germans that
   A. the Allies had more troops than they really had.
   B. an invasion of Britain would be futile.
   C. the Allies planned to invade the coast of Germany rather than France.
   D. the Allies planned to land their invasion forces in Pas-de-Calais.

_____ **19.** Iwo Jima was an important objective for the American military because
   A. the Japanese were using it as a base to attack the U.S. fleet.
   B. the main Japanese naval force was stationed there.
   C. U.S. planes could bomb Japan from there.
   D. the islands were an important link in the Japanese supply lines.

_____ **20.** The U.S. caused massive fires in Tokyo by dropping bombs filled with
   A. amphtrac.   **C.** DUKW.
   B. dynamite.   **D.** napalm.

DIRECTIONS: Essay Answer one of the following questions on a separate sheet of paper. *(20 points)*

21. Explain the purpose of the Doolittle Raid and the problems military planners had to solve to make it successful.

22. Complete the diagram by filling in the names of the branches of the United Nations. Then describe the makeup of each branch and its responsibilities.

The American Republic Since 1877

Chapter 20 Test, Form B

America and World War II

DIRECTIONS: Matching Match each item in Column A with the items in Column B.
Write the correct letters in the blanks. *(4 points each)*

Column A

_____ **1.** first time the Japanese used kamikaze attacks

_____ **2.** beginning of Operation Overlord

_____ **3.** first time American troops had to fight the German army
in North Africa

_____ **4.** name for French beach stormed by American invasion
forces

_____ **5.** Japanese American military unit

_____ **6.** limit availability of consumer products

_____ **7.** bomber that dropped the first atomic bomb

_____ **8.** first peacetime draft in American history

_____ **9.** African American military unit

_____ **10.** used to raise money for the war

Column B

A. Tuskegee Airmen

B. E bonds

C. Leyte Gulf

D. 442nd Regimental
Combat Team

E. Selective Service
and Training Act

F. Omaha

G. Kasserine Pass

H. *Enola Gay*

I. ration

J. D-Day

DIRECTIONS: Multiple Choice Choose the item that best completes each sentence
or answers each question. Write the letter in the blank. *(4 points each)*

_____ **11.** Over a third of all military equipment made during the war was
manufactured by the
   A. steel industry.   **C.** automobile industry.
   B. ship-building industry.   **D.** aircraft industry.

_____ **12.** The "Double V" campaign meant
   A. victory in Europe and victory in the Pacific.
   B. victory over Hitler's racism abroad and victory over racism at home.
   C. victory over the Nazis and victory over the Fascists.
   D. victory on land and victory on the seas.

_____ **13.** The Bataan Death March occurred in
   A. the Philippines.   **C.** Corregidor.
   B. North Africa.   **D.** the Soviet Union.

_____ **14.** A key to the American success at Midway was
   A. the use of new sonar and radar technology.
   B. breaking the Japanese Navy's secret code.
   C. the use of long-range B-25 bombers launched from aircraft carriers.
   D. American submarines.

(continued)

★ **Chapter 20 Test, Form B**

Score

_____ 15. The capture of Stalingrad was key to the success of Hitler's strategy to
  A. destroy the Soviet army.   **C.** draw China into the war.
  B. destroy Soviet morale.   **D.** destroy the Soviet economy.

_____ 16. Migrant farmworkers became an important part of the Southwest's agricultural system as a result of
  A. the planting of victory gardens.   **C.** the Bracero Program.
  B. a relaxation of immigration quotas. **D.** the Great Migration.

_____ 17. In the case *Korematsu* v. *the United States*, the Supreme Court ruled that relocation of Japanese Americans was
  A. constitutional, but the government had to pay them for property losses.
  B. unconstitutional, and they had to be released at once.
  C. constitutional because it was based on military urgency.
  D. unconstitutional because it was based on race.

_____ 18. As a result of the Allied attack on Sicily,
  A. the Italian king arrested Mussolini.   **C.** Mussolini surrendered Italy.
  B. Hitler removed Mussolini from power.   **D.** Mussolini took his own life.

_____ 19. The U.S. Marines had severe casualties at Tarawa in part because
  A. they had no air support.
  B. the shallow reef prevented many landing craft from reaching shore.
  C. the Japanese held the high ground of Mount Suribachi.
  D. the Japanese used kamikaze fighters against them.

_____ 20. Which of the following choices best completes the diagram?

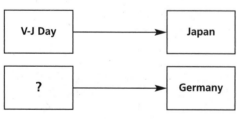

  A. D-Day   **C.** Double-V Day
  B. V-G Day   **D.** V-E Day

DIRECTIONS: Essay Answer one of the following questions on a separate sheet of paper. *(20 points)*

21. Describe zoot suiters and explain why they became the target of anger from many Americans.

22. Describe the different points of view in the debate over the use of the atomic bomb and explain why Truman finally decided to use it.

⭐ **Chapter 21**

Section Quiz 21-1

DIRECTIONS: Matching Match each item in Column A with the items in Column B.
Write the correct letters in the blanks. *(10 points each)*

Column A

_____ 1. located near Berlin; where Truman and Stalin met to work
out a deal on Germany

_____ 2. Eastern European countries that had to remain Communist
and friendly to the Soviet Union

_____ 3. issued by Roosevelt, Churchill, and Stalin and declared
"the right of all people to choose the form of government
under which they will live"

_____ 4. a Soviet resort on the Black Sea where Roosevelt, Churchill,
and Stalin met to plan the postwar world

_____ 5. an era of confrontation and competition between the United States
and the Soviet Union that lasted from about 1946 to 1990

Column B

A. Declaration of
Liberated Europe

B. satellite nations

C. Cold War

D. Potsdam

E. Yalta

DIRECTIONS: Multiple Choice In the blank at the left, write the letter of the choice
that best completes the statement or answers the question. *(10 points each)*

_____ 6. By 1945 what did President Roosevelt and his advisers think was the key
to keeping the world at peace?
  A. economic growth   **C.** atomic bombs
  B. a strong military   **D.** compromise

_____ 7. One of the major causes of the Cold War were arguments between the
United States and the Soviet Union over reparations and
  A. control of Japan.   **C.** economic policy in Germany.
  B. the use of the atomic bomb. **D.** immigration to the United States.

_____ 8. Roosevelt, Churchill, and Stalin agreed to divide Germany into four zones
controlled by the United States, Great Britain, the Soviet Union, and
  A. Italy.   **C.** Greece.
  B. Belgium.   **D.** France.

_____ 9. The presence of the Soviet army in Eastern Europe ensured that pro-
Soviet Communist governments would be established eventually in
Poland, Romania, Bulgaria, Hungary, and
  A. the Netherlands.   **C.** Switzerland.
  B. Czechoslovakia.   **D.** Austria.

_____ 10. As the war ended, what two factors influenced the Soviet leaders'
thinking?
  A. capitalism and democracy   **C.** security and communism
  B. trade and economic growth **D.** education and human rights

★ Chapter 21

Section Quiz 21-2

DIRECTIONS: Matching Match each item in Column A with the items in Column B.
Write the correct letters in the blanks. *(10 points each)*

Column A

_____ **1.** keeping communism within its present territory through the use of diplomatic, economic, and military actions

_____ **2.** the Soviet zone of Germany

_____ **3.** a war fought to achieve a limited objective such as containing communism

_____ **4.** gave European nations American aid to rebuild their economies

_____ **5.** when cargo planes supplied Berliners with food, medicine, and coal

Column B

A. East Germany

B. limited war

C. containment

D. Berlin airlift

E. Marshall Plan

DIRECTIONS: Multiple Choice In the blank at the left, write the letter of the choice
that best completes the statement or answers the question. *(10 points each)*

_____ **6.** To prevent a Communist revolution in Asia, the United States sent $2 billion in aid beginning in the mid-1940s to
   A. Mao Zedong's forces.
   B. North Korea.
   C. Japan.
   D. Chiang Kai-shek's forces.

_____ **7.** Where was the first of a string of crises that erupted in the spring and summer of 1946?
   A. Iran
   B. Turkey
   C. East Germany
   D. West Germany

_____ **8.** Where did Truman order United States naval and air power into action because he thought the Communist invasion of that country was a test of the containment policy?
   A. Turkey
   B. China
   C. South Korea
   D. Iran

_____ **9.** The United States, Great Britain, and France merged their zones to form West Germany and allowed the Germans to have their own
   A. military.
   B. government.
   C. containment.
   D. limited war.

_____ **10.** After the Korean War began, the United States embarked on a major
   A. military buildup.
   B. peace negotiation mission.
   C. trade agreement.
   D. capitalist education program.

The American Republic Since 1877

★ **Chapter 21**

Score

Section Quiz 21-3

DIRECTIONS: Matching Match each item in Column A with the items in Column B.
Write the correct letters in the blanks. *(10 points each)*

Column A

_____ **1.** formal disapproval

_____ **2.** the effort to secretly weaken a society and overthrow its
government

_____ **3.** blackening reputations with vague and unfounded charges

_____ **4.** built to protect people from the radiation left over after a
nuclear blast

_____ **5.** lying under oath

Column B

A. fallout shelters

B. McCarthyism

C. subversion

D. perjury

E. censure

DIRECTIONS: Multiple Choice In the blank at the left, write the letter of the choice
that best completes the statement or answers the question. *(10 points each)*

_____ **6.** In 1950, with the Korean War underway and McCarthy and others
arousing fears of Communist spies, Congress passed the Internal Security
Act, usually called the
  A. McCarthy Act.
  B. McCarran Act.
  C. Immigration Act.
  D. Hoover Act.

_____ **7.** What did President Truman establish in early 1947 to screen all federal
employees?
  A. House Un-American Activities Committee
  B. Project Venona
  C. loyalty review program
  D. McCarthy Review

_____ **8.** In 1949 the Red Scare intensified even further when the Soviet Union
tested an atomic bomb, and the Chinese fell to
  A. socialism.
  B. anarchy.
  C. McCarthyism.
  D. communism.

_____ **9.** In 1953 Americans were shocked when the Soviets tested the
  A. *Sputnik* satellite.
  B. first fallout shelters.
  C. hydrogen bomb.
  D. HUAC.

_____ **10.** What was the name of the project that cracked the Soviet spy code,
which confirmed extensive Soviet spying?
  A. Project Venona
  B. Rosenberg Project
  C. Project Red Spy
  D. Blacklist Project

Chapter 21

Section Quiz 21-4

DIRECTIONS: Matching Match each item in Column A with the items in Column B.
Write the correct letters in the blanks. *(10 points each)*

Column A

_____ **1.** formal face-to-face meeting of leaders from different
countries to discuss important issues

_____ **2.** policy of threatening to use nuclear weapons if a
Communist state tried to seize territory by force

_____ **3.** countries with primarily agricultural economies

_____ **4.** a relationship that developed between the military
establishment and the defense industry

_____ **5.** the first artificial satellite to orbit Earth

Column B

A. massive
retaliation

B. developing
nations

C. military-industrial
complex

D. *Sputnik*

E. summit

DIRECTIONS: Multiple Choice In the blank at the left, write the letter of the choice
that best completes the statement or answers the question. *(10 points each)*

_____ **6.** What did Congress create to coordinate research in rocket and space
technology?
    A. National Defense Education Act   **C.** Central Intelligence Agency
    B. National Aeronautics and Space   **D.** military-industrial complex
       Administration

_____ **7.** When Eisenhower declared a "New Look" was needed, he meant a new
look in
    A. education policy.   **C.** health policy.
    B. welfare programs.   **D.** defense policy.

_____ **8.** To prevent Communist revolutions in other countries, Eisenhower
decided to use covert, or hidden, operations conducted by the
    A. Central Intelligence Agency.   **C.** Federal Bureau of Investigation.
    B. National Aeronautics and Space   **D.** Navy.
       Administration.

_____ **9.** What island, which Eisenhower saw as part of the "anti-Communist
barrier," did the Chinese threaten to seize in 1954?
    A. Cuba   **C.** the Philippines
    B. Hawaii   **D.** Taiwan

_____ **10.** Who emerged as the leader of the Soviet Union three years after Stalin
died?
    A. Mohammed Mossadegh   **C.** Chiang Kai-shek
    B. Nikita Khrushchev   **D.** Jacobo Arbenz Guzmán

The American Republic Since 1877

★ Chapter 21 Test, Form A

The Cold War Begins

DIRECTIONS: Matching Match each item in Column A with the items in Column B. Write the correct letters in the blanks. *(4 points each)*

Column A

_____ **1.** U-2 pilot shot down over the Soviet Union

_____ **2.** wrote the novel *Tomorrow!* to educate the public about the horrors of atomic war

_____ **3.** leader of the Chinese Nationalists

_____ **4.** proposed the European Recovery Program that promised European nations American aid to rebuild their economies

_____ **5.** leader of the People's Republic of China

_____ **6.** FBI head who authorized wiretapping and infiltration of groups suspected of subversion

_____ **7.** "an iron curtain has descended across the continent"

_____ **8.** in charge of occupied Japan after World War II

_____ **9.** diplomat who tried to explain Soviet behavior in the "long telegram"

_____ **10.** the nation "must be prepared to use atomic weapons in all forms"

Column B

A. J. Edgar Hoover

B. Mao Zedong

C. Winston Churchill

D. Dwight D. Eisenhower

E. George C. Marshall

F. Francis Gary Powers

G. George Kennan

H. Douglas MacArthur

I. Chiang Kai-shek

J. Philip Wylie

DIRECTIONS: Multiple Choice Choose the item that best completes each sentence or answers each question. Write the letter in the blank. *(4 points each)*

_____ **11.** At Yalta, the leaders agreed to recognize the Polish government that the Soviets had set up if Stalin agreed to
    A. allow free enterprise in Poland.
    B. allow Poland to trade with the West.
    C. hold free elections there as soon as possible.
    D. give up his demand for reparations from Germany.

_____ **12.** Which of the following best completes the diagram?

Opposing Views at Potsdam

Allow Germany's economy to recover. ◁ U.S. View ◁   ▷ Soviet View ▷ **?**

    A. Germany must be Communist.
    B. Germany must be divided.
    C. Germany must make reparations.
    D. Berlin must be placed under Soviet control.

(continued)

The American Republic Since 1877

Chapter 21 Test, Form A

—— **13.** The Long Telegram resulted in
  A. the Marshall Plan.
  B. the establishment of the CIA.
  C. the Berlin airlift.
  D. the containment policy.

—— **14.** Truman said the Truman Doctrine and Marshall Plan were essential for
  A. containment.
  B. world economic recovery.
  C. world peace.
  D. American prosperity.

—— **15.** When the United States, Britain, and France merged their zones in Germany, the Soviet Union responded by
  A. threatening to declare war.
  B. building the Berlin Wall.
  C. blockading West Berlin.
  D. organizing a military alliance.

—— **16.** The Korean War pitted the military forces of North Korea and China against
  A. the United States.
  B. the Soviet Union.
  C. South Korea.
  D. the United Nations.

—— **17.** Ethel and Julius Rosenberg were charged with
  A. passing atomic secrets to the Soviets.
  B. plotting to overthrow the U.S.
  C. being Communist Party members.
  D. planning acts of terrorism.

—— **18.** Joseph McCarthy created the media frenzy that began his witch hunt by
  A. accusing Alger Hiss of being a Soviet spy.
  B. saying that there were spies in the United States Army.
  C. urging the House Un-American Activities Committee to hold open hearings.
  D. saying that he had a list of Communists employed by the State Department.

—— **19.** Popular support for Joseph McCarthy began to fade when
  A. he began to accuse popular film stars.
  B. millions watched him bully witnesses in televised hearings investigating the Army.
  C. he could not produce the list he said he had of known Communists.
  D. the Senate impeached him.

—— **20.** The Egyptians seized control of the Suez Canal in order to
  A. assure their own national security.
  B. expel Western influences from their country.
  C. use the canal's profits to pay for a dam.
  D. assure access to the canal for their ally, the Soviet Union.

DIRECTIONS: Essay Answer one of the following questions on a separate sheet of paper. *(20 points)*

21. In what ways did the Korean War mark a turning point in the Cold War?

22. Explain the reasoning behind "massive retaliation" and "brinkmanship," and describe how Eisenhower used these concepts to help end the Korean War.

The American Republic Since 1877

Chapter 21 Test, Form B

The Cold War Begins

DIRECTIONS: Matching Match each item in Column A with the items in Column B. Write the correct letters in the blanks. *(4 points each)*

Column A

_____ 1. threatening nuclear strikes to back down opponents

_____ 2. operated in developing countries to overthrow anti-American leaders

_____ 3. asserted "the right of all people to choose the form of government under which they will live"

_____ 4. created out of fear that the nation was falling behind in scientific research

_____ 5. Communist countries of Eastern Europe

_____ 6. border between North Korea and South Korea

_____ 7. era of confrontation between the U.S. and Soviet Union

_____ 8. deadly radiation left over after a nuclear blast

_____ 9. military alliance in Eastern Europe

_____ 10. daring attack that took the North Koreans by surprise

Column B

A. fallout

B. demilitarized zone

C. Cold War

D. Inchon

E. NASA

F. Declaration of Liberated Europe

G. CIA

H. satellite nations

I. brinkmanship

J. Warsaw Pact

DIRECTIONS: Multiple Choice Choose the item that best completes each sentence or answers each question. Write the letter in the blank. *(4 points each)*

_____ 11. At Yalta, the leaders agreed to
    A. divide Germany among the four Allied powers.
    B. allow half of Germany to be Communist and the other half democratic.
    C. help Germany's economy to recover.
    D. allow free elections in Germany.

_____ 12. Truman's first meeting with Soviet Foreign Minister Molotov marked a shift in Soviet-American relations because
    A. Truman gave in to most Soviet demands.
    B. Truman strongly confronted Molotov.
    C. Molotov gave in to most of Truman's demands.
    D. each official approached the other cautiously but diplomatically.

_____ 13. The Truman Doctrine resulted in
    A. the economic recovery of Europe.   **C.** the rearming of West Germany.
    B. a pledge to fight communism.   **D.** the Red Scare.

_____ 14. The purpose of the Marshall Plan was to
    A. punish Germany for World War II.   **C.** keep Communist countries weak.
    B. prevent Germany from rearming.   **D.** help Western Europe recover.

(continued)

⭐ **Chapter 21 Test, Form B**

—— **15.** NATO formed for the purpose of
   A. promoting free trade among members. **C.** mutual defense.
   B. spreading democracy. **D.** settling international disputes.

—— **16.** Truman fired MacArthur because
   A. MacArthur's mistakes caused his forces to lose the key port of Inchon.
   B. MacArthur ignored Truman's command to invade China.
   C. MacArthur wanted to withdraw American troops from China.
   D. MacArthur demanded Truman's approval to expand the war.

—— **17.** The purpose of Project Venona was to
   A. develop the atomic bomb. **C.** uncover Communists in the U.S.
   B. crack the Soviet spy code. **D.** spread anti-Communist propaganda.

—— **18.** The McCarran Act
   A. required all government employees to sign a loyalty oath.
   B. allowed the arrest of Communists in case of a national emergency.
   C. imposed the death penalty on anyone convicted of espionage.
   D. authorized the use of wiretaps to uncover suspected Communists.

—— **19.** The Korean War resulted in
   A. victory for North Korea. **C.** victory for the United Nations.
   B. victory for South Korea. **D.** containment but no victory.

—— **20.** To prevent Communists from staging revolutions within developing
   countries, Eisenhower used
   A. brinkmanship. **C.** embargoes.
   B. massive retaliation. **D.** covert operations.

DIRECTIONS: Essay Answer one of the following questions on a separate sheet of
paper. *(20 points)*

21. Tensions between the United States and the Soviet Union began to increase after
World War II because the two nations had different goals. Complete the diagram
below. Then use it to help you discuss the different concerns and beliefs that
contributed to the Cold War.

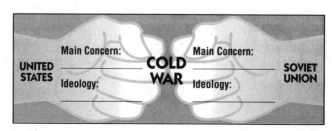

22. Describe the tactics of Joseph McCarthy and explain why few challenged him.

★ Chapter 22

Score

Section Quiz 22-1

DIRECTIONS: Matching Match each item in Column A with the items in Column B.
Write the correct letters in the blanks. *(10 points each)*

Column A

_____ 1. the largest public works program in American history

_____ 2. the practice of limiting work output in order to create more jobs

_____ 3. Eisenhower's term for the federal government's continuing aid to businesses

_____ 4. Truman's domestic policy

_____ 5. balancing economic conservatism with some activism

Column B

A. dynamic conservatism

B. featherbedding

C. "creeping socialism"

D. Fair Deal

E. Federal Highway Act

DIRECTIONS: Multiple Choice In the blank at the left, write the letter of the choice
that best completes the statement or answers the question. *(10 points each)*

_____ 6. In 1947 the conservative Congress set out to curb the power of organized labor by passing the
  A. Fair Deal.
  B. Federal Highway Act.
  C. Taft-Hartley Act.
  D. GI Bill.

_____ 7. Dwight Eisenhower's running mate in the presidential election of 1952 was
  A. Richard Nixon.
  B. Adlai Stevenson.
  C. Strom Thurmond.
  D. Thomas Dewey.

_____ 8. What did Eisenhower end that many conservatives had viewed as unnecessary federal control over the business community?
  A. government work programs
  B. the GI Bill
  C. government price and rent controls
  D. union shops

_____ 9. Truman won the election in 1948 with strong support from laborers, farmers, and
  A. wealthy socialites.
  B. Southern Democrats.
  C. the new Progressive Party.
  D. African Americans.

_____ 10. Eisenhower came to an agreement with Canada to build an American-Canadian waterway to aid international shipping called the
  A. Chesapeake Bay Seaway.
  B. Great Lakes-St. Lawrence Seaway.
  C. American-Canadian Seaway.
  D. St. Lawrence River locks.

★ **Chapter 22**

Section Quiz 22-2

DIRECTIONS: Matching Match each item in Column A with the items in Column B.
Write the correct letters in the blanks. *(10 points each)*

Column A

_____ **1.** one of the nation's earliest computers

_____ **2.** tested an injectable polio vaccine on himself, his wife, and his three sons

_____ **3.** one of the earliest suburbs, which was located 10 miles east of New York City

_____ **4.** a period from 1945 to 1961 when more than 65 million children were born in the United States

_____ **5.** economist who wrote the 1958 book *The Affluent Society*

Column B

A. Levittown

B. Jonas Salk

C. John Kenneth Galbraith

D. ENIAC

E. baby boom

DIRECTIONS: Multiple Choice In the blank at the left, write the letter of the choice
that best completes the statement or answers the question. *(10 points each)*

_____ **6.** What became the fastest-growing industry in the United States during the 1950s?

    A. construction   **C.** advertising

    B. food   **D.** medical research

_____ **7.** About 85 percent of new home construction in the 1950s was found in

    A. the suburbs.   **C.** rural towns.

    B. the city.   **D.** the South.

_____ **8.** Many large corporations competed with each other and some expanded overseas, creating

    A. conglomerates.   **C.** multinational franchises.

    B. franchises.   **D.** multinational corporations.

_____ **9.** What epidemic brought a wave of terror to postwar America?

    A. polio   **C.** influenza

    B. yellow fever   **D.** whooping cough

_____ **10.** What did John Bardeen, Walter H. Brattain, and William Shockley develop in 1947?

    A. a nuclear reaction   **C.** radiowaves

    B. the transistor   **D.** microwaves

The American Republic Since 1877

★ **Chapter 22**

Score

Section Quiz 22-3

DIRECTIONS: Matching Match each item in Column A with the items in Column B.
Write the correct letters in the blanks. *(10 points each)*

Column A

_____ **1.** cultural separation between children and their parents

_____ **2.** hosted *Toast of the Town*

_____ **3.** African American rock 'n' roll singer

_____ **4.** enjoyed television success with routines of bad violin playing and stingy behavior

_____ **5.** beat member who published *On the Road* in 1957

Column B

A. Ed Sullivan

B. Jack Kerouac

C. generation gap

D. Little Richard

E. Jack Benny

DIRECTIONS: Multiple Choice In the blank at the left, write the letter of the choice that best completes the statement or answers the question. *(10 points each)*

_____ **6.** While the film industry may not have been collapsing, it certainly did suffer after the war due to the popularity of
    A. live theater.   **C.** reading.
    B. television.   **D.** radio.

_____ **7.** What music had a loud and heavy beat that made it ideal for dancing?
    A. reggae   **C.** rock 'n' roll
    B. country   **D.** jazz

_____ **8.** With a few notable exceptions, television tended to shut out
    A. African Americans.   **C.** women.
    B. the middle class.   **D.** white-collar workers.

_____ **9.** Who eventually claimed the title of King of Rock 'n' Roll?
    A. Little Richard   **C.** Elvis Presley
    B. Allen Ginsberg   **D.** Alan Freed

_____ **10.** By 1957 how many television sets were in use in the United States?
    A. 3 million   **C.** 10 million
    B. 40 million   **D.** 5 million

★ Chapter 22

Section Quiz 22-4

DIRECTIONS: Matching Match each item in Column A with the items in Column B. Write the correct letters in the blanks. *(10 points each)*

Column A

Column B

_____ **1.** a figure the government set to reflect the minimum income required to support a family

_____ **2.** antisocial or criminal behavior of young people

_____ **3.** the federal government's withdrawal of all official recognition of Native American groups as legal entities

_____ **4.** chronicled poverty in the United States in his book, *The Other America*

_____ **5.** a conservative commentator

A. juvenile delinquency

B. poverty line

C. Bishop Fulton J. Sheen

D. termination policy

E. Michael Harrington

DIRECTIONS: Multiple Choice In the blank at the left, write the letter of the choice that best completes the statement or answers the question. *(10 points each)*

_____ **6.** By the middle of the 1900s, what group of people were the poorest in the nation?
  A. Native Americans
  B. African Americans
  C. Irish Americans
  D. German Americans

_____ **7.** The programs that tried to eliminate poverty by tearing down slums and erecting new high-rise buildings for poor residents were called
  A. tenements.
  B. soup kitchens.
  C. welfare.
  D. urban renewal.

_____ **8.** Due to the Bracero program during the 1940s and 1950s, the country witnessed a sharp rise in the number of immigrants from
  A. Italy.
  B. Mexico.
  C. Spain.
  D. Portugal.

_____ **9.** Studies of life in Appalachia revealed high rates of infant mortality and
  A. polio.
  B. juvenile delinquency.
  C. nutritional deficiency.
  D. suicide.

_____ **10.** The cores of numerous cities deteriorated as middle-class flight deprived urban areas of
  A. termination policies.
  B. minorities.
  C. tax dollars.
  D. cultural events.

The American Republic Since 1877

★ **Chapter 22 Test, Form A**

Postwar America

DIRECTIONS: Matching Match each item in Column A with the items in Column B. Write the correct letters in the blanks. *(4 points each)*

Column A

_____ **1.** African American actor who expressed resentment for having to play stereotypical roles in 1950s movies

_____ **2.** developed an injectable vaccine for polio

_____ **3.** African American singer who recorded hit songs in the fifties

_____ **4.** Dixiecrat Party candidate for president in 1948

_____ **5.** beat poet who blasted modern American life

_____ **6.** King of Rock 'n' Roll

_____ **7.** developed an oral vaccine for polio

_____ **8.** Eisenhower's vice president

_____ **9.** disc jockey who helped launch rock 'n' roll by playing African American music on the air

_____ **10.** "Every segment of our population has a right to expect from . . . government a fair deal."

Column B

A. Elvis Presley

B. Harry S Truman

C. Albert Sabin

D. Strom Thurmond

E. Sidney Poitier

F. Alan Freed

G. Richard Nixon

H. Chuck Berry

I. Jonas Salk

J. Allen Ginsberg

DIRECTIONS: Multiple Choice Choose the item that best completes each sentence or answers each question. Write the letter in the blank. *(4 points each)*

_____ **11.** As a result of the GI Bill, many returning soldiers
  A. found jobs in business.
  B. decided to make a career in the military.
  C. attended college.
  D. received awards and bonuses for their wartime service.

_____ **12.** President Truman ended the miners' strike by ordering government seizure of the mines while
  A. pressuring owners to grant most union demands.
  B. pressuring strikers to accept a minimal pay increase.
  C. pushing through a law that banned strikes in energy industries.
  D. pushing through a law that required mine owners to negotiate with unions.

_____ **13.** The States' Rights Party formed for the 1948 election as a reaction to
  A. the "Do-Nothing Congress."
  B. Truman's aggressive federal spending.
  C. Truman's support of civil rights.
  D. Truman's support of big business.

(continued)

_____ **14.** In Nixon's famous "Checkers speech," "Checkers" referred to
    A. his political opponents.   **C.** his daughters.
    B. the pieces of his defense plan.   **D.** his dog.

_____ **15.** Eisenhower used the term "creeping socialism" to refer to
    A. public support for national health care.   **C.** the expansion of the welfare system.
    B. the expansion of Social Security.   **D.** the federal government's continuing aid to businesses.

_____ **16.** To benefit from a cheaper labor pool, some businesses in the 1950s began to
    A. hire African Americans.   **C.** expand overseas.
    B. hire teenagers.   **D.** move to the Sunbelt.

_____ **17.** The development of the transistor made possible the
    A. mass production of radios.   **C.** development of the computer.
    B. miniaturization of radios.   **D.** mass production of computers.

_____ **18.** Rock 'n' roll grew out of the sounds of
    A. jazz.   **C.** rhythm and blues.
    B. swing.   **D.** ragtime.

_____ **19.** In his book *The Other America*, Michael Harrington wrote about
    A. the beat movement.   **C.** poverty.
    B. street gangs.   **D.** the generation gap.

_____ **20.** Topping the list of juvenile crimes in the 1950s was
    A. assault.   **C.** vandalism.
    B. shoplifting.   **D.** car theft.

DIRECTIONS: Essay Answer one of the following questions on a separate sheet of paper. *(20 points)*

21. As president, Eisenhower had a conservative side and an activist side. Describe some of his programs and actions that reflected these two sides.

22. The diagram shows three broad categories of factors that contributed to the baby boom. Explain each of these factors and how they contributed to the baby boom.

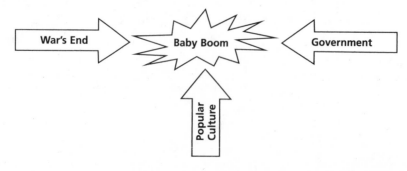

The American Republic Since 1877

⭐ **Chapter 22 Test, Form B**

Score

Postwar America

DIRECTIONS: Matching Match each item in Column A with the items in Column B.
Write the correct letters in the blanks. *(4 points each)*

Column A

_____ **1.** businesses in which a person owns and runs one or several stores of a chain operation

_____ **2.** banned union shops

_____ **3.** physical labor

_____ **4.** early computer that handled business data

_____ **5.** business in which new workers were required to join the union

_____ **6.** businesses that expanded overseas

_____ **7.** provided loans to veterans

_____ **8.** group of mostly white artists who sought to live unconventional lives

_____ **9.** forcing business owners to hire only union members

_____ **10.** movies shown on large, panoramic screens

Column B

A. multinational corporations

B. closed shop

C. right-to-work laws

D. franchises

E. GI Bill

F. cinemascope

G. blue-collar jobs

H. union shop

I. beats

J. UNIVAC

DIRECTIONS: Multiple Choice Choose the item that best completes each sentence
or answers each question. Write the letter in the blank. *(4 points each)*

_____ **11.** After World War II, labor unrest was triggered by
  A. rising inflation.   **C.** lack of jobs.
  B. falling wages.   **D.** poor working conditions.

_____ **12.** Which of the following choices best completes the diagram?

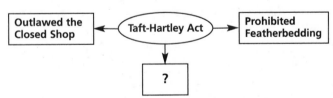

  A. supported unions' right to contribute to political campaigns   **C.** increased the minimum wage
  B. allowed right-to-work laws   **D.** outlawed strikes

_____ **13.** Congress passed all of the following parts of Truman's Fair Deal EXCEPT
  A. a minimum wage increase.   **C.** a national housing act.
  B. an expansion of Social Security.   **D.** a civil rights act.

(continued)

Chapter 22 Test, Form B

_____ **14.** President Eisenhower described his political beliefs as
  A. conservative.
  B. liberal.
  C. progressive.
  D. middle of the road.

_____ **15.** According to John Kenneth Galbraith, postwar America had an "economy of abundance" because of
  A. the huge numbers of new workers returning from the war.
  B. new business techniques and improved technology.
  C. the new consumer culture.
  D. the growth of suburbs.

_____ **16.** Some observers criticized suburbia because it
  A. lacked diversity.
  B. represented conspicuous consumption.
  C. represented a departure from traditional values.
  D. contributed to urban sprawl.

_____ **17.** Many of the early television comedy shows were adapted from popular
  A. movies.
  B. radio shows.
  C. novels.
  D. stage plays.

_____ **18.** Many quiz shows left the air when
  A. fraud was discovered in one of them.
  B. comedy became more popular.
  C. they were accused of gambling.
  D. young audiences lost interest.

_____ **19.** The government unwittingly encouraged residents of public housing to remain poor by
  A. increasing the rent as they earned more money.
  B. evicting them as soon as they began to earn any money.
  C. requiring them to pay for maintenance.
  D. locating the housing too far from available jobs.

_____ **20.** The federal government's termination policy was intended to
  A. end poverty in the inner city by replacing slums with new high-rise buildings.
  B. bring Native Americans into mainstream society.
  C. fight juvenile delinquency.
  D. end the dependence of poor Americans on government aid.

DIRECTIONS: Essay Answer one of the following questions on a separate sheet of paper. *(20 points)*

21. What were some reasons for the rapid growth of suburbia in the 1950s?

22. Describe how the rise of television affected Hollywood, and how Hollywood responded.

The American Republic Since 1877

⭐ **Unit 6 Posttest, Form A**

Score

Global Struggles

DIRECTIONS: Matching Match each item in Column A with the items in Column B. Write the correct letters in the blanks. *(4 points each)*

Column A

_____ **1.** willingness to go to the edge of war to force the other side to back down

_____ **2.** Japanese suicide pilots

_____ **3.** postwar border between North and South Korea

_____ **4.** Nazi camp with gas chambers built to kill 2,000 people at once

_____ **5.** led the team building the atomic bomb at a secret laboratory in Los Alamos, New Mexico

_____ **6.** early computer that launched the computer revolution

_____ **7.** first successful artificial satellite

_____ **8.** tearing down slums to erect new high-rise buildings

_____ **9.** brought about the deaths of millions in his own country

_____ **10.** brilliant commander of the German "Afrika Korps"

Column B

A. Robert Oppenheimer

B. demilitarized zone

C. UNIVAC

D. Auschwitz

E. Erwin Rommel

F. urban renewal

G. Joseph Stalin

H. brinkmanship

I. *Sputnik*

J. kamikazes

DIRECTIONS: Multiple Choice Choose the item that best completes each sentence or answers each question. Write the letter in the blank. *(4 points each)*

_____ **11.** Because of the Neutrality Act of 1935, Americans could not
   A. join another country's military.   **C.** travel into war zones.
   B. sell arms to any country at war.   **D.** join the Nazi or Fascist Party.

_____ **12.** Hitler made his first grab for territory by sending troops into
   A. the Sudetenland.   **C.** Poland.
   B. Czechoslovakia.   **D.** Austria.

_____ **13.** In the Nazi-Soviet nonaggression treaty, Germany and the Soviets secretly agreed to
   A. divide Poland between them.   **C.** exterminate Europe's Jews.
   B. set up Communist governments in Asia and Nazi governments in Europe.   **D.** join together to fight France and Britain.

_____ **14.** Roosevelt used the Lend-Lease Act to
   A. assure the return of borrowed American ships.
   B. get around the requirements of the Neutrality Act.
   C. bring in revenue needed for the American military buildup.
   D. spy on German U-boat activities.

(continued)

Unit 6 Posttest, Form A

Score

_____ **15.** Victory over Hitler's racism abroad and victory over racism at home was known as
A. the Pittsburgh coup.
B. the "Double V" campaign.
C. the Tuskegee Triumph.
D. the Bracero program.

_____ **16.** The turning point in the war against Japan was the Battle of
A. Midway.   **C.** Iwo Jima.
B. the Coral Sea.   **D.** Corregidor.

_____ **17.** How did the Allies fool the Germans into believing that the Allies would land at Pas-de-Calais?
A. They sent a message that they knew the Germans would intercept.
B. They surrendered their tanks at the Battle of Kasserine Pass.
C. They removed their soldiers stationed at Normandy.
D. They placed decoys along the coast across from Calais.

_____ **18.** The Japanese resisted the American demand for unconditional surrender because
A. they wanted their emperor to stay in power.
B. they feared mass executions by the Americans.
C. they hoped to complete their atomic bomb in time to save Japan.
D. they wanted immunity for their leaders from prosecution for war crimes.

_____ **19.** The containment policy resulted from
A. the Marshall Plan.   **C.** the Yalta Conference.
B. CIA intelligence.   **D.** the Long Telegram.

_____ **20.** How did the Korean War end?
A. with a victory for South Korea   **C.** with a victory for the United Nations
B. with a victory for North Korea   **D.** with containment but no victory

DIRECTIONS: Essay Answer one of the following questions on a separate sheet of paper. *(20 points)*

21. Describe Adolf Hitler's beliefs about different races and some of his actions that probably stemmed from these beliefs.

22. Describe McCarthyism and the events that finally brought about its end.

⭐ **Unit 6 Posttest, Form B**

Global Struggles

DIRECTIONS: Matching Match each item in Column A with the items in Column B. Write the correct letters in the blanks. *(4 points each)*

Column A

_____ **1.** attempt to end poverty by building new high-rise apartments for poor residents

_____ **2.** firebombs made of jellied gasoline

_____ **3.** large numbers of tanks massed together to break through and rapidly encircle enemy positions

_____ **4.** policy of President Eisenhower

_____ **5.** enabled the miniaturization of radios and calculators

_____ **6.** alliance of Communist nations after World War II

_____ **7.** dictator of Germany

_____ **8.** overall commander of Operation Overlord

_____ **9.** group of mostly white poets, writers, and artists who criticized 1950s American culture

_____ **10.** operation designed to defeat a Soviet blockade

Column B

A. blitzkrieg

B. Dwight D. Eisenhower

C. Berlin airlift

D. Adolf Hitler

E. transistor

F. napalm

G. dynamic conservatism

H. urban renewal

I. Warsaw Pact

J. beats

DIRECTIONS: Multiple Choice Choose the item that best completes each sentence or answers each question. Write the letter in the blank. *(4 points each)*

_____ **11.** The Axis Powers were Germany, Japan, and
   A. the Soviet Union.   **C.** Italy.
   B. Austria.   **D.** Bulgaria.

_____ **12.** The British and French declared war on Germany when Hitler's forces invaded
   A. Czechoslovakia.   **C.** Poland.
   B. the Sudetenland.   **D.** Austria.

_____ **13.** Many Jewish businesses and synagogues were destroyed in a night of anti-Jewish violence called
   A. blitzkrieg.   **C.** *Kristallnacht.*
   B. *Anschluss.*   **D.** Gestapo.

_____ **14.** The United States officially entered World War II when
   A. a German U-boat sunk the American passenger liner *Lusitania.*
   B. Germany invaded America's ally, Great Britain.
   C. Japan declared war on the United States.
   D. Japan attacked Pearl Harbor.

(continued)

★ **Unit 6 Posttest, Form B**

Score

_____ **15.** The American fleet was able to ambush the Japanese at Midway because of
   A. new radar technology that helped the U.S. Navy locate the Japanese fleet.
   B. intercepted Japanese transmissions in code that American code-breakers had cracked.
   C. long-range B-25 bombers that could be launched from aircraft carriers.
   D. American submarines patrolling the area.

_____ **16.** Secretary of War Stimson declared most of the West Coast a military zone and ordered
   A. all civilians to evacuate the area.
   B. all people of Japanese ancestry to relocate to internment camps.
   C. martial law in the area.
   D. the construction of hundreds of military bases along the coast.

_____ **17.** The Germans had very little left to prevent the Allies from entering Germany after
   A. the Battle of Stalingrad.   **C.** Operation Overlord.
   B. the Battle of the Bulge.   **D.** the Battle of Leyte Gulf.

_____ **18.** At the Potsdam conference, Stalin and Truman argued over the issue of
   A. a Communist government in Germany.
   B. the division of Germany.
   C. reparations from Germany.
   D. who would control Berlin.

_____ **19.** In which case did President Eisenhower NOT use brinkmanship?
   A. the Taiwan Crisis   **C.** the Korean War
   B. the Suez Crisis   **D.** the Guatemala Crisis

_____ **20.** The Taft-Hartley Act was intended to
   A. support workers' right to join a union.
   B. curb the power of organized labor.
   C. force businesses to negotiate with unions in good faith.
   D. create jobs for unemployed workers.

DIRECTIONS: Essay Answer one of the following questions on a separate sheet of paper. *(20 points)*

21. What was the Doolittle Raid, what problems had to be solved to make it successful, and what were the results?

22. What factors contributed to the rapid growth of suburbs in the 1950s?

The American Republic Since 1877

★ **Unit 7 Pretest, Form A**

Score

A Time of Upheaval

DIRECTIONS: Matching Match each item in Column A with the items in Column B. Write the correct letters in the blanks. *(4 points each)*

Column A

_____ **1.** young person of the 1960s counterculture

_____ **2.** doctrine that allowed segregation as long as equivalent facilities were provided for African Americans

_____ **3.** Nation of Islam

_____ **4.** president who established the Peace Corps

_____ **5.** chemical that killed insects and the birds that ate them

_____ **6.** provision in the Fourteenth Amendment that ensures that all people are treated the same by the court system

_____ **7.** militant African American group

_____ **8.** president who declared a war on poverty

_____ **9.** guerrilla army organized by Ho Chi Minh

_____ **10.** program of the Great Society

Column B

A. Black Panthers

B. Vietcong

C. due process

D. Medicare

E. Lyndon Johnson

F. separate-but-equal

G. Black Muslims

H. hippie

I. John F. Kennedy

J. DDT

DIRECTIONS: Multiple Choice Choose the item that best completes each sentence or answers each question. Write the letter in the blank. *(4 points each)*

_____ **11.** President Kennedy's goal in the space race with the Soviet Union was for the United States to be the first to

   A. put a man into space.   **C.** put a space station into orbit.

   B. put a man into orbit.   **D.** land a man on the moon.

_____ **12.** The purpose of the Bay of Pigs invasion was to

   A. support Fidel Castro's rebels, who were trying to overthrow a corrupt government.

   B. spark an uprising against Fidel Castro in Cuba.

   C. force the Soviets to remove their missiles from Cuba.

   D. take over Cuba and make it an American protectorate.

_____ **13.** Rosa Parks was arrested for

   A. trying to register to vote.

   B. drinking from a whites-only water fountain.

   C. refusing to give her bus seat to a white man.

   D. trying to register to enter an all-white school.

_____ **14.** Civil rights activists tried to integrate restaurants by using

   A. protest marches.   **C.** sit-ins.

   B. boycotts.   **D.** threats.

(continued)

Unit 7 Pretest, Form A

Score

_____ 15. The Freedom Riders intended to draw attention to
  A. discrimination against African Americans trying to register to vote.
  B. the South's refusal to integrate schools.
  C. violence against African Americans in the South.
  D. the South's refusal to integrate bus terminals.

_____ 16. President Johnson did not order a full-scale invasion of North Vietnam for fear that it might
  A. bring China into the war.   **C.** cost too many American lives.
  B. bring the Soviet Union into the war.   **D.** improve North Vietnamese morale.

_____ 17. Televised news coverage of the Vietnam War each night
  A. raised Johnson's approval ratings.
  B. united Americans behind the war effort.
  C. made Americans start to doubt government reports about the war.
  D. helped Americans understand why the war was taking so long.

_____ 18. Which of the following is true about the Great Society?
  A. It touched few aspects of American life.
  B. There were unlimited funds given to these programs.
  C. Programs grew quickly and were difficult to evaluate.
  D. No one questioned the intrusiveness of the programs.

_____ 19. Affirmative action required organizations to
  A. meet quotas in hiring African Americans.
  B. meet quotas in hiring African Americans and women.
  C. actively recruit African American employees.
  D. hire the best-qualified candidates, regardless of race, religion, or national origin.

_____ 20. What was true of President Eisenhower and civil rights?
  A. He ordered troops to protect school children.
  B. He wanted to roll back segregation through the courts.
  C. He agreed with Governor Faubus's tactics.
  D. He vetoed a civil rights act because it was too weak.

DIRECTIONS: Essay Answer one of the following questions on a separate sheet of paper. *(20 points)*

21. Who was Dr. Martin Luther King, Jr., and what approach did he take to ending segregation and racism?

22. What do you think the Vietnam War was like for American troops? What methods did the two sides use to fight? How did the terrain affect the fighting?

★ Unit 7 Pretest, Form B

Score

A Time of Upheaval

DIRECTIONS: Matching Match each item in Column A with the items in Column B. Write the correct letters in the blanks. *(4 points each)*

Column A

_____ **1.** shifted political power to urban areas

_____ **2.** Chief Justice during the Kennedy administration

_____ **3.** Kennedy's policy against Communist movements

_____ **4.** brilliant African American attorney

_____ **5.** leader of nonviolent civil rights movement

_____ **6.** site of first daring sit-in

_____ **7.** shared living arrangements among members of the counterculture

_____ **8.** money paid in order to vote

_____ **9.** chemical used to destroy the enemy's ability to hide in Vietnam's thick jungle

_____ **10.** speech given by Dr. Martin Luther King, Jr.

Column B

A. Earl Warren

B. communes

C. "I Have a Dream"

D. Thurgood Marshall

E. *Reynolds* v. *Sims*

F. Dr. Martin Luther King, Jr.

G. Agent Orange

H. "flexible response"

I. poll tax

J. Woolworth's

DIRECTIONS: Multiple Choice Choose the item that best completes each sentence or answers each question. Write the letter in the blank. *(4 points each)*

_____ **11.** Which of the following is true about John F. Kennedy's administration?
  A. The New Frontier won easy passage. **C.** Tax cuts were used.
  B. Women's rights were advanced. **D.** Deficit spending was outlawed.

_____ **12.** Which of the following was a major Great Society program?
  A. a breakfast program for the elderly **C.** Medicaid for the elderly
  B. a milk program for the elderly **D.** Medicare for the elderly

_____ **13.** Which event helped to advance the civil rights movement?
  A. the Southern Manifesto **C.** a Senate filibuster
  B. *Green* v. *Board of Education* **D.** a boycott of Montgomery buses

_____ **14.** The Black Power movement did NOT include
  A. Olympic athletes. **C.** Ralph Abernathy.
  B. the Black Panthers. **D.** Malcolm X.

(continued)

★ Unit 7 Pretest, Form B

_____ **15.** The war in Vietnam included all of the following EXCEPT
  A. the dropping of nuclear bombs.
  B. the use of jellied gasoline.
  C. the use of Agent Orange.
  D. weapons from China and the Soviet Union.

_____ **16.** Which of the following did NOT occur during 1968?
  A. the Tet offensive against American troops
  B. Nixon's announcement of his plan to end the war
  C. Johnson's decision not to run again for president
  D. a decrease in American bombing to help Hubert Humphrey's campaign

_____ **17.** A leading figure in the women's movement and editor of *Ms.* magazine was
  A. Betty Friedan.
  B. Dolores Huerta.
  C. Gloria Steinem.
  D. Phyllis Schlafly.

_____ **18.** Which of the following was NOT connected to the counterculture of the 1960s?
  A. religious movements such as the Hare Krishna
  B. changes in fashion, music, and dance
  C. rebellious yuppies
  D. the pop art of Warhol and Lichtenstein

_____ **19.** Rachel Carson's book *Silent Spring* warned that one day few birds would be left to usher in the spring because of
  A. over-hunting.
  B. habitat destruction.
  C. air pollution.
  D. pesticides.

_____ **20.** In the 1970s, the high occurrence of health problems among residents of Love Canal resulted because
  A. local factories were releasing harmful gases into the air.
  B. local factories were dumping toxic waste into the canal.
  C. pesticides sprayed on nearby farmlands were leaking into the canal.
  D. contents of an old toxic waste dump under the community was leaking into the ground.

DIRECTIONS: Essay Answer one of the following questions on a separate sheet of paper. *(20 points)*

21. If you had been an activist during the civil rights movement, which group might you have joined, and why?

22. What was the Berlin Wall, what purpose did it serve, and what did it come to symbolize?

★ **Chapter 23**

Section Quiz 23-1

DIRECTIONS: Matching Match each item in Column A with the items in Column B.
Write the correct letters in the blanks. *(10 points each)*

Column A

_____ **1.** the way in which states draw up political districts based on changes in population

_____ **2.** President Kennedy's legislative agenda

_____ **3.** nominated to become the Chief Justice of the United States in 1953

_____ **4.** suspicion that the United States lagged behind the Soviets in weaponry

_____ **5.** ensures that all people are treated the same by the court system

Column B

A. Earl Warren

B. due process

C. New Frontier

D. missile gap

E. reapportionment

DIRECTIONS: Multiple Choice In the blank at the left, write the letter of the choice that best completes the statement or answers the question. *(10 points each)*

_____ **6.** Compared to earlier campaigns, the 1960 presidential race made new use of
   A. the courts.
   B. newspapers.
   C. radio.
   D. television.

_____ **7.** The Supreme Court's decision in *Reynolds* v. *Sims* shifted political power throughout the country to
   A. urban areas.
   B. rural areas.
   C. the suburbs.
   D. the South.

_____ **8.** In an effort to increase growth and create more jobs, Kennedy advocated the New Deal strategy of
   A. conservative spending.
   B. deficit spending.
   C. reapportionment.
   D. balancing the budget.

_____ **9.** In *Gideon* v. *Wainwright*, the Supreme Court ruled that a defendant in a state court had the right to
   A. a telephone call.
   B. remain silent.
   C. a lawyer.
   D. a speedy trial.

_____ **10.** Republicans as well as Southern Democrats viewed the New Frontier as
   A. too conservative.
   B. too big and too costly.
   C. elitist policies.
   D. sound economic policies.

Chapter 23

Section Quiz 23-2

DIRECTIONS: Matching Match each item in Column A with the items in Column B. Write the correct letters in the blanks. *(10 points each)*

Column A

_____ **1.** banned the testing of nuclear weapons in the atmosphere

_____ **2.** astronaut who stepped onto the moon

_____ **3.** national commission to investigate the assassination of President Kennedy

_____ **4.** program aimed at helping less developed nations fight poverty

_____ **5.** Cuban exiles who were secretly trained and armed by the CIA

Column B

A. La Brigada

B. Warren Commission

C. Peace Corps

D. test ban treaty

E. Neil Armstrong

DIRECTIONS: Multiple Choice In the blank at the left, write the letter of the choice that best completes the statement or answers the question. *(10 points each)*

_____ **6.** On April 17, 1961, armed Cuban exiles landed on the south coast of Cuba at
   A. New Delhi.
   B. Santiago de Cuba.
   C. the Bay of Pigs.
   D. Havanna.

_____ **7.** The man accused of killing President Kennedy appeared to be a confused and embittered Marxist named
   A. Fidel Castro.
   B. Jack Ruby.
   C. Earl Warren.
   D. Lee Harvey Oswald.

_____ **8.** On October 22, 1962, President Kennedy announced that American spy planes had taken aerial photographs showing that the Soviet Union had placed long-range missiles in
   A. Cuba.
   B. Germany.
   C. the Bahamas.
   D. Central America.

_____ **9.** President Kennedy pushed for a buildup of conventional troops and weapons that would allow the United States to fight with
   A. a flexible response.
   B. nuclear threats.
   C. nuclear weapons.
   D. a rigid response.

_____ **10.** To improve relations between the United States and Latin America, President Kennedy proposed a series of cooperative aid projects with Latin American governments called
   A. La Brigada.
   B. Alliance for Progress.
   C. the Peace Corps.
   D. the Bay of Pigs.

The American Republic Since 1877

⭐ **Chapter 23**

Section Quiz 23-3

DIRECTIONS: Matching Match each item in Column A with the items in Column B.
Write the correct letters in the blanks. *(10 points each)*

Column A

_____ **1.** qualifies certain categories of Americans to benefits

_____ **2.** project directed at disadvantaged preschool children

_____ **3.** general agreement

_____ **4.** put young people with high ideals to work in poor school districts

_____ **5.** Johnson's Republican opponent in the 1964 presidential election

Column B

A. entitlements

B. VISTA

C. Barry Goldwater

D. Head Start

E. consensus

DIRECTIONS: Multiple Choice In the blank at the left, write the letter of the choice
that best completes the statement or answers the question. *(10 points each)*

_____ **6.** Who was the first African American to serve in the cabinet as the secretary of the Department of Housing and Urban Development?
   A. Rosa Parks
   B. Marion Barry
   C. Robert Weaver
   D. Jesse Jackson

_____ **7.** What was President Johnson's vision of the more perfect and equitable society the United States could and should become called?
   A. Fair Deal
   B. New Deal
   C. New Age
   D. Great Society

_____ **8.** What did the Immigration Reform Act of 1965 eliminate that played a key role in changing the composition of the American population?
   A. all European immigration
   B. the "national origins" system
   C. Asian immigration
   D. Mexican immigration

_____ **9.** Before the end of 1964, Johnson won passage of a tax cut, a major civil rights bill, and a significant
   A. anti-poverty program.
   B. reforestation program.
   C. cut in welfare.
   D. highway system.

_____ **10.** At Johnson's urging, what did Congress set up in 1964 to create jobs and fight poverty?
   A. Medicare
   B. Department of Housing and Urban Development
   C. Office of Economic Opportunity
   D. Project Head Start

The American Republic Since 1877

★ Chapter 23 Test, Form A

The New Frontier and the Great Society

DIRECTIONS: Matching Match the Great Society programs in the diagram to the descriptions of them in Column A. Write the letters from the diagram in the blanks provided. *(4 points each)*

Building a Great Society

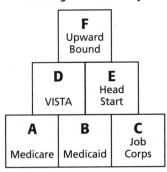

Column A

_____ **1.** government-sponsored health care for people living below the poverty line

_____ **2.** preschool program for the disadvantaged

_____ **3.** government-funded health insurance for the elderly

_____ **4.** put young people to work in poor neighborhoods

_____ **5.** provided college preparation for low-income teenagers

_____ **6.** helped young unemployed people find jobs

DIRECTIONS: Matching Match each item in Column A with the items in Column B. Write the correct letters in the blanks. *(4 points each)*

Column A

_____ **7.** first African American to serve in a cabinet

_____ **8.** director of the Women's Bureau of the Department of Labor in the Kennedy Administration

_____ **9.** Chief Justice of the Supreme Court

_____ **10.** first astronaut to step on the moon

Column B

A. Robert Weaver

B. Earl Warren

C. Esther Peterson

D. Neil Armstrong

DIRECTIONS: Multiple Choice Choose the item that best completes each sentence or answers each question. Write the letter in the blank. *(4 points each)*

_____ **11.** In the 1960 presidential campaign, television was used for the first time to
    A. report election results.
    B. broadcast candidates' speeches.
    C. advertise candidates.
    D. poll voters.

_____ **12.** The outcome of the 1960 presidential election was strongly influenced by
    A. Nixon's "Checkers speech."
    B. the televised debates.
    C. Kennedy's stand on communism.
    D. reapportionment.

_____ **13.** Kennedy's legislative agenda was called the
    A. Great Society.
    B. New Frontier.
    C. Fair Deal.
    D. Square Deal.

(continued)

Chapter 23 Test, Form A

Score

_____ **14.** Kennedy convinced Congress to invest more funds in
   A. defense and space exploration.   **C.** urban affairs.
   B. health insurance for the elderly.   **D.** education.

_____ **15.** In response to the recommendations of the Presidential Commission on the Status of Women, President Kennedy
   A. appointed a woman to his cabinet.
   B. ordered an end to gender discrimination in the federal civil service.
   C. established Mother's Day as a national holiday.
   D. established a minimum wage for women in the workplace.

_____ **16.** The decision in the case of *Reynolds* v. *Sims* was important because it shifted political power
   A. from the North to the South and West.   **C.** from rural areas to urban areas.
   B. from urban areas to rural areas.   **D.** from urban areas to suburban areas.

_____ **17.** Kennedy's "flexible response" plan called for
   A. a buildup of nuclear weapons.   **C.** establishing military bases around the world.
   B. a buildup of conventional weapons.   **D.** building alliances around the world.

_____ **18.** During the space race, Kennedy's goal for the nation was to be the first to
   A. put a man into space.   **C.** land a man on the moon.
   B. put a man into orbit.   **D.** build a space station.

_____ **19.** The purpose of the Warren Commission was to
   A. find out who was at fault for the disastrous invasion of Cuba.
   B. make recommendations for ending gender discrimination in employment.
   C. make recommendations for ending racial discrimination in employment.
   D. find out if more than one person was involved in the Kennedy assassination.

_____ **20.** Johnson's goals for a better America were supported by
   A. the hardships caused by the slumping economy.
   B. the prosperity resulting from the strong economy.
   C. the success of unions in organizing workers.
   D. the failure of business to create enough jobs.

DIRECTIONS: Essay Answer one of the following questions on a separate sheet of paper. *(20 points)*

21. Compare presidential candidates Kennedy and Nixon.

22. Describe the nature of United States involvement in Latin America before Kennedy took office, and the response of Latin Americans to this involvement.

⭐ **Chapter 23 Test, Form B**

Score

The New Frontier and the Great Society

DIRECTIONS: Matching Match each item in Column A with the items in Column B.
Write the correct letters in the blanks. *(4 points each)*

Column A

_____ **1.** accused has the right to an attorney during police
questioning

_____ **2.** desegregation of public accommodations established in the
Civil Rights Act of 1964 is legal

_____ **3.** congressional reapportionment must follow idea of "one
person, one vote"

_____ **4.** unlawfully seized evidence is inadmissible at trial

_____ **5.** state-mandated Bible reading in school banned

_____ **6.** prohibiting the sale and use of birth control devices
violated citizens' constitutional right to privacy

_____ **7.** celebrities may only sue the media for libel in certain
circumstances

_____ **8.** state-mandated prayer in school banned

_____ **9.** government may not ban interracial marriage

_____ **10.** felony suspects are entitled to court-appointed attorney if
unable to afford one on their own

Column B

A. *Mapp* v. *Ohio*

B. *Loving* v. *Virginia*

C. *Engel* v. *Vitale*

D. *Griswold* v.
Connecticut

E. *New York Times*
v. *Sullivan*

F. *Escobedo* v. *Illinois*

G. *Abington School
District* v. *Schempp*

H. *Gideon* v.
Wainwright

I. *Reynolds* v. *Sims*

J. *Heart of Atlanta
Motel* v. *United
States*

DIRECTIONS: Multiple Choice Choose the item that best completes each sentence
or answers each question. Write the letter in the blank. *(4 points each)*

_____ **11.** To soothe religious concerns during the campaign, Kennedy spoke in
support of
A. school prayer.
B. individual choice over prayer in
school.
C. teaching creationism in school.
D. separation of church and state.

_____ **12.** Kennedy was unable to pass many of his domestic programs because
A. the Republicans held a large majority in the Senate.
B. the Republicans held a large majority in the House of Representatives.
C. Republicans controlled the most influential committees in Congress.
D. many Democrats in Congress did not feel that he helped them win their seats.

_____ **13.** In an effort to increase growth and create more jobs, Kennedy advocated
A. deficit spending.
B. public works programs.
C. price controls.
D. raising taxes for the wealthiest
Americans.

(continued)

⭐ **Chapter 23 Test, Form B**

_____ **14.** To get the economy moving, Kennedy adopted the supply-side idea of
    A. reducing taxes.
    C. lowering interest rates.
    B. increasing taxes.
    D. raising interest rates.

_____ **15.** The principle of "one man, one vote" meant that
    A. all citizens of voting age should be allowed to register to vote.
    B. all citizens' votes should have equal weight.
    C. discriminatory voting practices should end.
    D. the House of Representatives should have voting power equal to senators.

_____ **16.** Reapportionment required by the Warren Court boosted the political power of
    A. poor rural farmers.
    C. African Americans.
    B. Southern conservatives.
    D. big business.

_____ **17.** The Fourteenth Amendment requires
    A. trial by jury.
    C. habeas corpus.
    B. due process.
    D. that all defendants have a lawyer.

_____ **18.** The Alliance for Progress was a
    A. series of programs to improve life in American inner cities.
    B. job program that sent young people to work in poor American school districts.
    C. series of cooperative aid projects with Latin American governments.
    D. free-trade agreement between the United States and Latin American countries.

_____ **19.** Which of the following choices best completes the diagram about the agreement ending the Cuban missile crisis?

Agreement Ending the Cuban Missile Crisis

| Kennedy promised *publicly* not to invade Cuba. | Kennedy promised *privately* to: ? | Khrushchev promised to remove Soviet missiles from Cuba. |

    A. remove missiles from Florida.
    C. remove missiles from China.
    B. remove missiles from Alaska.
    D. remove missiles from Turkey.

_____ **20.** The Office of Economic Opportunity was a major part of Johnson's
    A. health care reform program.
    C. war on poverty.
    B. education reform program.
    D. consumer protection program.

DIRECTIONS: Essay Answer one of the following questions on a separate sheet of paper. *(20 points)*

21. What was the "Kennedy mystique"?

22. Describe Lyndon Johnson's leadership style.

Chapter 24

Section Quiz 24-1

DIRECTIONS: Matching Match each item in Column A with the items in Column B.
Write the correct letters in the blanks. *(10 points each)*

Column A

_____ **1.** governor who ordered troops from the Arkansas National Guard to prevent African American students from entering school

_____ **2.** set out to eliminate segregation from American society and to encourage African Americans to register to vote

_____ **3.** segregation by custom and tradition

_____ **4.** challenged segregation in court and launched the modern civil rights movement

_____ **5.** African American attorney who was the NAACP's chief counsel

Column B

A. Thurgood Marshall

B. Southern Christian Leadership Conference

C. Orval Faubus

D. Rosa Parks

E. de facto segregation

DIRECTIONS: Multiple Choice In the blank at the left, write the letter of the choice that best completes the statement or answers the question. *(10 points each)*

_____ **6.** The dramatic ruling in *Brown* v. *Board of Education* threatened
     A. segregation.   **C.** racial equality.
     B. education.   **D.** civil rights.

_____ **7.** The *Plessy* v. *Ferguson* ruling of 1896 established that laws segregating African Americans were permitted in the so-called
     A. de facto segregation ruling.   **C.** separate-but-equal doctrine.
     B. Southern Manifesto.   **D.** constitutional segregation doctrine.

_____ **8.** After the *Brown* v. *Board of Education* decision, many states adopted an elaborate set of requirements other than race that schools could use to prevent African Americans from attending white schools called
     A. "prompt and reasonable start laws."   **C.** "Jim Crow" laws.
     B. pupil assignment laws.   **D.** separate-but-equal laws.

_____ **9.** Outraged by Rosa Parks's arrest, Jo Ann Robinson, head of a local organization called the Women's Political Council, called on African Americans to
     A. stage a sit-in at the courthouse.   **C.** go on strike.
     B. boycott Montgomery's buses.   **D.** elect new city officials.

_____ **10.** Dr. Martin Luther King, Jr., believed that the only moral way to end segregation and racism was through
     A. violence and riots.   **C.** education.
     B. the political system.   **D.** nonviolent passive resistance.

Score

Section Quiz 24-2

DIRECTIONS: Matching Match each item in Column A with the items in Column B. Write the correct letters in the blanks. *(10 points each)*

Column A

_____ **1.** when a small group of senators take turns speaking and refuse to stop the debate and allow a bill to come to vote

_____ **2.** teams of African Americans and white Americans who traveled into the South to draw attention to the South's refusal to integrate bus terminals

_____ **3.** African American air force veteran who applied for a transfer to the University of Mississippi

_____ **4.** former sharecropper and Student Nonviolent Coordinating Committee organizer

_____ **5.** a march from Selma to Montgomery, Alabama, organized by Dr. King and the SNCC

Column B

A. Fannie Lou Hamer

B. filibuster

C. "march for freedom"

D. James Meredith

E. Freedom Riders

DIRECTIONS: Multiple Choice In the blank at the left, write the letter of the choice that best completes the statement or answers the question. *(10 points each)*

_____ **6.** The first chairperson of the Student Nonviolent Coordinating Committee (SNCC) was
   A. Jesse Jackson.
   B. Dr. Martin Luther King, Jr.
   C. Ella Baker.
   D. Marion Barry.

_____ **7.** What did President Johnson sign into law on July 2, 1964?
   A. Voting Rights Act of 1964
   B. Civil Rights Act of 1964
   C. Cloture Act of 1964
   D. Interstate Travel Act of 1964

_____ **8.** President Kennedy eventually ordered the Interstate Commerce Commission to tighten its regulations against
   A. freedom marches.
   B. sit-ins.
   C. segregated bus terminals.
   D. Freedom Riders.

_____ **9.** The brutal attack by law enforcement officers against peaceful demonstrators in Selma, Alabama, became known as
   A. Bloody Sunday.
   B. the Selma Massacre.
   C. the Televised Beatings.
   D. Sad Saturday.

_____ **10.** The passage of what law marked a turning point in the civil rights movement?
   A. Civil Rights Act of 1964
   B. Segregation Act of 1965
   C. Voting Rights Act of 1965
   D. Discrimination Act of 1964

Chapter 24

Score

Section Quiz 24-3

DIRECTIONS: Matching Match each item in Column A with the items in Column B. Write the correct letters in the blanks. *(10 points each)*

Column A

_____ **1.** to most African Americans, this term meant they should control the social, political, and economic direction of their struggle for equality

_____ **2.** prejudice toward someone because of his or her race

_____ **3.** the philosophy of incorporating different racial or cultural groups into the dominant society

_____ **4.** an African American neighborhood in Los Angeles where a race riot broke out

_____ **5.** trusted assistant to Dr. King who led the Poor People's Campaign in King's absence

Column B

A. black power

B. Reverend Ralph Abernathy

C. Watts

D. racism

E. cultural assimilation

DIRECTIONS: Multiple Choice In the blank at the left, write the letter of the choice that best completes the statement or answers the question. *(10 points each)*

_____ **6.** The goals of the civil rights movement until 1965—ending segregation and restoring the voting rights of African Americans—could be achieved through new laws and
　　A. court decisions.　　　　　　**C.** changing attitudes.
　　B. abolishing racism.　　　　　**D.** changing values.

_____ **7.** Who had become a symbol of the black power movement that was sweeping the nation by the early 1960s?
　　A. Reverend Ralph Abernathy　　**C.** Malcolm X
　　B. Stokely Carmichael　　　　　**D.** Eldridge Cleaver

_____ **8.** In support of a strike by African American sanitation workers, Dr. King went to Memphis, Tennessee, where on April 4, 1968, he was
　　A. awarded the Nobel Peace Prize.　**C.** arrested.
　　B. assassinated.　　　　　　　　**D.** beaten by union members.

_____ **9.** What group urged African Americans to arm themselves and confront white society in order to force whites to grant them equal rights?
　　A. Black Panthers　　　　　　　**C.** Black Muslims
　　B. Black Power　　　　　　　　**D.** SNCC

_____ **10.** Despite their name, the Black Muslims do not hold the same beliefs as mainstream Muslims, but preach
　　A. nonviolence.　　　　　　　　**C.** cultural assimilation.
　　B. black nationalism.　　　　　　**D.** integration.

Chapter 24 Test, Form A

The Civil Rights Movement

DIRECTIONS: Matching Match the court cases in the diagram with their rulings in Column A. Write the letters from the diagram in the blanks provided. *(4 points each)*

Column A

_____ **1.** state law schools had to admit qualified African American applicants even if parallel black law schools existed

_____ **2.** segregation in public schools was unconstitutional

_____ **3.** exclusion of African Americans from juries violated their right to equal protection under the law

_____ **4.** segregation on interstate buses was unconstitutional

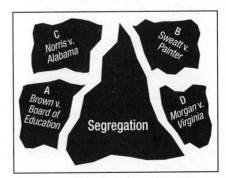

DIRECTIONS: Matching Match each item in Column A with the items in Column B. Write the correct letters in the blanks. *(4 points each)*

Column A

_____ **5.** assassination of Dr. Martin Luther King, Jr.

_____ **6.** "march for freedom" in which state troopers and deputized citizens brutally attacked marchers in full view of television

_____ **7.** violence against demonstrators, viewed by millions on television, that prompted Kennedy to prepare a new civil rights bill

_____ **8.** first time since the Civil War that a state's armed forces were used to oppose the authority of the federal government

_____ **9.** sit-in at Woolworth's that sparked a new mass movement for civil rights

_____ **10.** successful bus boycott

Column B

A. Memphis, Tennessee

B. Montgomery, Alabama

C. Selma, Alabama

D. Greensboro, North Carolina

E. Birmingham, Alabama

F. Little Rock, Arkansas

DIRECTIONS: Multiple Choice Choose the item that best completes each sentence or answers each question. Write the letter in the blank. *(4 points each)*

_____ **11.** In response to the arrest of Rosa Parks, African Americans
  A. organized restaurant sit-ins.
  B. organized a bus boycott.
  C. formed the first Black Panther group.
  D. started riots.

_____ **12.** CORE successfully integrated many restaurants by using
  A. protest marches.
  B. boycotts.
  C. sit-ins.
  D. threats.

(continued)

The American Republic Since 1877

★ Chapter 24 Test, Form A

_____ **13.** The Southern Manifesto encouraged
  A. white Southerners to defy Court rulings.
  B. African Americans to register to vote.
  C. segregation.
  D. students to march for civil rights.

_____ **14.** Dr. Martin Luther King, Jr., drew on the philosophy and techniques of
  A. Abraham Lincoln.
  B. Frederick Douglass.
  C. Thurgood Marshall.
  D. Mohandas Gandhi.

_____ **15.** In Little Rock, Arkansas, the governor tried to prevent African American students from entering a white high school by
  A. closing the school.
  B. redrawing the school district.
  C. hiring the Ku Klux Klan.
  D. deploying the National Guard.

_____ **16.** The organization founded by student civil rights activists was
  A. SNCC.
  B. CORE.
  C. NAACP.
  D. SCLC.

_____ **17.** At first President Kennedy acted slowly on civil rights because
  A. he was not sure such laws were really needed.
  B. he needed support from many Southern senators to get other programs passed.
  C. he believed that civil rights had to evolve gradually, as people's values changed.
  D. he did not want to provoke violence in the South.

_____ **18.** At the march on Washington, Dr. Martin Luther King, Jr.,
  A. was assassinated.
  B. was arrested.
  C. gave his "I have a dream" speech.
  D. organized the SCLC.

_____ **19.** Dr. King selected Selma, Alabama, for a protest march because
  A. African Americans were the majority, but only a fraction had jobs.
  B. African Americans were the majority, but only a fraction were registered to vote.
  C. violence against Freedom Riders in Selma had been well-documented.
  D. opposition to school desegregation was particularly intense in Selma.

_____ **20.** The Kerner Commission blamed the majority of the inner-city problems on
  A. white society and white racism.
  B. lack of job skills.
  C. the nonviolence of African Americans.
  D. militant African Americans.

DIRECTIONS: Essay Answer one of the following questions on a separate sheet of paper. *(20 points)*

21. Describe the ideas Dr. King expressed in his "Letter from a Birmingham Jail."

22. Describe three meanings that the term "black power" held for African Americans.

★ **Chapter 24 Test, Form B**

Score

The Civil Rights Movement

DIRECTIONS: Matching Match each item in Column A with the items in Column B. Write the correct letters in the blanks. *(4 points each)*

Column A

_____ **1.** leader of SNCC who believed in black power

_____ **2.** student who was barred from the neighborhood school

_____ **3.** one of the organizers of the Black Panthers, who wrote *Soul on Ice*, articulating many of the organization's objectives

_____ **4.** symbol of the black power movement

_____ **5.** minister whose vision and nonviolent methods helped the civil rights movement transform American society

_____ **6.** helped organize the Mississippi Freedom Democratic Party

_____ **7.** one of the founders of the Congress of Racial Equality

_____ **8.** first African American student to attend the University of Mississippi

_____ **9.** NAACP's chief counsel

_____ **10.** SNCC's first chairperson, who later served as the mayor of Washington, D.C.

Column B

A. Dr. Martin Luther King, Jr.

B. Fannie Lou Hamer

C. Thurgood Marshall

D. James Farmer

E. Malcolm X

F. Eldridge Cleaver

G. Stokely Carmichael

H. James Meredith

I. Linda Brown

J. Marion Barry

DIRECTIONS: Multiple Choice Choose the item that best completes each sentence or answers each question. Write the letter in the blank. *(4 points each)*

_____ **11.** The ruling in *Plessy* v. *Ferguson* in 1896 had established
   A. the right of African Americans to vote.
   B. the right of all Americans to peaceful protest.
   C. the separate-but-equal doctrine.
   D. the right of all Americans to equal protection under the law.

_____ **12.** Dr. Martin Luther King, Jr., believed the way to end segregation was through
   A. economic self-improvement.   **C.** separation from white society.
   B. riots and vandalism.   **D.** nonviolent passive resistance.

_____ **13.** When first established, the Southern Christian Leadership Conference set out to
   A. end segregation and encourage African Americans to register to vote.
   B. end lynching and segregation.
   C. promote education for African Americans and encourage them to register to vote.
   D. end segregation and promote education for African Americans.

(continued)

⭐ **Chapter 24 Test, Form B**

_____ **14.** The Civil Rights Act of 1957, the first since Reconstruction, was intended to
   A. protect African Americans' voting rights.
   B. end lynching.
   C. end segregation.
   D. end discrimination in hiring.

_____ **15.** SNCC's Voter Education Project focused on
   A. rural areas of the North.
   B. rural areas of the Deep South.
   C. urban slums of the North.
   D. urban slums of the Deep South.

_____ **16.** The Freedom Riders were organized to draw attention to the South's refusal to
   A. promote voter registration.
   B. end school segregation.
   C. stop violence against voters.
   D. integrate bus terminals.

_____ **17.** Robert Kennedy tried to help African Americans register to vote by
   A. sending U.S. Marshals to the South.
   B. directing the news media to cover the marches in the South.
   C. having the Justice Department file lawsuits throughout the South.
   D. proposing a voting rights bill in Congress.

_____ **18.** The Civil Rights Act of 1964 did little to
   A. guarantee the right to vote.
   B. end segregation in public places.
   C. end discrimination in employment.
   D. end school segregation.

_____ **19.** Until 1965, the civil rights movement focused on
   A. changing attitudes rather than creating jobs.
   B. violent protest rather than peaceful confrontation.
   C. economic rather than social problems.
   D. segregation and voting rights rather than economic and social problems.

_____ **20.** After his pilgrimage to Makkah, Malcolm X concluded that
   A. an integrated society was possible.
   B. integration was not possible.
   C. black power meant self-sufficiency.
   D. assimilation was key to success.

DIRECTIONS: Essay Answer one of the following questions on a separate sheet of paper. *(20 points)*

21. The diagram shows two factors that contributed to the new political power for African Americans. Describe how these two events resulted in this new power.

22. Describe the provisions of the Civil Rights Act of 1964.

★ **Chapter 25**

Section Quiz 25-1

DIRECTIONS: Matching Match each item in Column A with the items in Column B.
Write the correct letters in the blanks. *(10 points each)*

Column A

_____ **1.** nationalist leader in the South after the Geneva Accords

_____ **2.** nationalist group organized by Ho Chi Minh

_____ **3.** belief that if Vietnam fell to communism, so too would the other nations of Southeast Asia

_____ **4.** founder of the Indochinese Communist Party

_____ **5.** Vietnam, Laos, and Cambodia when under French rule

Column B

A. Ho Chi Minh

B. Ngo Dinh Diem

C. domino theory

D. French Indochina

E. Vietminh

DIRECTIONS: Multiple Choice In the blank at the left, write the letter of the choice
that best completes the statement or answers the question. *(10 points each)*

_____ **6.** What troops returned to Vietnam in 1946 and drove the Vietminh's forces into hiding in the countryside?
   A. Japanese
   B. French
   C. Chinese
   D. American

_____ **7.** In 1941 the Vietminh united both Communists and non-Communists in the struggle to expel the
   A. French.
   B. Chinese.
   C. Japanese forces.
   D. United States advisers.

_____ **8.** On May 7, 1954, where did a French force fall to the Vietminh?
   A. Saigon
   B. Cambodia
   C. Geneva
   D. Dien Bien Phu

_____ **9.** Who was in control of North Vietnam after the Geneva Accords temporarily divided the country?
   A. Ho Chi Minh and the Vietminh
   B. Ngo Dinh Diem and a pro-Western regime
   C. the Japanese
   D. the United States

_____ **10.** American officials did not think France should control Vietnam, but they did not want Vietnam to be
   A. Communist.
   B. part of Indochina.
   C. Socialist.
   D. part of China.

Chapter 25

Section Quiz 25-2

DIRECTIONS: Matching Match each item in Column A with the items in Column B. Write the correct letters in the blanks. *(10 points each)*

Column A

_____ **1.** special fortified villages created by the South Vietnamese

_____ **2.** chemical that strips leaves from trees and shrubs, turning farmland and forests into wasteland

_____ **3.** network of jungle paths through Cambodia and Laos that bypassed the border between North and South Vietnam

_____ **4.** sustained bombing campaign against North Vietnam by the United States

_____ **5.** a guerrilla army organized by Ho Chi Minh to reunify the nation

Column B

A. Operation Rolling Thunder

B. Vietcong

C. Ho Chi Minh trail

D. Agent Orange

E. strategic hamlets

DIRECTIONS: Multiple Choice In the blank at the left, write the letter of the choice that best completes the statement or answers the question. *(10 points each)*

_____ **6.** To counter the enemy's tactics, American troops went on missions called

    A. "hit-and-run."   **C.** Agent Orange.

    B. "search and destroy."   **D.** counter-guerrilla missions.

_____ **7.** Diem made himself even more unpopular by discriminating against one of the country's most widely practiced religions,

    A. Catholicism.   **C.** Buddhism.

    B. Judaism.   **D.** Hinduism.

_____ **8.** On August 7, 1964, Congress, in effect, handed its war powers over to the president when it passed the

    A. Domino Theory Resolution.   **C.** Geneva Accords.

    B. Vietnam Resolution.   **D.** Gulf of Tonkin Resolution.

_____ **9.** North Vietnam received military weapons and other support from the Soviet Union and

    A. China.   **C.** Italy.

    B. Japan.   **D.** East Germany.

_____ **10.** American aircraft struck North Vietnam less than 14 hours after a Vietcong attack on a base at

    A. a strategic hamlet.   **C.** Pleiku.

    B. My Lai.   **D.** the Gulf of Tonkin.

⭐ **Chapter 25**

Section Quiz 25-3

DIRECTIONS: Matching Match each item in Column A with the items in Column B. Write the correct letters in the blanks. *(10 points each)*

Column A

_____ **1.** those who wanted the United States to withdraw from Vietnam

_____ **2.** a left-wing student organization

_____ **3.** those who insisted the United States stay and fight in Vietnam

_____ **4.** surprise attack launched during the Vietnamese New Year by the Vietcong and North Vietnamese

_____ **5.** reported that the Vietnamese enemy was on the brink of defeat

Column B

A. Students for a Democratic Society

B. hawks

C. General William Westmoreland

D. doves

E. Tet offensive

DIRECTIONS: Multiple Choice In the blank at the left, write the letter of the choice that best completes the statement or answers the question. *(10 points each)*

_____ **6.** Young protesters especially focused on what they saw as an unfair
    A. draft system.   **C.** teach-in.
    B. credibility gap.   **D.** division of Vietnam.

_____ **7.** The year 1968 saw a shocking political announcement, a pair of traumatic assassinations, and finally, a violent political convention in
    A. New York.   **C.** Chicago.
    B. Miami.   **D.** San Francisco.

_____ **8.** The violence and chaos associated with the Democratic Party benefited the 1968 Republican presidential candidate,
    A. Hubert Humphrey.   **C.** George Wallace.
    B. Richard Nixon.   **D.** Eugene McCarthy.

_____ **9.** What developed in the view of many Americans when, day after day, they saw images of wounded and dead Americans in Vietnam but were told the enemy was on the brink of defeat?
    A. the need for teach-ins   **C.** a credibility gap
    B. a domino theory   **D.** guerrilla warfare

_____ **10.** Who appeared to be on his way to winning the Democratic nomination until he was gunned down on June 5, 1968, in a California hotel?
    A. Dr. Martin Luther King, Jr.   **C.** George Wallace
    B. Robert Kennedy   **D.** Hubert Humphrey

⭐ **Chapter 25**

Score

Section Quiz 25-4

DIRECTIONS: Matching Match each item in Column A with the items in Column B.
Write the correct letters in the blanks. *(10 points each)*

Column A

_____ **1.** reestablished some limits on executive power

_____ **2.** the most destructive air raids of the entire Vietnam War

_____ **3.** Harvard professor given wide authority to use diplomacy
   to end the Vietnam War

_____ **4.** a plan calling for the gradual withdrawal of American
   troops and for the South Vietnamese army to assume more
   of the fighting

_____ **5.** Democratic candidate for president in 1972

Column B

A. Vietnamization

B. "Christmas
   bombings"

C. Henry Kissinger

D. War Powers Act

E. George McGovern

DIRECTIONS: Multiple Choice In the blank at the left, write the letter of the choice
that best completes the statement or answers the question. *(10 points each)*

_____ **6.** After the United States ended its direct involvement in Vietnam, the
   North Vietnamese captured Saigon and united Vietnam under
   A. a democratic system.   **C.** rule of the United Nations.
   B. nationalist rule.   **D.** Communist rule.

_____ **7.** What country did American troops invade in an effort to destroy
   Vietcong military bases there?
   A. Laos   **C.** China
   B. Cambodia   **D.** Taiwan

_____ **8.** Long after troops were home, the war lingered on for the hundreds of
   American families whose relatives and friends were classified as missing
   in action or
   A. prisoners of war.   **C.** defectors.
   B. draft dodgers.   **D.** absent without leave.

_____ **9.** What confirmed that the government had not been honest with
   Americans?
   A. the "Christmas bombings"   **C.** the Pentagon Papers
   B. the Cambodian invasion   **D.** the massacre at My Lai

_____ **10.** Henry Kissinger tried to improve relations with the Soviet Union and
   China so he could persuade them to cut back on their aid to Vietnam in a
   policy he called
   A. diplomacy.   **C.** Vietnamization.
   B. arms negotiation.   **D.** linkage.

⭐ **Chapter 25 Test, Form A**

The Vietnam War

DIRECTIONS: Matching Match each item in Column A with the items in Column B.
Write the correct letters in the blanks. *(4 points each)*

Column A

_____ 1. Nixon's special assistant for national security affairs

_____ 2. Democratic candidate assassinated in a California hotel

_____ 3. feared the Vietnam War would draw attention from the civil rights movement

_____ 4. South Vietnam's president at the end of the Vietnam War

_____ 5. American commander in South Vietnam

_____ 6. outspoken segregationist who won over 13% of the popular vote as an independent candidate in the 1968 election

_____ 7. peace negotiator for the North Vietnamese

_____ 8. Communist leader who organized a guerrilla army to fight to reunify Vietnam

_____ 9. former Defense Department worker who leaked the Pentagon Papers to the *New York Times*

_____ 10. pro-Western leader of South Vietnam early in the war who was overthrown in a coup and executed

Column B

A. Le Duc Tho

B. Dr. Martin Luther King, Jr.

C. Daniel Ellsberg

D. Ho Chi Minh

E. Nguyen Van Thieu

F. Robert Kennedy

G. Ngo Dinh Diem

H. George Wallace

I. William Westmoreland

J. Henry Kissinger

DIRECTIONS: Multiple Choice Choose the item that best completes each sentence or answers each question. Write the letter in the blank. *(4 points each)*

_____ 11. The Vietminh formed initially in Vietnam to
    A. create a Communist government.   **C.** win independence from France.
    B. create a pro-Western government.   **D.** win independence from Japan.

_____ 12. What two events convinced Truman to help France in Vietnam?
    A. the fall of China to communism and the outbreak of the Korean War
    B. Japan's surrender in World War II and the fall of China to communism
    C. the establishment of a Communist government in Vietnam and the Korean War
    D. the establishment of a Communist government in Vietnam and the fall of China

_____ 13. When the French left Vietnam, the United States stepped in to
    A. make sure free elections were held, as specified by the Geneva Accords.
    B. protect the pro-Western government in the South.
    C. act as peacekeeper along the border between North and South Vietnam.
    D. try to cause a popular uprising against the Communist ruler in North Vietnam.

(continued)

Chapter 25 Test, Form A

Score

_____ 14. The Vietcong's power continued to increase in part because of
   A. the Vietcong's use of terror.
   B. the use of terror by South Vietnam.
   C. the strong belief in communism.
   D. the Vietnamese distrust of the U.S.

_____ 15. With the Gulf of Tonkin Resolution, Congress
   A. declared war on North Vietnam.
   B. committed to a limited war only.
   C. increased aid to South Vietnam.
   D. gave its war powers to the president.

_____ 16. The goal of Agent Orange was to
   A. infiltrate the Vietcong military.
   B. sabotage Vietcong equipment.
   C. destroy the ability to hide in jungles.
   D. cut Vietcong supply lines.

_____ 17. A main reason President Johnson refused to order a full-scale invasion of North Vietnam was his fear that it would
   A. bring China into the war.
   B. strengthen the North Vietnamese will to fight.
   C. result in a staggering loss of American lives.
   D. horrify the American public, ruining him politically.

_____ 18. The "educational hearings" on Vietnam were intended to
   A. boost public support for the war.
   B. protest the war.
   C. explain the war to the Senate.
   D. explain the war to the public.

_____ 19. After the Tet offensive, the mainstream American media began to
   A. appeal to American patriotism to support the war effort.
   B. give less air time to antiwar protesters.
   C. give more air time to antiwar protesters.
   D. openly criticize the war effort.

_____ 20. Nixon's decision to invade Cambodia angered Congress, resulting in
   A. a vote of censure.
   B. impeachment hearings.
   C. a repeal of the Gulf of Tonkin Resolution.
   D. a repeal of the War Powers Act.

DIRECTIONS: Essay Answer one of the following questions on a separate sheet of paper. *(20 points)*

21. Describe the Vietcong's battle tactics and ways that American troops tried to counter these tactics.

22. Explain what the circle graphs show, and discuss how the draft system at the beginning of the war could have contributed to this situation.

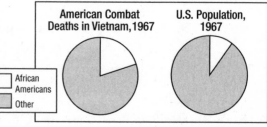

American Combat Deaths in Vietnam, 1967   U.S. Population, 1967

☐ African Americans
▨ Other

Chapter 25 Test, Form B

The Vietnam War

DIRECTIONS: Matching Match each item in Column A with the items in Column B. Write the correct letters in the blanks. *(4 points each)*

Column A

_____ **1.** massacre of South Vietnamese civilians by U.S. troops

_____ **2.** forces made up of North and South Vietnamese, but supplied by North Vietnam

_____ **3.** chemical that strips leaves from trees and shrubs

_____ **4.** temporarily divided Vietnam along the 17th Parallel

_____ **5.** soldier whose fate was undetermined

_____ **6.** jellied gasoline that explodes on contact

_____ **7.** renamed Ho Chi Minh City after reunification

_____ **8.** fear that a Communist Vietnam would lead to other Southeast Asian Communist governments

_____ **9.** strategy that led troops to count bodies after battles

_____ **10.** improving relations with the Soviet Union and China to persuade them to cut back their aid to North Vietnam

Column B

A. napalm

B. MIA

C. domino theory

D. war of attrition

E. Agent Orange

F. Saigon

G. Geneva Accords

H. My Lai

I. Vietcong

J. linkage

DIRECTIONS: Multiple Choice Choose the item that best completes each sentence or answers each question. Write the letter in the blank. *(4 points each)*

_____ **11.** As a result of the battle at Dien Bien Phu,
  A. President Johnson decided to send American troops into Vietnam.
  B. regular North Vietnamese army units joined the Vietcong.
  C. President Nixon decided to pull American troops out of Vietnam.
  D. the French withdrew from Indochina.

_____ **12.** As the fighting began between the Vietcong and South Vietnamese army, President Eisenhower tried to help South Vietnam by sending
  A. food.   **C.** military advisers.
  B. napalm.   **D.** American troops.

_____ **13.** Kennedy felt he needed to stand up to communism in Vietnam because
  A. he needed to overcome the American humiliation in the Korean War.
  B. many Republicans blamed the Truman administration for losing China to communism.
  C. most Southern Democrats strongly supported the war.
  D. he could justify to Congress the need for increases in military spending.

_____ **14.** In South Vietnam, a monk set himself on fire to protest
  A. the war.   **C.** extreme religious ceremonies.
  B. Western influences in his country. **D.** discrimination against Buddhists.

(continued)

Chapter 25 Test, Form B

Score

_____ **15.** Operation Rolling Thunder was
  A. an invasion of North Vietnam.
  B. an invasion of Cambodia.
  C. the first combat operation in which American ground troops participated.
  D. a sustained bombing campaign against North Vietnam.

_____ **16.** President Johnson refused to allow a full-scale attack on North Vietnam's main supply line because
  A. such an attack would result in heavy American casualties.
  B. it passed through the territory of countries not involved in the war.
  C. he feared such an attack would bring the Soviet Union into the war.
  D. its route continually changed, making it hard to locate and destroy.

_____ **17.** Nightly news coverage of the Vietnam War on television helped
  A. raise Johnson's ratings in the polls.   **C.** create a credibility gap.
  B. unify Americans behind the war.   **D.** support the nation's "hawks."

_____ **18.** The Tet offensive marked a major turning point in the Vietnam War because
  A. Communist forces scored a major military victory.
  B. Communist forces scored a major political victory.
  C. American and South Vietnamese forces scored a major military victory.
  D. American and South Vietnamese forces scored a major political victory.

_____ **19.** In 1968 antiwar protesters and police clashed outside the
  A. Democratic National Convention.   **C.** White House.
  B. Republican National Convention.   **D.** Lincoln Memorial.

_____ **20.** The Pentagon Papers revealed that
  A. many more Americans had died in Vietnam than had been reported.
  B. American soldiers had massacred Vietnamese civilians at My Lai.
  C. American prisoners of war were being tortured in North Vietnamese prisons.
  D. the government had not been honest with the public about Vietnam.

DIRECTIONS: Essay Answer one of the following questions on a separate sheet of paper. *(20 points)*

21. Fill in the diagram. Then use it to help you explain the credibility gap that developed during the Vietnam War.

22. Explain the outcomes and significance of the Tet offensive.

★ **Chapter 26**

Section Quiz 26-1

DIRECTIONS: Matching Match each item in Column A with the items in Column B.
Write the correct letters in the blanks. *(10 points each)*

Column A

_____ **1.** one of the most famous rock 'n' roll groups

_____ **2.** derived its subject matter from elements of the popular culture

_____ **3.** defined the views of the Students for a Democratic Society

_____ **4.** group living arrangements in which members shared everything and worked together

_____ **5.** young men and women with alternative ways of life, commonly called "hippies"

Column B

A. counterculture

B. Port Huron Statement

C. pop art

D. The Beatles

E. communes

DIRECTIONS: Multiple Choice In the blank at the left, write the letter of the choice
that best completes the statement or answers the question. *(10 points each)*

_____ **6.** Many of the religious groups embraced by members of the counterculture centered around
    A. communes.
    B. Catholicism.
    C. authoritarian leaders.
    D. individualism.

_____ **7.** The early 1960s saw a phenomenon that fueled the youth movement—the rapid increase in
    A. college enrollments.
    B. military enlistments.
    C. high school dropouts.
    D. immigration.

_____ **8.** The 1960s gave birth to a conspicuous youth movement, which challenged the American political and social system and conventional
    A. elections.
    B. utopian ideals.
    C. political parties.
    D. middle-class values.

_____ **9.** What movement was sparked in Berkeley, California, when the university decided to restrict the students' rights to distribute literature and to recruit volunteers for political causes on campus?
    A. Counterculture Movement
    B. Free Speech Movement
    C. Hippie Movement
    D. Commune Movement

_____ **10.** Where did SDS leaders orchestrate an eight-day occupation of several buildings to protest the administration's plan to build a new gym in an area that served as a neighborhood park?
    A. University of Chicago
    B. Kent State University
    C. University of Michigan
    D. Columbia University in New York City

Chapter 26

Section Quiz 26-2

DIRECTIONS: Matching Match each item in Column A with the items in Column B.
Write the correct letters in the blanks. *(10 points each)*

Column A

_____ **1.** a leading figure of the women's movement and editor of *Ms.* magazine

_____ **2.** in most cases outlawed paying men more than women for the same job

_____ **3.** the belief that men and women should be equal politically, economically, and socially

_____ **4.** wrote the book *The Feminine Mystique*, which led to the rise of a new feminist movement

_____ **5.** prohibited federally funded schools from discriminating against girls and young women in nearly all aspects of their operations, from admissions to athletics

Column B

A. feminism

B. Title IX

C. Betty Friedan

D. Equal Pay Act

E. Gloria Steinem

DIRECTIONS: Multiple Choice In the blank at the left, write the letter of the choice
that best completes the statement or answers the question. *(10 points each)*

_____ **6.** One of the forces that helped bring the women's movement to life was
   A. the counterculture.
   B. Phyllis Schlafly.
   C. the President's Commission on the Status of Women.
   D. the bus boycotts.

_____ **7.** What outlawed job discrimination by private employers not only on the basis of race, color, religion, and national origin, but also of gender?
   A. Equal Rights Amendment
   B. Title VII of the 1964 Civil Rights Act
   C. Equal Employment Opportunity Act
   D. Title IX

_____ **8.** The big change in abortion laws came with the 1973 Supreme Court decision in
   A. *Roe* v. *Wade.*
   B. *Plessy* v. *Ferguson.*
   C. *Reynolds* v. *Sims.*
   D. *Gideon* v. *Wainwright.*

_____ **9.** A new organization, the idea of Betty Friedan, reflected the diverse goals of the modern feminist movement and was named the
   A. Women for a Democratic Society.
   B. National Woman's Party.
   C. National Organization for Women.
   D. Equal Rights Organization.

_____ **10.** Although about 40 percent of American women were in the workforce in the 1960s, generally they were shut out of
   A. clerical positions.
   B. higher paying and prestigious professions.
   C. factory jobs.
   D. cashier positions.

The American Republic Since 1877

★ Chapter 26

Section Quiz 26-3

DIRECTIONS: Matching Match each item in Column A with the items in Column B.
Write the correct letters in the blanks. *(10 points each)*

Column A

_____ **1.** organized by African American members of Congress to represent the legislative concerns of African Americans

_____ **2.** the practice of teaching immigrant students in their own language while they also learned English

_____ **3.** a militant group of Native Americans who viewed the government's reform efforts as too modest

_____ **4.** called for companies and institutions doing business with the government to recruit African American employees

_____ **5.** a manifesto calling for policies to create greater economic opportunities on reservations

Column B

A. American Indian Movement

B. affirmative action

C. bilingualism

D. Declaration of Indian Purpose

E. Congressional Black Caucus

DIRECTIONS: Multiple Choice In the blank at the left, write the letter of the choice that best completes the statement or answers the question. *(10 points each)*

_____ **6.** In 1966 César Chávez and Dolores Huerta merged their organizations that fought for the rights of farmworkers to form the
   A. United Farm Workers.
   B. American Federation of Labor.
   C. National Farmers Organization.
   D. Farm Bureau.

_____ **7.** The Indian Civil Rights Act recognized the legitimacy of local reservation law and guaranteed reservation residents the protections of
   A. affirmative action.
   B. bilingualism.
   C. the Bill of Rights.
   D. the military.

_____ **8.** Who founded the political party *La Raza Unida*, which called for job-training programs and greater access to financial institutions?
   A. César Chávez
   B. Dolores Huerta
   C. Jesse Jackson
   D. José Angel Gutiérrez

_____ **9.** Leaders of the civil rights movement began to focus their energies on gaining good jobs for African Americans and
   A. voting rights.
   B. desegregation.
   C. adequate education.
   D. bilingualism.

_____ **10.** Who founded People United to Save Humanity, or PUSH, a group aimed at registering voters, developing African American businesses, and broadening educational opportunities?
   A. Jesse Jackson
   B. Maynard Jackson
   C. Ruth Baston
   D. Allan Bakke

Chapter 26

Section Quiz 26-4

DIRECTIONS: Matching Match each item in Column A with the items in Column B. Write the correct letters in the blanks. *(10 points each)*

Column A

_____ **1.** notable figure of the consumer protection movement

_____ **2.** a nuclear facility where low levels of radiation escaped from the reactor

_____ **3.** created to set and enforce pollution standards, promote research, and coordinate anti-pollution activities with state and local governments

_____ **4.** wrote *Silent Spring,* one of the most controversial and powerful books of the 1960s

_____ **5.** leader of residents at Love Canal who banded together and demanded the government address local health threats

Column B

A. Lois Gibbs

B. Environmental Protection Agency

C. Three Mile Island

D. Rachel Carson

E. Ralph Nader

DIRECTIONS: Multiple Choice In the blank at the left, write the letter of the choice that best completes the statement or answers the question. *(10 points each)*

_____ **6.** Supporters of nuclear energy hailed it as a cleaner and less expensive alternative to

A. wind power.   **C.** fossil fuels.

B. hydroelectric power.   **D.** solar power.

_____ **7.** Congress passed the National Traffic and Motor Vehicle Safety Act in 1966 and for the first time set federal safety regulations for the

A. automobile industry.   **C.** workers in automobile factories.

B. highway system.   **D.** automobile, train, and airline industries.

_____ **8.** Scientists established the Environmental Defense Fund and used its contributions for a series of legal actions across the country to halt

A. unsafe automobiles.   **C.** DDT spraying.

B. the Environmental Protection Agency.   **D.** nuclear power.

_____ **9.** Many observers point to April 1970, as the clearest beginning of the environmental movement with the celebration of

A. Love Canal.   **C.** Three Mile Island.

B. Earth Day.   **D.** the Endangered Species Act.

_____ **10.** What act established emissions standards for factories and automobiles?

A. National Traffic and Motor Vehicle Act   **C.** Clean Air Act

B. Environmental Protection Act   **D.** Clean Water Act

The American Republic Since 1877

⭐ **Chapter 26 Test, Form A**

Score

The Politics of Protest

DIRECTIONS: Matching Match each item in Column A with the items in Column B.
Write the correct letters in the blanks. *(4 points each)*

Column A

_____ **1.** founded the National Organization for Women

_____ **2.** first African American mayor of Atlanta whose efforts opened job opportunities for minority contractors

_____ **3.** organized a group that fought for the rights of farmworkers

_____ **4.** sounded the alarm on the effect of pesticides on birds

_____ **5.** master of the electric guitar

_____ **6.** leader of the Unification Church

_____ **7.** editor of *Ms.*

_____ **8.** main author of the Port Huron Statement

_____ **9.** civil rights leader who founded PUSH

_____ **10.** pop artist who often used images of famous people

Column B

A. Andy Warhol

B. Jimi Hendrix

C. Gloria Steinem

D. Tom Hayden

E. Maynard Jackson

F. Betty Friedan

G. Jesse Jackson

H. Dolores Huerta

I. Sun Myung Moon

J. Rachel Carson

DIRECTIONS: Multiple Choice Choose the item that best completes each sentence or answers each question. Write the letter in the blank. *(4 points each)*

_____ **11.** The Port Huron Statement expressed the views of the
    A. Hare Krishna movement.
    B. American Indian Movement.
    C. Free Speech Movement.
    D. Students for a Democratic Society.

_____ **12.** The Free Speech Movement was sparked by restrictions on students' rights to
    A. make speeches voicing opposition to university policies.
    B. distribute literature and recruit volunteers for political causes.
    C. distribute literature and recruit people to join non-mainstream religious groups.
    D. distribute drug-related literature and publicly speak in favor of drug use.

_____ **13.** Many of the new religious groups of the 1960s centered around
    A. individualism.
    B. the drug culture.
    C. witchcraft and satanism.
    D. authoritarian leaders.

_____ **14.** A rock festival that drew hundreds of thousands of people in 1969 was at
    A. Haight-Ashbury.
    B. San Francisco.
    C. Woodstock.
    D. Berkeley.

_____ **15.** After 1920 the women's movement split into two camps with opposing views on
    A. right-to-work laws.
    B. laws protecting women.
    C. woman suffrage.
    D. women's role in society.

(continued)

Chapter 26 Test, Form A

_____ **16.** For her book *The Feminine Mystique,* Betty Friedan interviewed Smith College graduates and found that most of the women
   A. made far less money than did men in comparable jobs.
   B. preferred to stay home rather than take jobs outside the home.
   C. wanted to work outside the home, but few could find jobs.
   D. reported having everything they could want, but still felt unfulfilled.

_____ **17.** In *University of California Regents* v. *Bakke,* the Supreme Court ruled that
   A. schools could not use race in determining admissions.
   B. schools could use racial quotas for determining admissions.
   C. schools could use race but not quotas for determining admissions.
   D. affirmative action was a form of discrimination and was therefore unconstitutional.

_____ **18.** To push for better wages and benefits for farmworkers, César Chávez organized a successful
   A. march on Washington.   **C.** advertising and publicity campaign.
   B. sit-down strike.   **D.** grape boycott.

_____ **19.** Some opponents of bilingualism argued that
   A. it would prevent students from learning English.
   B. total immersion in English was the soundest road to educational success.
   C. it would hold back the education of native-English-speaking students.
   D. the Constitution established English as the nation's only official language.

_____ **20.** The incident at Three Mile Island left many people in great doubt about the
   A. safety of nuclear energy.   **C.** healthfulness of the water they drink.
   B. ability of the government to protect   **D.** long-term survival of the planet.
      them from corporate polluters.

DIRECTIONS: Essay Answer one of the following questions on a separate sheet of paper. *(20 points)*

21. Describe counterculture fashions and their effect on the mainstream.

22. Complete the chart about the two sides of the nuclear power debate. Then describe the event at Three Mile Island and its effects on the debate.

Debate Over Nuclear Energy

Arguments for:	Arguments against:

⭐ **Chapter 26 Test, Form B**

The Politics of Protest

DIRECTIONS: Matching Match each item in Column A with the items in Column B.
Write the correct letters in the blanks. *(4 points each)*

Column A

_____ **1.** claim that qualified white workers were kept from jobs

_____ **2.** living arrangement popular among the counterculture

_____ **3.** youth culture that represented a rebellion against the dominant culture

_____ **4.** coal, oil, and natural gas

_____ **5.** seized and occupied for 70 days by American Indians

_____ **6.** celebration that marked the beginning of the environmental movement

_____ **7.** policy that prompted "white flight" to private schools

_____ **8.** believed that a few wealthy elites controlled politics

_____ **9.** kills insects and the birds that eat them

_____ **10.** popular destination for youths of the counterculture

Column B

A. Earth Day

B. Wounded Knee

C. fossil fuels

D. Students for a Democratic Society

E. Haight-Ashbury

F. DDT

G. reverse discrimination

H. hippie

I. busing

J. commune

DIRECTIONS: Multiple Choice Choose the item that best completes each sentence
or answers each question. Write the letter in the blank. *(4 points each)*

_____ **11.** The youth movement included
  A. resentment against the "beats."
  B. volunteers in Johnson's Peace Corps.
  C. disinterest in college education.
  D. the Port Huron statement.

_____ **12.** Who was Rachel Carson?
  A. the founder of Earth Day
  B. the environmentalist who wrote *Silent Spring*
  C. the head of the Environmental Protection Agency
  D. the author of the Endangered Species Act

_____ **13.** The part of the Educational Amendments that prohibited federally
  funded schools from discriminating against girls and young women in
  nearly all aspects of their operations was
  A. Title VII.
  B. Title VIII.
  C. Title IX.
  D. Title X.

_____ **14.** In *Roe* v. *Wade*, the Supreme Court ruled that
  A. states could not regulate a woman's right to have an abortion.
  B. a woman's right to an abortion would be determined on a state-by-state basis.
  C. states could not regulate abortion in the first three months of pregnancy.
  D. states could ban abortion at any time during the pregnancy.

(continued)

★ **Chapter 26 Test, Form B**

Score

_____ **15.** Affirmative action called for companies and institutions to
   A. meet quotas in hiring African Americans.
   B. actively recruit African American employees.
   C. hire the best-qualified candidates, regardless of race, religion, or national origin.
   D. provide diversity training for all employees.

_____ **16.** In *Swann* v. *Charlotte-Mecklenburg Board of Education,* the Supreme Court ruled that
   A. busing was constitutional.   **C.** affirmative action was constitutional.
   B. busing was unconstitutional.   **D.** affirmative action was unconstitutional.

_____ **17.** *La Raza Unida* was a Mexican American
   A. political party.   **C.** protest movement.
   B. immigrant-aid organization.   **D.** farmworkers union.

_____ **18.** The Indian Civil Rights Act
   A. returned a number of land and water rights to Native American groups.
   B. legalized casinos on reservation land.
   C. recognized the legitimacy of local reservation law.
   D. authorized reparations to several groups for land lost to white settlement.

_____ **19.** At Love Canal, residents experienced health problems because
   A. local factories were releasing harmful gases into the air.
   B. local factories were dumping toxic waste into the canal.
   C. paint containing lead covered the walls of many of their homes.
   D. an old toxic waste dump under the community was leaking into the ground.

_____ **20.** The book *Unsafe at Any Speed* led to
   A. a ban on the use of DDT.   **C.** safety standards for car designs.
   B. tougher traffic safety laws.   **D.** lower speed limits on highways.

DIRECTIONS: Essay Answer one of the following questions on a separate sheet of paper. *(20 points)*

21. The diagram shows three factors that helped bring about the youth movement in the 1960s. Explain how the effects of these factors contributed to the movement.

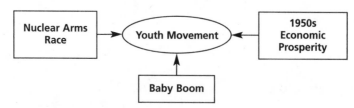

22. Describe some examples of stereotypes and unequal treatment of women that reawakened the women's movement in the 1960s.

The American Republic Since 1877

⭐ **Unit 7 Posttest, Form A**

Score

A Time of Upheaval

DIRECTIONS: Matching Match each item in Column A with the items in Column B. Write the correct letters in the blanks. *(4 points each)*

Column A

_____ 1. part of the Educational Amendments that prohibited discrimination against girls and young women in federally funded schools

_____ 2. head of the President's Commission on the Status of Women

_____ 3. site of symbolic Native American protest in 1969

_____ 4. schools could use race but not quotas for determining admissions

_____ 5. set and enforced pollution standards

_____ 6. part of the Civil Rights Act of 1964 that became the decisive legal basis for advances by the women's movement

_____ 7. site of a huge rock festival in 1969

_____ 8. resulted because many Americans watched nightly televised news reports about the Vietnam War

_____ 9. segregation in public schools is unconstitutional

_____ 10. revealed that the government had not been honest about the Vietnam War

Column B

A. Alcatraz Island

B. credibility gap

C. *Brown* v. *Board of Education*

D. Title IX

E. Woodstock

F. Eleanor Roosevelt

G. Pentagon Papers

H. Environmental Protection Agency

I. Title VII

J. *University of California Regents* v. *Bakke*

DIRECTIONS: Multiple Choice Choose the item that best completes each sentence or answers each question. Write the letter in the blank. *(4 points each)*

_____ 11. A key to Kennedy's defeat of Nixon in 1960 was
   A. Nixon's "Checkers speech."
   B. the televised debates.
   C. Kennedy's religion.
   D. reapportionment.

_____ 12. To make sure that everyone in the court system receives equal treatment, the Fourteenth Amendment requires
   A. trial by jury.
   B. due process.
   C. habeas corpus.
   D. all people on trial to have a lawyer.

_____ 13. In the agreement ending the Cuban missile crisis, Khrushchev promised to remove Soviet missiles from Cuba in exchange for Kennedy's public promise
   A. not to invade Cuba.
   B. to stop testing nuclear weapons in the atmosphere.
   C. to remove American missiles from China on the Soviet border.
   D. to remove American missiles from Alaska near the Soviet Union.

(continued)

Copyright © by The McGraw-Hill Companies, Inc.

Unit 7 Posttest, Form A

_____ **14.** The purpose of pupil assignment laws was to
   A. integrate public schools.
   B. prevent African Americans from attending white schools.
   C. improve education in African American schools.
   D. send the brightest, most motivated African American students to all-white schools.

_____ **15.** Which of the following was NOT connected to the sit-in movement?
   A. Jesse Jackson   **C.** Ella Baker
   B. Marion Barry   **D.** Rosa Parks

_____ **16.** The Freedom Riders traveled to the South to
   A. register African American voters.
   B. protest school segregation.
   C. draw attention to violence against African Americans in the South.
   D. draw attention to the South's refusal to integrate bus terminals.

_____ **17.** The Civil Rights Act of 1964 helped protect civil rights, but it did not
   A. guarantee the right to vote.   **C.** end discrimination in employment.
   B. end segregation in public places.   **D.** end school segregation.

_____ **18.** Nixon's Vietnamization plan called for
   A. a simultaneous withdrawal of troops by North Vietnam and the United States.
   B. South Vietnam to assume more of the fighting as American troops withdrew.
   C. a massive invasion of North Vietnam to finally end the war.
   D. a withdrawal of American troops from North Vietnam.

_____ **19.** Which of the following happened during the Kennedy administration?
   A. a decline in the numbers of Special Forces and Green Berets
   B. the successful domination of space by the United States
   C. the organization of the Peace Corps for American volunteers
   D. the creation of the Alliance for Progress with Eastern European countries

_____ **20.** Which of the following did NOT occur in 1970?
   A. the Three Mile Island disaster   **C.** the creation of the EPA
   B. the first Earth Day   **D.** the passage of the Clean Air Act

DIRECTIONS: Essay Answer one of the following questions on a separate sheet of paper. *(20 points)*

21. Describe the legacy of Johnson's Great Society. How successful was it? What are some of its lasting effects?

22. What was the Gulf of Tonkin Resolution? What incidents led up to it and what was its significance?

The American Republic Since 1877

★ **Unit 7 Posttest, Form B**

Score

A Time of Upheaval

DIRECTIONS: Matching Match each item in Column A with the items in Column B. Write the correct letters in the blanks. *(4 points each)*

Column A

_____ 1. program that employed young people to work in poor school districts in the United States

_____ 2. belief that men and women should be equal

_____ 3. investigated the assassination of President Kennedy

_____ 4. established the separate-but-equal doctrine

_____ 5. police must inform suspects of their rights during the arrest process

_____ 6. site of "Bloody Sunday" where state troopers and deputized civilians brutally attacked marchers

_____ 7. preschool program for disadvantaged children

_____ 8. his efforts led to safety standards for automobiles

_____ 9. firebombs of jellied gasoline

_____ 10. announced in April 1970 that American troops had invaded Cambodia

Column B

A. napalm

B. VISTA

C. Selma, Alabama

D. *Miranda* v. *State of Arizona*

E. *Plessy* v. *Ferguson*

F. feminism

G. Head Start

H. Richard Nixon

I. Warren Commission

J. Ralph Nader

DIRECTIONS: Multiple Choice Choose the item that best completes each sentence or answers each question. Write the letter in the blank. *(4 points each)*

_____ 11. Reapportionment as required by the Warren Court shifted more political power to
    A. poor rural farmers.
    B. Southern whites.
    C. African Americans.
    D. corporations.

_____ 12. Which of the following was NOT a crisis of the Cold War during Kennedy's administration?
    A. the building of the Berlin Wall
    B. the Soviet missile crisis
    C. the findings of the Warren Commission
    D. the Bay of Pigs invasion

_____ 13. Rosa Parks's action resulted in a
    A. restaurant sit-in.
    B. bus boycott.
    C. Supreme Court case that overturned school segregation.
    D. riot.

(continued)

_____ **14.** To end segregation and racism, Dr. Martin Luther King, Jr., advocated
    A. educational self-improvement.
    B. riots and vandalism.
    C. separation from white society.
    D. nonviolent passive resistance.

_____ **15.** The SNCC was founded by
    A. students.
    B. ministers.
    C. farmers.
    D. environmentalists.

_____ **16.** Dr. Martin Luther King, Jr., gave his "I have a dream" speech during the
    A. Selma March.
    B. Watts riot.
    C. March on Washington.
    D. Poor People's Campaign in Memphis.

_____ **17.** President Johnson did not order a full-scale attack on the Ho Chi Minh trail because
    A. heavy American casualties would likely result.
    B. it passed through Cambodia and Laos, which were not involved in the war.
    C. he feared such an attack would bring the Soviet Union into the war.
    D. it was mostly underground tunnels, making it hard to locate enemy forces.

_____ **18.** The Tet offensive, a turning point in the Vietnam War, resulted in
    A. the entrance of China into the war on the Communist side.
    B. the capture of Saigon by the Communist forces.
    C. the entrance of the Soviet Union into the war on the Communist side.
    D. a major political victory for the Communist forces.

_____ **19.** The results of the Vietnam War included which of the following?
    A. fewer than 50,000 American deaths
    B. a South Vietnamese victory
    C. democracy in Saigon
    D. the end of America's longest war

_____ **20.** A leading figure in the women's movement and editor of *Ms.* magazine was
    A. Betty Friedan.
    B. Dolores Huerta.
    C. Gloria Steinem.
    D. Phyllis Schlafly.

DIRECTIONS: Essay Answer one of the following questions on a separate sheet of paper. *(20 points)*

21. Who were the Black Muslims, and what did they believe?

22. Describe the 1960s counterculture. Who participated, what did they want, and how did they behave?

★ **Unit 8 Pretest, Form A**

Score

A Changing Society

DIRECTIONS: Matching Match each item in Column A with the items in Column B. Write the correct letters in the blanks. *(4 points each)*

Column A

_____ 1. winner of the 1968 presidential election

_____ 2. Democratic candidate in the 1968 presidential election

_____ 3. third-party candidate in the 1968 presidential election

_____ 4. created the Department of Energy

_____ 5. advocated yoga, martial arts, and chanting

_____ 6. new openness in the Soviet Union that allowed more freedom of religion and speech

_____ 7. Jerry Falwell's movement

_____ 8. advocate free speech and privacy

_____ 9. global information system that operates commercially rather than through the government

_____ 10. a combination of rising prices and economic stagnation

Column B

A. *glasnost*

B. Hubert Humphrey

C. New Age movement

D. Moral Majority

E. Internet

F. Jimmy Carter

G. Richard Nixon

H. liberals

I. George Wallace

J. stagflation

DIRECTIONS: Multiple Choice Choose the item that best completes each sentence or answers each question. Write the letter in the blank. *(4 points each)*

_____ 11. In the 1970s, the American economy fell into a recession, partly as a result of an oil embargo imposed by
   A. NATO.
   B. OPEC.
   C. NAFTA.
   D. the Warsaw Pact.

_____ 12. Nixon's foreign policy was characterized by all of the following EXCEPT
   A. making Henry Kissinger national security adviser.
   B. a visit to Communist China.
   C. the signing of SALT I.
   D. détente with Cuba.

_____ 13. The music craze in the 1970s was
   A. rock 'n' roll.
   B. bluegrass.
   C. disco.
   D. jazz.

(continued)

Unit 8 Pretest, Form A

Score

14. President Reagan's domestic policy included
  A. a proposal to increase many social programs.
  B. an increase of government regulation of industry.
  C. a 25 percent tax rate cut passed by Congress.
  D. a steady decline in the median American income.

15. The Iran-Contra scandal involved selling weapons to Iran to
  A. support the guerrillas fighting against the pro-Soviet government in Iran.
  B. support Iran's effort to defeat Iraq.
  C. gain freedom for the American hostages being held in the Middle East.
  D. improve relations with the Iranian government, so that it would not look to the Soviets for aid.

16. The space shuttle was a breakthrough because, unlike earlier spacecraft, it could
  A. travel outside of Earth's orbit.   **C.** carry more than two passengers.
  B. remain in space for more that a week. **D.** be reused.

17. Why were the 1980s called a decade of indulgence?
  A. There was strong economic growth.   **C.** Racial difficulties were resolved.
  B. There were fewer baby boomers.   **D.** Economic statistics were stagnant.

18. A gas in our atmosphere that protects us from cancer-causing ultraviolet rays of the sun is
  A. hydrogen.   **C.** ozone.
  B. carbon dioxide.   **D.** hydrocarbon.

19. The result of the 2000 election was finally determined by a
  A. recount of votes in Florida.   **C.** vote of the Electoral College.
  B. Supreme Court ruling.   **D.** vote of the House of Representatives.

20. On September 11, 2001, terrorists attacked the United States using
  A. airplanes carrying bombs.   **C.** anthrax spores.
  B. hijacked airplanes.   **D.** suicide bombers with bombs tied to their bodies.

DIRECTIONS: Essay Answer one of the following questions on a separate sheet of paper. *(20 points)*

21. What was "Watergate"? What were its results?

22. Describe three technological advances in media entertainment that developed in the 1980s and that you enjoy today.

⭐ **Unit 8 Pretest, Form B**

Score

A Changing Society

DIRECTIONS: Matching Match each item in Column A with the items in Column B.
Write the correct letters in the blanks. *(4 points each)*

Column A

_____ **1.** became president when Nixon resigned

_____ **2.** name of the European Union's monetary unit

_____ **3.** head of al-Qaeda

_____ **4.** global computer network

_____ **5.** music of the 1970s

_____ **6.** believe that raising interest rates will lower inflation

_____ **7.** have a fundamental distrust of the power of government

_____ **8.** agreement between the Soviet Union and United States to limit nuclear arms

_____ **9.** governments that secretly support terrorist groups with money, weapons, and training

_____ **10.** famous evangelical Protestant minister

Column B

A. Osama bin Laden

B. state-sponsored terrorism

C. Billy Graham

D. conservatives

E. SALT I

F. Gerald Ford

G. Internet

H. disco

I. euro

J. monetarists

DIRECTIONS: Multiple Choice Choose the item that best completes each sentence
or answers each question. Write the letter in the blank. *(4 points each)*

_____ **11.** Nixon's election included which of the following?
   A. a presidential ballot that included only two candidates
   B. an appeal to Middle America and the silent majority
   C. a fight with Strom Thurmond over his vice presidential candidate
   D. a loss of the electoral votes of all Southern states

_____ **12.** Which of the following led to the Watergate scandal?
   A. Gerald Ford's creation of the Committee to Re-elect the President
   B. a burglary by the Democrats
   C. the enemies list made by the president
   D. thievery by members of the Democratic National Committee

_____ **13.** Economic conditions during the 1970s included
   A. an embargo of oil to OPEC nations.
   B. decreasing prices for gasoline and consumer products.
   C. OPEC using oil as a weapon.
   D. Jimmy Carter's tax cut.

(continued)

Unit 8 Pretest, Form B

_____ **14.** Which did NOT occur during the Ford administration?
  A. The Helsinki Accords were signed.
  B. Cambodia seized an American ship.
  C. The "Whip Inflation Now" plan was introduced.
  D. Richard Nixon went to jail.

_____ **15.** All of the following were part of the "Me" decade EXCEPT
  A. a search for fulfillment with the New Age movement.
  B. a general move away from fads.
  C. disco music and *Saturday Night Fever.*
  D. television shows about racism.

_____ **16.** Which of the following is NOT connected to the revival of conservatism?
  A. President Lyndon Johnson   **C.** Barry Goldwater
  B. William F. Buckley   **D.** Proposition 13

_____ **17.** President George Bush faced all of the following foreign policy crises EXCEPT
  A. protests in China's Tiananmen Square.   **C.** the grassroots movement.
  B. a crisis in Panama.   **D.** the invasion of Kuwait.

_____ **18.** Intel revolutionized computers by
  A. developing the integrated circuit.
  B. developing the microprocessor.
  C. creating the first practical and affordable home computer.
  D. inventing the mouse.

_____ **19.** President Clinton's domestic program included all of the following EXCEPT
  A. deficit spending.   **C.** the Brady Bill.
  B. health benefits.   **D.** AmeriCorps.

_____ **20.** In the September 11, 2001, terrorist attack, the most lives were lost in
  A. Washington, D.C.   **C.** western Pennsylvania.
  B. the Pentagon.   **D.** the World Trade Center.

DIRECTIONS: Essay Answer one of the following questions on a separate sheet of paper. *(20 points)*

21. President Jimmy Carter boycotted the 1980 summer Olympic Games. Why did he do this, and do you agree with his decision? Explain.

22. What happened in Tiananmen Square, and how did this event affect U.S. relations with China?

★ Chapter 27

Section Quiz 27-1

DIRECTIONS: Matching Match each item in Column A with the items in Column B. Write the correct letters in the blanks. *(10 points each)*

Column A

_____ **1.** chosen by Nixon to replace Chief Justice Warren

_____ **2.** "... not a love fest ... [but] an understanding between nations ..."

_____ **3.** granted federal funds to state and local agencies

_____ **4.** Nixon's effort to win Southerners to the Republican Party

_____ **5.** a plan the United States and Soviet Union worked out to limit nuclear arms

Column B

A. Strategic Arms Limitation Treaty

B. revenue-sharing bills

C. détente

D. Southern strategy

E. Warren Burger

DIRECTIONS: Multiple Choice In the blank at the left, write the letter of the choice that best completes the statement or answers the question. *(10 points each)*

_____ **6.** President Nixon's Republican constituency favored dismantling a number of federal programs and giving more control to state and local governments in what he called
   A. New Federalism.
   B. the New Deal.
   C. State Power.
   D. New Southernism.

_____ **7.** To gain Southern support, Nixon promised several things to the powerful senator from South Carolina,
   A. George Wallace.
   B. Strom Thurmond.
   C. John Mitchell.
   D. Hubert Humphrey.

_____ **8.** President Nixon once expressed the hope that a "competent cabinet" of advisers could run the country, which would allow him to focus his energies on the subject that truly fascinated him,
   A. memoir writing.
   B. negotiating.
   C. education.
   D. foreign affairs.

_____ **9.** Shortly after the public learned of U.S. negotiations with China, the Soviets proposed an American-Soviet high-level diplomatic meeting, or
   A. détente.
   B. revenue sharing.
   C. summit.
   D. New Federalism.

_____ **10.** Rather than a bipolar notion of the world, Nixon believed the world of the future demanded a
   A. nationalistic approach.
   B. multipolar approach.
   C. conservative approach.
   D. unilateral approach.

★ Chapter 27

Section Quiz 27-2

DIRECTIONS: Matching Match each item in Column A with the items in Column B.
Write the correct letters in the blanks. *(10 points each)*

Column A

_____ 1. principle that White House conversations should remain confidential to protect national security

_____ 2. member of Nixon's inner circle who leveled allegations against Nixon

_____ 3. limited campaign contributions and established an independent agency to administer stricter election laws

_____ 4. appointed by President Nixon to handle the Watergate cases and eventually fired at Nixon's request

_____ 5. senator from North Carolina and head of the Senate's Select Committee on Presidential Campaign Activities

Column B

A. John Dean

B. Federal Campaign Act Amendments

C. Sam J. Ervin

D. executive privilege

E. Archibald Cox

DIRECTIONS: Multiple Choice In the blank at the left, write the letter of the choice
that best completes the statement or answers the question. *(10 points each)*

_____ 6. What was the scandal called that originated from the Nixon administration's attempts to cover up its involvement in the break-in at the Democratic National Committee headquarters?
  A. Southern strategy **C.** Watergate
  B. Revenue Sharing **D.** Woodward-Bernstein

_____ 7. John Dean testified that the Watergate break-in had been ordered by
  A. Attorney General John Mitchell. **C.** Vice President Agnew.
  B. President Nixon. **D.** Alexander Butterfield.

_____ 8. What revealed that on June 23, 1972, just six days after the Watergate burglary, President Nixon had ordered the CIA to stop the FBI's investigation of the break-in?
  A. written documents **C.** audiotapes
  B. videotapes **D.** phone taps

_____ 9. Vice President Spiro Agnew was forced to resign in disgrace when investigators found he had
  A. accepted bribes. **C.** a criminal record.
  B. stolen the White House tapes. **D.** lied while campaigning.

_____ 10. The Watergate crisis prompted a series of new laws intended to limit the power of
  A. campaign contributors. **C.** political deals.
  B. the executive branch. **D.** the legislative branch.

The American Republic Since 1877

★ **Chapter 27**

Section Quiz 27-3

DIRECTIONS: Matching Match each item in Column A with the items in Column B. Write the correct letters in the blanks. *(10 points each)*

Column A

_____ **1.** a combination of rising prices and economic stagnation

_____ **2.** a historic peace treaty between Israel and Egypt that was brokered by President Carter

_____ **3.** religious leader and head of the new regime in Iran

_____ **4.** a rise in the cost of goods

_____ **5.** first African American ambassador to the United Nations

Column B

A. Andrew Young

B. inflation

C. Camp David Accords

D. stagflation

E. Ayatollah Khomeini

DIRECTIONS: Multiple Choice In the blank at the left, write the letter of the choice that best completes the statement or answers the question. *(10 points each)*

_____ **6.** What virtually collapsed under the Carter administration?
  A. the Cold War
  B. the economic crisis
  C. human rights
  D. détente

_____ **7.** Two things that economists who emphasized the demand-side of economic theory, including supporters of Keynesianism, did not think could occur at the same time were recession and
  A. a bull market.
  B. peace.
  C. inflation.
  D. stagflation.

_____ **8.** In August 1975, President Ford met with leaders of NATO and the Warsaw Pact to sign the
  A. Helsinki Accords.
  B. Camp David Accords.
  C. OPEC Agreement.
  D. Nixon pardon.

_____ **9.** President Carter felt that the nation's most serious problem was its dependence on
  A. détente.
  B. foreign oil.
  C. the federal government.
  D. industry.

_____ **10.** The Organization of Petroleum Exporting Countries announced that its members would embargo, or stop shipping, petroleum to countries that supported
  A. Iraq.
  B. Egypt.
  C. Iran.
  D. Israel.

Chapter 27

Section Quiz 27-4

DIRECTIONS: Matching Match each item in Column A with the items in Column B.
Write the correct letters in the blanks. *(10 points each)*

Column A

_____ **1.** allowed drivers to talk to each other over a two-way
frequency within a range of a few miles

_____ **2.** religious movement led by Maharishi Mahesh Yogi

_____ **3.** situation comedy that placed an unmarried woman with a
meaningful career at its center

_____ **4.** popular singer in tune with the new meditative
atmosphere

_____ **5.** marked the biggest turning point in television
programming

Column B

A. *All in the Family*

B. CBs

C. John Denver

D. *The Mary Tyler
Moore Show*

E. transcendental
meditation

DIRECTIONS: Multiple Choice In the blank at the left, write the letter of the choice
that best completes the statement or answers the question. *(10 points each)*

_____ **6.** What fell to an all-time low in 1976?
    A. birthrate   **C.** divorce rate
    B. oil prices   **D.** college enrollment

_____ **7.** What reached its peak after the 1977 movie, *Saturday Night Fever*?
    A. punk rock   **C.** rock 'n' roll
    B. disco mania   **D.** ballroom dancing

_____ **8.** Disenchanted with the conventional religions of their parents, some
young men and women sought fulfillment through the host of secular
movements and activities that made up the
    A. hippie movement.   **C.** counterculture.
    B. fitness movement.   **D.** New Age movement.

_____ **9.** The hard-driving rock of the tumultuous 1960s gave way to
    A. salsa sounds.   **C.** softer sounds.
    B. classical music.   **D.** rap music.

_____ **10.** What popular exercise was a way to achieve fitness without the
drudgery and isolation that often accompanies exercise?
    A. skiing   **C.** golf
    B. aerobics   **D.** calisthenics

⭐ **Chapter 27 Test, Form A**

Score

Politics and Economics

DIRECTIONS: Matching Match each item in Column A with the items in Column B. Write the correct letters in the blanks. *(4 points each)*

Column A

_____ **1.** Watergate burglar and ex-CIA official

_____ **2.** counsel who leveled allegations against Nixon

_____ **3.** special prosecutor who took Nixon to court to force him to turn over the tapes

_____ **4.** became Nixon's vice president after Spiro Agnew resigned

_____ **5.** accused of ordering the Watergate break-in

_____ **6.** judge hearing the case of the Watergate burglars

_____ **7.** testified that Nixon had ordered a taping system installed in the White House

_____ **8.** asked the CIA to stop the FBI from inquiring into the source of the money paid to the Watergate burglars

_____ **9.** chaired the Senate's Select Committee on Presidential Campaign Activities

_____ **10.** *Washington Post* reporter who broke the Watergate story

Column B

A. Sam J. Ervin

B. John Mitchell

C. Bob Woodward

D. Gerald Ford

E. Richard Nixon

F. John J. Sirica

G. John Dean

H. Archibald Cox

I. Alexander Butterfield

J. James McCord

DIRECTIONS: Multiple Choice Choose the item that best completes each sentence or answers each question. Write the letter in the blank. *(4 points each)*

_____ **11.** Richard Nixon won Southern support in the 1968 election by promising to
   A. support busing.
   B. push for repeal of the Civil Rights Act.
   C. appoint a Southerner to the Supreme Court.
   D. win the Vietnam War.

_____ **12.** To make good on his campaign promise to fight crime, Nixon targeted
   A. Communists.
   B. African Americans.
   C. organized crime syndicates.
   D. antiwar protesters.

_____ **13.** The first American president ever to visit the Soviet Union was
   A. Richard Nixon.
   B. Gerald Ford.
   C. Jimmy Carter.
   D. Ronald Reagan.

_____ **14.** Burglars broke into the Watergate complex intending to
   A. tap the phone of Nixon's Democratic opponent who lived there.
   B. take campaign funds the Democrats stored in their headquarters.
   C. destroy documents that implicated Nixon in illegal activities.
   D. steal campaign information from the Democratic Party headquarters.

(continued)

_____ **15.** Evidence on Watergate seems to show that Nixon
    A. was never directly involved in it.   **C.** ordered the cover-up.
    B. ordered the break-in.   **D.** ordered the break-in and the cover-up.

_____ **16.** Spiro Agnew resigned because investigators discovered that he had
    A. played a direct role in the Watergate break-in.   **C.** leaked information about Watergate to the press.
    B. taken bribes.   **D.** illegally evaded taxes.

_____ **17.** The prosperity of the 1950s and 1960s rested in large part on easy access to raw materials around the world and
    A. increased consumer spending.   **C.** a strong manufacturing industry.
    B. low unemployment.   **D.** low inflation.

_____ **18.** By the 1970s, the U.S. economy had become heavily dependent on
    A. imported oil.   **C.** steadily rising profits.
    B. steadily increasing production.   **D.** government regulation.

_____ **19.** The energy crisis of the 1970s was in large part a result of OPEC price increases and
    A. price gouging by the oil industry.   **C.** increased demand for oil.
    B. government regulation of the oil industry.   **D.** a shortage of alternative fuels.

_____ **20.** President Carter imposed an embargo on the sale of grain to the Soviet Union as a result of the Soviet
    A. invasion of Afghanistan.   **C.** expansion in the Middle East.
    B. boycott of the Summer Olympic Games.   **D.** aid to the Arab nations during the Yom Kippur War.

DIRECTIONS: Essay Answer one of the following questions on a separate sheet of paper. *(20 points)*

21. Complete the diagram about the results of revenue sharing. Then explain what revenue sharing was and why the actual results differed from the intended results.

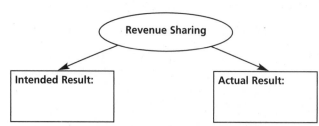

22. Describe the beliefs and activities typical of the New Age movement.

★ **Chapter 27 Test, Form B**

Politics and Economics

DIRECTIONS: Matching Match each item in Column A with the items in Column B.
Write the correct letters in the blanks. *(4 points each)*

Column A

_____ **1.** voluntary cut backs on oil and gas consumption

_____ **2.** counteracted the effects of oil industry deregulation

_____ **3.** played a major role in Carter's loss to Reagan in 1980

_____ **4.** recognized the borders of Eastern Europe established at the end of World War II in exchange for a Soviet promise to uphold human rights

_____ **5.** firing of the special prosecutor investigating Watergate

_____ **6.** enlightenment

_____ **7.** relaxation of tensions between the United States and its two major Communist rivals, the Soviet Union and China

_____ **8.** Nixon's name for the many Americans who supported the government and longed for an end to the violence and turmoil of the 1960s

_____ **9.** a well-known guru

_____ **10.** historic peace treaty between Israel and Egypt

Column B

A. Camp David Accords

B. Helsinki Accords

C. Zen

D. détente

E. windfall profits tax

F. Whip Inflation Now

G. Maharishi Mahesh Yogi

H. Iran hostage crisis

I. silent majority

J. Saturday Night Massacre

DIRECTIONS: Multiple Choice Choose the item that best completes each sentence or answers each question. Write the letter in the blank. *(4 points each)*

_____ **11.** As part of his Southern strategy, Nixon took steps to
  A. increase school funding.
  B. slow desegregation.
  C. balance the budget.
  D. support prices for farm products.

_____ **12.** As part of Nixon's New Federalism policy, Congress passed
  A. new civil rights laws.
  B. revenue-sharing bills.
  C. the Aid to Families with Dependent Children Act.
  D. the Ethics in Government Act.

_____ **13.** A main purpose of Nixon's trip to China was to
  A. confront the Chinese government about its human rights violations.
  B. negotiate an arms limitation treaty with the Chinese government.
  C. encourage the Soviets to more actively pursue diplomacy.
  D. negotiate a treaty of alliance with China against the Soviet Union.

(continued)

Chapter 27 Test, Form B

_____ **14.** As part of the Strategic Arms Limitation Treaty, Nixon and Brezhnev agreed to
- **A.** exchange weapons technology.
- **B.** exchange prisoners.
- **C.** end the Cold War.
- **D.** exchange scientific information.

_____ **15.** Nixon's "enemies list" was composed of anyone he suspected of being a
- **A.** Communist sympathizer.
- **B.** threat to his presidency.
- **C.** spy for the Soviet Union.
- **D.** member of organized crime.

_____ **16.** Nixon tried to avoid turning over the Watergate tapes by claiming that the tapes
- **A.** would compromise national security.
- **B.** were private property.
- **C.** did not exist.
- **D.** did not contain any information relevant to the investigation.

_____ **17.** Watergate investigators found indisputable evidence against the president when a tape revealed that Nixon had
- **A.** paid for the break-in.
- **B.** paid "hush money" to the burglars.
- **C.** edited out important information.
- **D.** ordered the CIA to stop the FBI investigation.

_____ **18.** Which of the following choices best completes the diagram?

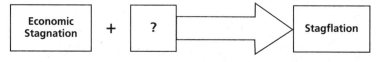

- **A.** recession
- **B.** deflation
- **C.** rising unemployment
- **D.** rising prices

_____ **19.** President Ford's approval rating plunged when he
- **A.** froze wages.
- **B.** rationed gasoline.
- **C.** pardoned Richard Nixon.
- **D.** sent marines to Cambodia.

_____ **20.** The 1978 Panama Canal treaties transferred control of the Panama Canal from
- **A.** Panama to the United States.
- **B.** Colombia to Panama.
- **C.** Panama to Britain.
- **D.** the United States to Panama.

DIRECTIONS: Essay Answer one of the following questions on a separate sheet of paper. *(20 points)*

21. Discuss Watergate's impact on government and Americans' view of government. Include a discussion of at least three new laws or guidelines passed as a result of Watergate.

22. Describe five fads of the 1970s.

★ **Chapter 28**

Section Quiz 28-1

DIRECTIONS: Matching Match each item in Column A with the items in Column B.
Write the correct letters in the blanks. *(10 points each)*

Column A

_____ **1.** a movement founded by Jerry Falwell that built up a
network of ministers to register new voters who backed
conservative candidates and issues

_____ **2.** a referendum question on the state ballot in California that
greatly reduced property taxes

_____ **3.** the South and West

_____ **4.** conservative Republican nominee for president in 1964

_____ **5.** Protestant minister with a national following

Column B

A. Sunbelt

B. Billy Graham

C. Moral Majority

D. Proposition 13

E. Barry Goldwater

DIRECTIONS: Multiple Choice In the blank at the left, write the letter of the choice
that best completes the statement or answers the question. *(10 points each)*

_____ **6.** The largest religious group within the social conservative movement was
evangelical
   A. Unitarians.   **C.** Protestant Christians.
   B. Shakers.   **D.** revivalists.

_____ **7.** Unlike liberals, conservatives fundamentally distrust the power of
   A. large corporations.   **C.** the wealthy elite.
   B. the church.   **D.** government.

_____ **8.** Republicans learned through Barry Goldwater's presidential candidacy
that the best way to attract Southern votes was to support
   A. conservative policies.   **C.** civil rights.
   B. liberal policies.   **D.** regulation of growth.

_____ **9.** Who founded the conservative magazine *National Review* and helped
revive conservative ideas in the United States?
   A. Jerry Falwell   **C.** William F. Buckley
   B. Billy Graham   **D.** Barry Goldwater

_____ **10.** Although liberals favor government intervention in the economy, they
are suspicious of any attempt to use the government to regulate
   A. higher education.   **C.** the states.
   B. social behavior.   **D.** business.

★ **Chapter 28**

Score

Section Quiz 28-2

DIRECTIONS: Matching Match each item in Column A with the items in Column B. Write the correct letters in the blanks. *(10 points each)*

Column A

_____ **1.** Ronald Reagan became president of this union in 1947

_____ **2.** nominated to the Supreme Court

_____ **3.** rebels in Nicaragua who overthrew a pro-American dictator

_____ **4.** nicknamed "Star Wars," it called for the development of weapons that could intercept and destroy incoming missiles

_____ **5.** first woman to run for vice president for a major party

Column B

A. Sandinistas

B. Geraldine Ferraro

C. Strategic Defense Initiative

D. Sandra Day O'Connor

E. Screen Actors Guild

DIRECTIONS: Multiple Choice In the blank at the left, write the letter of the choice that best completes the statement or answers the question. *(10 points each)*

_____ **6.** Who became the leader of the Soviet Union in 1985 and agreed to resume arms control talks?

    A. Mikhail Gorbachev   **C.** Nikita Krushchev

    B. Boris Yeltsin   **D.** Mikhail Rehnquist

_____ **7.** President Reagan encouraged the Federal Reserve to raise interest rates and asked Congress to pass a massive tax cut in what critics called

    A. monetarist theory.   **C.** Reaganomics.

    B. supply-side economics.   **D.** stagflation.

_____ **8.** Reagan's first act as president was to sign an executive order eliminating price controls on

    A. corn and soybeans.   **C.** exports and imports.

    B. coal and solar power.   **D.** oil and gasoline.

_____ **9.** What did Reagan launch the largest peacetime buildup of in American history?

    A. the military   **C.** surplus wheat

    B. the bills in Congress   **D.** U.S. oil reserves

_____ **10.** A scandal emerged when individuals in President Reagan's administration secretly sold weapons to Iran in exchange for the release of American hostages being held in the Middle East, and then sent the profits from these sales to the

    A. Sandinistas in Nicaragua.   **C.** *mujahadeen* in Afghanistan.

    B. contras in Nicaragua.   **D.** Marxists in Grenada.

The American Republic Since 1877

⭐ **Chapter 28**

Section Quiz 28-3

DIRECTIONS: Matching Match each item in Column A with the items in Column B. Write the correct letters in the blanks. *(10 points each)*

Column A

_____ **1.** young, ambitious, and hardworking moneymakers

_____ **2.** environmental group

_____ **3.** first video arcade game

_____ **4.** disease that weakens the immune system, lowering resistance to illnesses

_____ **5.** orbiting platforms where continuous observation of the universe could take place

Column B

A. Sierra Club

B. yuppies

C. AIDS

D. *Pong*

E. space stations

DIRECTIONS: Multiple Choice In the blank at the left, write the letter of the choice that best completes the statement or answers the question. *(10 points each)*

_____ **6.** Like other singers, actors, and entertainers of the time, Bruce Springsteen, a singer and social activist, gave concerts to benefit food banks and
   A. the yuppies.
   B. the space program.
   C. AARP.
   D. the homeless.

_____ **7.** Congress, under pressure from environmental groups, blocked many plans of the Secretary of the Interior,
   A. Bob Geldof.
   B. Donald Trump.
   C. James Watt.
   D. Larry King.

_____ **8.** Who pioneered a new type of broadcasting in 1975?
   A. Robert Johnson
   B. Ted Turner
   C. Sam Walton
   D. Arthur Blank

_____ **9.** The worst disaster in NASA's history was the explosion and deaths of the crew on the space shuttle
   A. *Challenger.*
   B. *Mir.*
   C. *Columbia.*
   D. *Skylab.*

_____ **10.** A new sound of the 1980s had rhythmic lyrics frequently focusing on the African American experience in the inner city and was called
   A. rap.
   B. rock 'n' roll.
   C. punk rock.
   D. alternative.

★ Chapter 28

Score

Section Quiz 28-4

DIRECTIONS: Matching Match each item in Column A with the items in Column B. Write the correct letters in the blanks. *(10 points each)*

Column A

_____ **1.** term used by Jesse Jackson for a broad group of minorities and the poor

_____ **2.** openness; a principle of Gorbachev's plan

_____ **3.** tax paid by businesses and investors when they sell stocks or real estate for a profit

_____ **4.** Russian president

_____ **5.** laying off workers and managers to become more efficient

Column B

A. Boris Yeltsin

B. rainbow coalition

C. capital gains tax

D. *glasnost*

E. downsizing

DIRECTIONS: Multiple Choice In the blank at the left, write the letter of the choice that best completes the statement or answers the question. *(10 points each)*

_____ **6.** While President Bush struggled to deal with events in Eastern Europe and China, a crisis developed in
    A. France.
    B. Mexico.
    C. Cuba.
    D. Panama.

_____ **7.** By what means were Communist rulers replaced with democratically elected governments in Poland, Hungary, Czechoslovakia, Romania, and Bulgaria?
    A. foreign intervention
    B. bloody wars
    C. peaceful revolutions
    D. coups

_____ **8.** Who sent his army to invade oil-rich Kuwait in August 1990?
    A. Manuel Noriega
    B. Saddam Hussein
    C. Norman Schwarzkopf
    D. Mikhail Gorbachev

_____ **9.** In late December 1991, Mikhail Gorbachev announced the end of
    A. *perestroika.*
    B. Operation Desert Storm.
    C. the Soviet Union.
    D. the Berlin Wall.

_____ **10.** In May 1989, students and workers held demonstrations for democracy in
    A. China.
    B. Germany.
    C. Panama.
    D. Kuwait.

The American Republic Since 1877

★ **Chapter 28 Test, Form A**

Resurgence of Conservatism

DIRECTIONS: Matching Match each item in Column A with the items in Column B.
Write the correct letters in the blanks. *(4 points each)*

Column A

_____ 1. high taxes take too much money away from investors, weakening the economy

_____ 2. movement founded by Jerry Falwell

_____ 3. beginning of the Gay Liberation movement

_____ 4. restructuring of the Soviet economy to allow some private enterprise and profit-making

_____ 5. raising interest rates will fight inflation

_____ 6. young urban professionals

_____ 7. pro-democracy demonstration violently crushed by Chinese government forces

_____ 8. rebels who overthrew the pro-American dictator in Nicaragua in 1979 and set up a socialist government

_____ 9. marked the beginning of the end of the Cold War

_____ 10. Star Wars

Column B

A. Tiananmen Square

B. Strategic Defense Initiative

C. monetarism

D. Intermediate-Range Nuclear Forces Treaty

E. supply-side economics

F. *perestroika*

G. Moral Majority

H. Stonewall riot

I. yuppies

J. Sandinistas

DIRECTIONS: Multiple Choice Choose the item that best completes each sentence or answers each question. Write the letter in the blank. *(4 points each)*

_____ 11. Liberals generally believe in
    A. religious faith as the best way to solve social problems.
    B. transferring more power from the federal government to state governments.
    C. free speech and privacy.
    D. reducing government regulation of business.

_____ 12. Many conservatives believe that most social problems can be solved through
    A. limiting the power of big business.   **C.** government welfare programs.
    B. limiting the power of the wealthy.   **D.** religious faith and private efforts.

_____ 13. Conservatives built a coalition that could elect a president when
    A. Westerners began shifting their votes to the Republican Party.
    B. Southerners began shifting their votes to the Republican Party.
    C. liberals began moving to the suburbs in large numbers.
    D. conservatives began moving to the Northeast in large numbers.

_____ 14. Before Ronald Reagan became governor of California, he was
    A. a lawyer.   **C.** an actor.
    B. a shoe salesman.   **D.** a televangelist.

(continued)

★ **Chapter 28 Test, Form A**

_____ **15.** Supply-side economists believed that tax cuts would result in
  A. a severe budget deficit. **C.** too much money in circulation.
  B. business expansion and new jobs. **D.** high inflation.

_____ **16.** All of the following resulted from Reagan's policy of deregulation EXCEPT
  A. increased use of public lands for oil drilling. **C.** relaxed fuel efficiency requirements for cars.
  B. voluntary price caps on airline tickets. **D.** fewer safety checks on pesticides.

_____ **17.** Reagan followed the foreign policy of
  A. containment. **C.** strict constructionism.
  B. détente. **D.** peace through strength.

_____ **18.** Reagan believed that massive Soviet defense spending would
  A. collapse the Communist system. **C.** maintain peace.
  B. lead to nuclear war. **D.** reduce U.S.–Soviet tensions.

_____ **19.** In the Iran-Contra scandal, officials sold weapons to Iran to
  A. support the guerrillas fighting against the pro-Soviet government in Iran.
  B. support the pro-Western government in Iran in its fight against communism.
  C. gain freedom for the American hostages in Iran.
  D. improve relations with the Iranian government.

_____ **20.** As opposition to reforms mounted in the Soviet Union, Boris Yeltsin
  A. removed Gorbachev from power. **C.** denounced a coup.
  B. announced the end of the USSR. **D.** fled to the United States.

DIRECTIONS: Essay Answer one of the following questions on a separate sheet of paper. *(20 points)*

21. Complete the diagram by writing "liberal" or "conservative" in the appropriate box. Then explain the beliefs behind these opposing views on taxation.

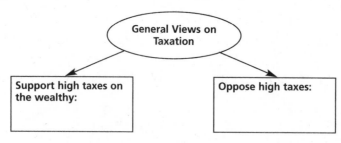

General Views on Taxation

Support high taxes on the wealthy:

Oppose high taxes:

22. Describe five new developments in media news and entertainment that occurred in the 1980s.

Chapter 28 Test, Form B

Score

Resurgence of Conservatism

DIRECTIONS: Matching Match each item in Column A with the items in Column B. Write the correct letters in the blanks. *(4 points each)*

Column A

_____ **1.** first woman on the Supreme Court

_____ **2.** teacher who died in the *Challenger* disaster

_____ **3.** increased the amount of public land corporations could use for oil drilling, mining, and logging

_____ **4.** founded the Moral Majority movement

_____ **5.** first woman to run for vice president for a major party

_____ **6.** appointed by Reagan to succeed Warren Burger as Chief Justice

_____ **7.** founded Young Americans for Freedom

_____ **8.** tried to create a "rainbow coalition"

_____ **9.** sparked the Persian Gulf War

_____ **10.** first American woman in space

Column B

A. Geraldine Ferraro

B. James Watt

C. Sally Ride

D. William F. Buckley

E. Jesse Jackson

F. Christa McAuliffe

G. Jerry Falwell

H. Saddam Hussein

I. Sandra Day O'Connor

J. William Rehnquist

DIRECTIONS: Multiple Choice Choose the item that best completes each sentence or answers each question. Write the letter in the blank. *(4 points each)*

_____ **11.** Conservatives generally support
   A. government regulation of the economy.
   B. the split of government power between state and federal levels.
   C. social programs sponsored by government to help disadvantaged Americans.
   D. shifting wealth to reduce the gap between rich and poor.

_____ **12.** Some Americans turned to conservatism during the Cold War because they believed that
   A. liberal economic ideas were slowly leading the nation toward communism.
   B. liberal organizations included many members of the Communist Party.
   C. liberals would not go to war, if necessary, to stop communism.
   D. the liberal policy of confronting communism would lead the country into war.

_____ **13.** California's Proposition 13 was a conservative effort to
   A. reduce taxes.   **C.** reduce regulation of business.
   B. win approval of prayer in schools. **D.** limit abortion rights.

_____ **14.** To keep the deficit under control, Reagan proposed
   A. increasing taxes.   **C.** cutting social programs.
   B. decreasing interest rates.   **D.** issuing more government bonds.

(continued)

_____ 15. Which of the following choices best completes the diagram?

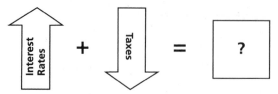

A. monetarism

B. Keynesianism

C. supply-side economics

D. Reaganomics

_____ 16. Reagan wanted to appoint justices who would

A. follow the original intent of the Constitution.

B. interpret the Constitution more broadly.

C. expand the Constitution to better fit present-day problems.

D. limit application of the Constitution.

_____ 17. Investigations into the Iran-Contra scandal revealed that Reagan had

A. approved the sale of arms to Iran and the diversion of money to the contras.

B. approved the sale of arms to Iran but not the diversion of money to the contras.

C. not approved the sale of arms to Iran but did approve sending money to the contras.

D. not approved the sale of arms to Iran or the diversion of money to the contras.

_____ 18. Reagan's Strategic Defense Initiative called for the

A. deployment of nuclear weapons in Western Europe.

B. development of weapons that could destroy incoming missiles.

C. deployment of nuclear missiles in space, targeted at the Soviet Union.

D. development of missiles that could reach the Soviet Union from silos in the U.S.

_____ 19. In May 1989, Chinese students and workers held demonstrations for

A. higher wages.

B. halting war.

C. democracy.

D. a capitalist economy.

_____ 20. The United Nations went to war in the Persian Gulf because

A. Saudi Arabia invaded Kuwait.

B. Kuwait invaded Iraq.

C. Iraq invaded Kuwait.

D. Iraq invaded Saudi Arabia.

DIRECTIONS: Essay Answer one of the following questions on a separate sheet of paper. *(20 points)*

21. Describe some of the problems in government, the economy, and society that brought together a new conservative coalition in the late 1970s.

22. Explain how the end of the Cold War contributed to the recession that began in 1990.

Chapter 29

Section Quiz 29-1

DIRECTIONS: Matching Match each item in Column A with the items in Column B.
Write the correct letters in the blanks. *(10 points each)*

Column A

_____ **1.** economy spawned by the Internet

_____ **2.** improved medical research after it was decoded

_____ **3.** complete electronic circuit on a single chip of the element silicon

_____ **4.** doing jobs via a computer without going to an office

_____ **5.** world's first electronic digital computer

Column B

A. telecommute

B. DNA

C. dot.com

D. ENIAC

E. integrated circuit

DIRECTIONS: Multiple Choice In the blank at the left, write the letter of the choice
that best completes the statement or answers the question. *(10 points each)*

_____ **6.** As Steven Jobs and Stephen Wozniak were creating Apple, 19-year-old
Harvard dropout Bill Gates co-founded Microsoft to design PC
A. software.
B. hardware.
C. Web sites.
D. Internet connections.

_____ **7.** The Telecommunications Act passed in 1996 allowed all of the following
EXCEPT
A. telephone companies to compete.
B. telephone companies to send television signals.
C. cable companies to regulate cellular phones.
D. cable companies to offer telephone service.

_____ **8.** What had its roots in a computer networking system that the U.S.
Defense Department's Advanced Research Project Agency established?
A. the Windows operating system
B. ENIAC
C. integrated circuits
D. the Internet

_____ **9.** Who deciphered the structure of DNA?
A. James Watson and Gordon Moore
B. James Watson and Francis Crick
C. Gordon Moore and Robert Noyce
D. Steven Jobs and Stephen Wozniak

_____ **10.** Intel, a company formed in 1968, revolutionized computers by
combining several integrated circuits that contained both memory and
computing functions on a single chip called
A. graphical-user interfaces.
B. genomes.
C. microprocessors.
D. personal computers.

Chapter 29

Section Quiz 29-2

DIRECTIONS: Matching Match each item in Column A with the items in Column B.
Write the correct letters in the blanks. *(10 points each)*

Column A

_____ **1.** put students to work improving low-income housing, teaching children to read, and cleaning up the environment

_____ **2.** Kenneth Starr argued that President Clinton had committed this

_____ **3.** a plan for creating a Palestinian government

_____ **4.** a peace plan regarding Bosnia

_____ **5.** limited people to no more than two consecutive years on welfare and required them to work to receive benefits

Column B

A. Welfare Reform Act

B. Dayton Accords

C. Declaration of Principles

D. AmeriCorps

E. perjury

DIRECTIONS: Multiple Choice In the blank at the left, write the letter of the choice
that best completes the statement or answers the question. *(10 points each)*

_____ **6.** In Bosnia, one of the former Yugoslav republics, a vicious three-way civil war erupted between Bosnian Muslims, Catholic Croatians, and
   A. Palestinians.
   B. Orthodox Christian Serbs.
   C. Kurds.
   D. Communists.

_____ **7.** A law Congress passed that gave workers up to 12 weeks per year of unpaid family leave for the birth or adoption of a child or for the illness of a family member was called
   A. the Health Care Plan.
   B. AmeriCorps.
   C. the Family Medical Leave Act.
   D. the Adoption and Safe Families Act.

_____ **8.** Despite strong opposition from many Republicans and the National Rifle Association, the Democrats in Congress passed a gun-control law known as the
   A. Firearms Act.
   B. Brady Bill.
   C. Contract with America.
   D. HOPE Bill.

_____ **9.** Who led congressional Republicans in creating the Contract with America?
   A. Newt Gingrich
   B. Ross Perot
   C. Kenneth Starr
   D. Bob Dole

_____ **10.** Seeking to topple the military dictatorship and restore democracy, the Clinton administration convinced the United Nations to impose a trade embargo on
   A. Iraq.
   B. Kosovo.
   C. Bosnia.
   D. Haiti.

Name _____ Date _____ Class _____

 Chapter 29

Score

Section Quiz 29-3

DIRECTIONS: Matching Match each item in Column A with the items in Column B.
Write the correct letters in the blanks. *(10 points each)*

Column A

_____ **1.** an increase in average world temperatures over time

_____ **2.** joined Canada, the United States, and Mexico in a free-trade zone

_____ **3.** when Americans purchased more from foreign nations than American industry and agriculture sold abroad

_____ **4.** spread of nuclear weapons to new nations

_____ **5.** created to promote economic and political cooperation among the many European nations

Column B

A. nuclear proliferation

B. global warming

C. European Union

D. North American Free Trade Agreement

E. trade deficit

DIRECTIONS: Multiple Choice In the blank at the left, write the letter of the choice that best completes the statement or answers the question. *(10 points each)*

_____ **6.** From World War II to the present, Republican and Democratic administrations have both tried to lower the barriers to
   A. democracy.
   B. trade deficits.
   C. cheap labor.
   D. international trade.

_____ **7.** Central to the effort to promote a global economy was the
   A. Asia Pacific Economic Cooperation.
   B. Kyoto Protocol.
   C. World Trade Organization.
   D. European Union.

_____ **8.** In the latter part of the 1900s, economies around the world had become much more
   A. nationalistic.
   B. isolated.
   C. regulated.
   D. interdependent.

_____ **9.** The European Union created a common bank and a common currency for member nations called the
   A. euro.
   B. European coins.
   C. union euro.
   D. free trade currency.

_____ **10.** At an international conference on global warming in Japan in 1997, 38 nations and the EU signed an agreement to reduce emissions by 2008 known as the
   A. Kyoto Protocol.
   B. Reduction of Global Warming Initiative.
   C. Japanese Accords.
   D. Global Warming Protocol.

⭐ **Chapter 29**

Section Quiz 29-4

DIRECTIONS: Matching Match each item in Column A with the items in Column B.
Write the correct letters in the blanks. *(10 points each)*

Column A

_____ **1.** Democratic presidential candidate in 2000

_____ **2.** consumer advocate and Green Party candidate

_____ **3.** a piece of cardboard punched out of a ballot

_____ **4.** Republican presidential candidate in 2000

_____ **5.** Bush's program to develop missiles that could shoot down
nuclear missiles

Column B

A. Ralph Nader

B. strategic defense

C. George W. Bush

D. Al Gore

E. chad

DIRECTIONS: Multiple Choice In the blank at the left, write the letter of the choice
that best completes the statement or answers the question. *(10 points each)*

_____ **6.** To win the presidency, candidates have to win a majority of state
electoral votes, not the overall
  A. chad count.
  B. African American vote.
  C. popular vote.
  D. Sunbelt vote.

_____ **7.** The presidential election came down to the vote in which state?
  A. Florida
  B. Texas
  C. Georgia
  D. Tennessee

_____ **8.** The United States Supreme Court ruled that the hand recounts of ballots
  A. was constitutional.
  B. violated the equal protection clause.
  C. should be done by the state Supreme Court.
  D. was fair and impartial.

_____ **9.** In his inaugural address, George W. Bush promised to improve the
nation's public schools, to reform Social Security and Medicare, to build
up the nation's defenses, and to
  A. increase welfare programs.
  B. reduce interest rates.
  C. reform the election process.
  D. cut taxes.

_____ **10.** George W. Bush selected this former defense secretary as his vice
presidential running mate—
  A. John McCain.
  B. Ralph Nader.
  C. Richard Cheney.
  D. Joseph Lieberman.

The American Republic Since 1877

★ **Chapter 29**

Section Quiz 29-5

DIRECTIONS: Matching Match each item in Column A with the items in Column B. Write the correct letters in the blanks. *(10 points each)*

Column A

_____ **1.** "the Base"

_____ **2.** lethal bacteria

_____ **3.** Muslim fundamentalists in Afghanistan

_____ **4.** intended to frighten governments into changing their policies

_____ **5.** region in northern India

Column B

A. terrorism

B. the Taliban

C. anthrax

D. Kashmir

E. al-Qaeda

DIRECTIONS: Multiple Choice In the blank at the left, write the letter of the choice that best completes the statement or answers the question. *(10 points each)*

_____ **6.** The coalition of Afghan groups who were allied with the United States is known as
  A. the Taliban.
  B. the Northern Alliance.
  C. the Southern Alliance.
  D. the Afghan Resistance.

_____ **7.** What American warship was bombed by terrorists in 1999?
  A. USS *Maine*
  B. USS *Enterprise*
  C. USS *Kennedy*
  D. USS *Cole*

_____ **8.** What did some devout Muslims fear would happen as the contact between the Middle East and Western society increased?
  A. that traditional values and beliefs would be weakened
  B. that the United States would launch terrorist attacks against them
  C. that wealthy Middle Eastern families would enslave them
  D. that Palestinians would want their own nation

_____ **9.** The new federal agency created in response to the terrorist attacks was the
  A. CIA.
  B. Office of Terrorist Activity.
  C. Department of Homeland Security.
  D. Terrorism Defense Agency.

_____ **10.** Governments of Libya, Syria, Iraq, and Iran have all participated in
  A. state-sponsored terrorism.
  B. Afghan resistance efforts.
  C. direct acts of war against the U.S.
  D. hijacking American airplanes.

⭐ **Chapter 29 Test, Form A**

Score

Into a New Century

DIRECTIONS: Matching Match each item in Column A with the items in Column B. Write the correct letters in the blanks. *(4 points each)*

Column A

Column B

_____ 1. software that enabled Internet users to click links to jump from Web site to Web site

_____ 2. IBM's first compact computer

_____ 3. policy of the Serbs to brutally expel Bosnian Muslims from the region

_____ 4. Muslim fundamentalists who controlled Afghanistan

_____ 5. lying under oath

_____ 6. genetic material in cells that determines all forms of life

_____ 7. early computer operating system developed for the PC

_____ 8. environmental threat that could lead to droughts

_____ 9. chemical used in air conditioners and refrigerators that could potentially deplete the earth's protective atmosphere

_____ 10. program of 10 proposed changes that helped Republicans win the majority in both houses of Congress in 1994

A. DNA

B. global warming

C. Personal Computer

D. Taliban

E. ethnic cleansing

F. Contract with America

G. Web browser

H. chlorofluoro-carbon

I. MS-DOS

J. perjury

DIRECTIONS: Multiple Choice Choose the item that best completes each sentence or answers each question. Write the letter in the blank. *(4 points each)*

_____ 11. The first practical and affordable home computer was
    A. ENIAC.
    B. Apple I.
    C. Apple II.
    D. Personal Computer.

_____ 12. Bill Gates co-founded the company
    A. Intel.
    B. Apple Computer.
    C. IBM.
    D. Microsoft.

_____ 13. The Brady Bill was a
    A. gun-control law.
    B. health care reform law.
    C. welfare reform law.
    D. tax increase.

_____ 14. A problem Clinton faced in trying to reduce the federal deficit was
    A. the military.
    B. schools.
    C. public works programs.
    D. entitlement programs.

_____ 15. Opponents of a global economy feared that lowering trade barriers might
    A. increase the U.S. budget deficit.
    B. cost the U.S. industrial jobs.
    C. reduce investments in the U.S.
    D. cause inflation in the U.S.

(continued)

Chapter 29 Test, Form A

_____ **16.** In the period after NAFTA passed,
   A. unemployment rose in the United States.
   B. wages fell in the United States.
   C. American workers shifted to less skilled industrial jobs.
   D. American workers shifted to more skilled jobs or to the service industry.

_____ **17.** The goal of the Kyoto Protocol was to
   A. stop nuclear proliferation.
   B. open free trade among member nations.
   C. bring peace to troubled areas in the former Yugoslavia.
   D. reduce emissions worldwide.

_____ **18.** George W. Bush pushed through an immediate tax rebate to
   A. reduce inflation.
   B. prevent a recession.
   C. help parents send their children to private schools if their public schools were doing a poor job.
   D. help people save for retirement rather than depend on Social Security.

_____ **19.** The al-Qaeda group is a
   A. Palestinian group fighting Israel for a homeland.
   B. Muslim terrorist group behind the attack of September 11, 2001.
   C. Serb group trying to drive Muslims from Bosnia.
   D. Bosnian Muslim group trying to win independence from Serbia.

_____ **20.** Terrorists carried out their attacks on September 11, 2001, by
   A. using truck bombs.   **C.** planting bombs on airplanes.
   B. hijacking airplanes.   **D.** attaching bombs to their targets.

DIRECTIONS: Essay Answer one of the following questions on a separate sheet of paper. *(20 points)*

21. Why was President Clinton impeached, and what was the outcome?

22. Study the illustration of the ballot below to help you answer the following question: How did little chads cause big problems in the 2000 presidential election?

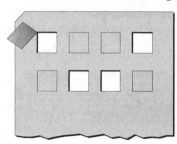 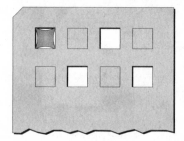

The American Republic Since 1877

★ **Chapter 29 Test, Form B**

Into a New Century

DIRECTIONS: Matching Match each item in Column A with the items in Column B.
Write the correct letters in the blanks. *(4 points each)*

Column A

_____ **1.** gas in the atmosphere that protects life on Earth from cancer-causing ultraviolet rays of the sun

_____ **2.** use of violence by nongovernmental groups against civilians to achieve a political goal

_____ **3.** first computer to use on-screen graphic icons that users could manipulate with a mouse

_____ **4.** element used in computer chips

_____ **5.** Israeli prime minister who was assassinated by a right-wing Israeli who opposed the peace plan with the PLO

_____ **6.** independent counsel appointed to investigate Clinton

_____ **7.** Serbian leader who ordered a crackdown on Albanians

_____ **8.** presidential candidate of the Green Party in 2000

_____ **9.** terrorist leader behind the attacks on Americans

_____ **10.** leader of the Palestine Liberation Organization

Column B

A. silicon

B. Osama bin Laden

C. Yitzhak Rabin

D. Macintosh

E. Yasir Arafat

F. Ralph Nader

G. ozone

H. terrorism

I. Slobodan Milosevic

J. Kenneth Starr

DIRECTIONS: Multiple Choice Choose the item that best completes each sentence or answers each question. Write the letter in the blank. *(4 points each)*

_____ **11.** Which electronics company popularized mouse-activated, on-screen graphic icons?
   A. Microsoft
   B. Apple Computer
   C. IBM
   D. Intel

_____ **12.** A global information system that operated commercially rather than through the government was called
   A. ARPANET.
   B. the Internet.
   C. hypertext transport protocol.
   D. the integrated circuit.

_____ **13.** In an unprecedented role for a first lady, Hillary Rodham Clinton accepted her husband's appointment to
   A. the cabinet.
   B. the Supreme Court.
   C. head a task force on health care reform.
   D. act as his foreign policy adviser.

_____ **14.** The Dayton Accords was an agreement intended to bring peace to
   A. Bosnia.
   B. Kosovo.
   C. Haiti.
   D. Afghanistan.

(continued)

Chapter 29 Test, Form B

Score

_____ **15.** What is the result for the United States of the situation presented in the diagram?

| Europe, Africa, and Asia | Products exported to other countries $$$$$ | U.S. |

Products imported from other countries $$$$$$$$$$$

   A. budget deficit   **C.** trade deficit
   B. budget surplus   **D.** trade surplus

_____ **16.** The free-trade agreement that represented the fastest-growing region in the world was
   A. APEC.   **C.** WTO.
   B. NAFTA.   **D.** EU.

_____ **17.** The Republican candidate in the 2000 presidential election was
   A. George W. Bush.   **C.** Al Gore.
   B. Bill Clinton.   **D.** Ralph Nader.

_____ **18.** Congress passed Bush's proposal for
   A. federal funds to private schools.
   B. setting up the AmeriCorps program.
   C. annual reading and math tests in public schools for grades 3 to 8.
   D. reducing emissions from automobiles and factories.

_____ **19.** George W. Bush's military program called for
   A. stockpiling nuclear weapons.
   B. encouraging nuclear proliferation.
   C. developing devices that could shoot down nuclear missiles.
   D. a reduction in defense spending.

_____ **20.** September 11, 2001, was the day that terrorists attacked
   A. the USS *Cole*.   **C.** Israel to try to gain a Palestinian state.
   B. the American embassies in Kenya   **D.** the World Trade Center and Pentagon.
      and Tanzania.

DIRECTIONS: Essay Answer one of the following questions on a separate sheet of paper. *(20 points)*

21. What do many experts believe causes global warming, and why is the issue controversial?

22. What were some of Osama bin Laden's beliefs that led him to call on Muslims to kill Americans?

⭐ **Unit 8 Posttest, Form A**

A Changing Society

DIRECTIONS: Matching Match each item in Column A with the items in Column B.
Write the correct letters in the blanks. *(4 points each)*

Column A

_____ **1.** believe tax cuts will spur investment, helping businesses
expand and create new jobs

_____ **2.** common currency of the European Union

_____ **3.** agreement of the United States, Canada, and Mexico to
form a free-trade zone

_____ **4.** Nixon's name for "Middle Americans" who longed for an
end to turmoil and a return to more conservative values

_____ **5.** forerunner of the Internet

_____ **6.** brutal expulsion of a people from a geographic area

_____ **7.** set up a socialist government in Nicaragua in 1979

_____ **8.** believe that raising interest rates will lower inflation

_____ **9.** guerrilla forces fighting the socialist government in
Nicaragua

_____ **10.** new openness instituted in the Soviet Union

Column B

A. *glasnost*

B. monetarists

C. supply-side
economists

D. contras

E. Sandinistas

F. ARPANET

G. ethnic cleansing

H. silent majority

I. euro

J. NAFTA

DIRECTIONS: Multiple Choice Choose the item that best completes each sentence
or answers each question. Write the letter in the blank. *(4 points each)*

_____ **11.** An unintended result of Nixon's revenue-sharing legislation was
   A. increased power of the federal government over the states.
   B. dependence of needy people on welfare payments.
   C. increased independence of the states, limiting the federal government's power.
   D. no difference in income for needy people who found jobs and left welfare.

_____ **12.** Five Nixon supporters broke into the Watergate complex to try to
   A. record phone conversations of Nixon's Democratic opponent who lived there.
   B. steal campaign funds the Democrats stored in their headquarters.
   C. destroy documents the Democrats had that implicated Nixon in illegal activities.
   D. steal campaign information from the Democratic Party headquarters.

_____ **13.** Which of the following occurred during the Carter administration?
   A. The Department of Energy was dissolved.
   B. The president and Congress agreed on many issues.
   C. Americans were taken as hostages.
   D. The Camp David Accords were signed between Israel and Lebanon.

(continued)

Unit 8 Posttest, Form A

Score

_____ 14. The economic slow-down of the 1970s resulted in part from the nation's heavy dependence on

    A. imported oil.

    B. ever-increasing production.

    C. constantly rising profits.

    D. government welfare.

_____ 15. The Reagan Doctrine called for the United States to

    A. seek better relations with China and the Soviet Union.

    B. build a missile defense system.

    C. support guerrillas fighting to overthrow pro-Soviet governments.

    D. build up its supplies of non-nuclear weapons.

_____ 16. Which of the following would be true in a comparison of liberalism and conservatism?

    A. Liberals are in favor of government supporting religious belief.

    B. Liberals are in favor of the government regulating the economy.

    C. Conservatives have a general trust in governmental power.

    D. Conservatives believe that taxes encourage investment.

_____ 17. Boris Yeltsin responded to Gorbachev's reforms in the Soviet Union by

    A. removing Gorbachev from power.

    B. announcing the end of the USSR.

    C. denouncing a military coup.

    D. fleeing to the United States.

_____ 18. The Persian Gulf War was touched off by

    A. Saudi Arabia's invasion of Kuwait.

    B. Kuwait's invasion of Iraq.

    C. Iraq's invasion of Kuwait.

    D. Iraq's invasion of Saudi Arabia.

_____ 19. The United States participated in peacekeeping missions in Bosnia along with

    A. the United Nations.

    B. NATO.

    C. the European Union.

    D. the French and British.

_____ 20. The United States and 22 other nations agreed to phase out production of chlorofluorocarbons after seeing evidence of

    A. global warming.

    B. radioactivity from the sun reaching the earth.

    C. a hole in the ozone layer above Antarctica.

    D. melting of the ice at the poles.

DIRECTIONS: Essay Answer one of the following questions on a separate sheet of paper. *(20 points)*

21. What was Richard Nixon's philosophy on dealing with Communist rivals? Describe the new approach to foreign policy that resulted from this philosophy.

22. Describe conservative beliefs on the role of government in the economy.

★ **Unit 8 Posttest, Form B**

A Changing Society

DIRECTIONS: Matching Match each item in Column A with the items in Column B. Write the correct letters in the blanks. *(4 points each)*

Column A

_____ **1.** Camp David Accords were signed between Israel and this nation

_____ **2.** Arab response to nations supporting Israel in the Yom Kippur War

_____ **3.** Osama bin Laden's terrorist organization

_____ **4.** Russian word for "restructuring"

_____ **5.** high-level diplomatic meetings

_____ **6.** used oil as a political and economic weapon in the 1970s

_____ **7.** peace plan to settle civil war in Bosnia

_____ **8.** argument used by Nixon in refusing to turn over tapes

_____ **9.** boycott led by President Carter

_____ **10.** computer chip that combines both memory and computing functions

Column B

A. al-Qaeda

B. oil embargo

C. *perestroika*

D. OPEC

E. 1980 Summer Olympic Games

F. microprocessor

G. summits

H. Egypt

I. Dayton Accords

J. executive privilege

DIRECTIONS: Multiple Choice Choose the item that best completes each sentence or answers each question. Write the letter in the blank. *(4 points each)*

_____ **11.** To encourage the Soviets to more actively pursue diplomacy, Nixon
  A. threatened war.
  B. praised communism.
  C. visited China.
  D. visited Soviet satellites.

_____ **12.** The conservative movement grew in the 1980s, particularly in the
  A. Rust Belt.   **C.** Northeast.
  B. Sunbelt.   **D.** Democratic Party.

_____ **13.** In 1985 _____ became the leader of the Soviet Union.
  A. Leon Jaworski   **C.** Boris Yeltsin
  B. Francis Crick   **D.** Mikhail Gorbachev

_____ **14.** The plan to boost the economy by raising interest rates while dramatically cutting taxes was called
  A. monetarism.   **C.** supply-side economics.
  B. Keynesianism.   **D.** Reaganomics.

(continued)

_____ **15.** The Reagan Doctrine was a policy of
   A. cutting federal funds to social programs.
   B. supporting groups who were fighting to overthrow Communist governments.
   C. eliminating price controls on oil and gasoline.
   D. reducing taxes and increasing the budget deficit.

_____ **16.** The spread of *glasnost* across Eastern Europe resulted in
   A. peaceful revolutions to replace the Communist rulers with elected governments.
   B. bloody revolutions to overthrow the Communist rulers.
   C. Soviet troops invading Eastern Europe to support the Communist rulers.
   D. peaceful protests, often crushed by force by the Communist rulers.

_____ **17.** American troops invaded Panama during the Bush administration to
   A. regain control of the Panama Canal.
   B. help Panama's government defend the Panama Canal against rebel forces.
   C. support Panama's pro-American government against Communist rebels.
   D. arrest Panama's ruler on drug charges.

_____ **18.** In the Whitewater Development scandal, President Clinton was accused of
   A. arranging illegal loans for a real estate company.
   B. committing perjury in court testimony about his financial dealings.
   C. taking bribes to award government contracts.
   D. using inside information to make money on real estate transactions.

_____ **19.** The organization that administered international trade agreements and helped settle disputes was
   A. the UN.   **C.** APEC.
   B. the WTO.   **D.** the EU.

_____ **20.** In *Bush* v. *Gore*, the Supreme Court ruled that the recount of votes in Florida during the 2000 election violated
   A. state sovereignty.
   B. local and national voting laws.
   C. the due process clause of the Constitution.
   D. the equal protection clause of the Constitution.

DIRECTIONS: Essay Answer one of the following questions on a separate sheet of paper. *(20 points)*

21. What were the Watergate tapes, and what role did they play in the investigation?

22. What role did oil play in spawning terrorism?

UNIT 1 PRETEST, FORM A

Matching

1. H	**2.** F	**3.** D	**4.** G	**5.** A
6. I	**7.** J	**8.** E	**9.** C	**10.** B

Multiple Choice

11. D	**12.** A	**13.** A	**14.** C	**15.** D
16. B	**17.** A	**18.** C	**19.** C	**20.** B

Essay

21. Europeans and Native Americans exchanged foods, inventions, knowledge, and, unfortunately, diseases. Europeans took many Native American foods back to Europe. Many of these, especially corn and potatoes, became important crops throughout Europe. Europeans introduced new crops as well as domestic livestock to Native Americans. Europeans adopted many Native American farming methods and inventions, such as canoes and hammocks. Europeans introduced Native Americans to a range of technologies, including new metalworking techniques and firearms. Both groups introduced the other to foreign diseases to which they were not immune. As a result, millions died, mostly Native Americans.

22. Answers will vary, but students should note that most African Americans living in the colonies had come or were descendants of those who had come aboard slave ships. Most enslaved African Americans supported the Southern agricultural system by toiling under poor conditions in the fields. They had no rights or freedoms and were under the control of the slaveholder. Most had no way to earn or gain their freedom. The free African Americans held jobs, organized churches and voluntary associations, and some became prosperous.

UNIT 1 PRETEST, FORM B

Matching

1. G	**2.** F	**3.** A	**4.** C	**5.** H
6. D	**7.** I	**8.** J	**9.** B	**10.** E

Multiple Choice

11. D	**12.** D	**13.** C	**14.** C	**15.** B
16. B	**17.** C	**18.** B	**19.** C	**20.** C

Essay

21. European culture changed as strong states emerged and as technology changed. Increased revenue from trade allowed kings to gather power. They wanted to expand their power and find new avenues for trade. This led them to finance explorers who sought new trade routes and new sources of natural resources such as gold. Scientific advances that occurred during the Renaissance, such as improved navigational tools, gave these explorers the tools they needed to travel to new lands.

African cultures had also seen the development of strong empires based on trade in precious commodities such as gold and salt. Muslim conquest had brought African cultures into contact with other parts of the world, especially the Muslim world.

African and European cultures met as the Europeans explored the coast of Africa. Europeans became involved in the slave trade as they expanded their sugar plantations. Eventually, Europeans transported enslaved Africans to the Americas.

22. The United States expanded its territory through purchases such as the Louisiana Purchase, through claims such as the Northwest Territory, through annexation such as Texas, and through treaties such as the treaty in which Spain ceded Florida to the United States. In some cases, the United States simply took land that was claimed by the Native Americans with little or no payment for the land.

SECTION QUIZ 1-1

Matching

1. D	**2.** A	**3.** C	**4.** B	**5.** E

Multiple Choice

6. B	**7.** C	**8.** A	**9.** B	**10.** D

SECTION QUIZ 1-2

Matching

1. C	**2.** E	**3.** B	**4.** A	**5.** D

Multiple Choice

6. A	**7.** B	**8.** A	**9.** D	**10.** C

SECTION QUIZ 1-3

Matching

1. B	**2.** D	**3.** A	**4.** E	**5.** C

Multiple Choice

6. A	**7.** D	**8.** A	**9.** A	**10.** B

SECTION QUIZ 1-4

Matching

1. E	**2.** B	**3.** A	**4.** D	**5.** C

Multiple Choice

6. C	**7.** B	**8.** B	**9.** A	**10.** A

CHAPTER 1 TEST, FORM A

Matching

1. H	**2.** D	**3.** E	**4.** B	**5.** F
6. B	**7.** A	**8.** C	**9.** G	**10.** I

Multiple Choice

11. B	**12.** D	**13.** D	**14.** D	**15.** C
16. D	**17.** B	**18.** C	**19.** D	**20.** A

Essay

21. Slavery had existed in Africa and other parts of the world for centuries. At first, most African slaves were war captives who were eventually ransomed back to their people or absorbed into their captors' culture. West African slavery began to change with the arrival of Arab traders, who exchanged horses, cotton, and other goods for slaves. The gold trade and the development of sugarcane plantations, however, increased the demand for slaves. Both gold mining and sugarcane cultivation required much manual labor. More workers meant greater production.

22. At the top were the *peninsulares.* These were people born in Spain and appointed to the highest government and church positions. Next were the *criollos,* who were people born in the colonies to Spanish parents. Many were wealthy. At the next lower level were the *mestizos.* These were people of Spanish and Native American parents. Their social status varied greatly. A few were accepted at the top of society. Others worked as artisans, merchants, and shopkeepers. Most, however, were poor and lived at the lowest level of society. The lowest level also included Native Americans, Africans, and people of mixed Spanish and African or African and Native American ancestry. These people labored for New Spain's farms, mines, and ranches.

CHAPTER 1 TEST, FORM B

Matching

1. I	**2.** G	**3.** J	**4.** F	**5.** D
6. H	**7.** B	**8.** A	**9.** C	**10.** E

Multiple Choice

11. C	**12.** C	**13.** D	**14.** A	**15.** A
16. D	**17.** A	**18.** D	**19.** B	**20.** D

Essay

21. For centuries the Roman Empire had dominated much of Europe. When the Roman political and economic system collapsed, western Europe became isolated from the rest of the world. Trade declined, cities and roads fell into disrepair, law and order vanished, and money was no longer used. With the weakening of central government, feudalism developed in western Europe. Under this political system, kings would give estates to nobles in exchange for their military support. The nobles could raise their own armies, dispense justice, and mint their own coins. Most built fortified castles for defense.

22. Europeans and Native Americans exchanged foods, inventions, knowledge, and, unfortunately, diseases. Europeans took many Native American foods back to Europe. Many of these, especially corn and potatoes, became important crops throughout Europe. Europeans introduced new crops as well as domestic livestock to Native Americans. Europeans adopted many Native American farming methods and inventions, such as canoes and hammocks. Europeans introduced Native Americans to a range of technologies, including new metalworking techniques and firearms. Both groups introduced the other to foreign diseases to which they were not immune. As a result, millions died, mostly Native Americans.

SECTION QUIZ 2-1

Matching

1. E	**2.** B	**3.** D	**4.** C	**5.** A

Multiple Choice

6. D	**7.** A	**8.** C	**9.** B	**10.** C

SECTION QUIZ 2-2

Matching

1. D	**2.** A	**3.** E	**4.** C	**5.** B

Multiple Choice

6. D	**7.** A	**8.** D	**9.** B	**10.** C

SECTION QUIZ 2-3

Matching

1. C	**2.** A	**3.** E	**4.** D	**5.** B

Multiple Choice

6. A	**7.** D	**8.** D	**9.** A	**10.** A

SECTION QUIZ 2-4

Matching

1. C	**2.** B	**3.** E	**4.** D	**5.** A

Multiple Choice

6. D	**7.** A	**8.** B	**9.** C	**10.** C

SECTION QUIZ 2-5

Matching

1. E	**2.** A	**3.** C	**4.** B	**5.** D

Multiple Choice

6. B	7. B	8. D	9. C	10. A

CHAPTER 2 TEST, FORM A

Matching

1. G	2. H	3. J	4. I	5. A
6. D	7. B	8. E	9. F	10. C

Multiple Choice

11. D	12. C	13. A	14. C	15. B
16. B	17. A	18. B	19. B	20. D

Essay

21. The English government had little money, and Cabot found no wealth to spur migration. Furthermore, Spain had claimed America. At the time, Spain and England were allies. Any attempt to settle America would have upset the alliance.

22. The Enlightenment encouraged people to use reason and natural law to shape society. Thinkers believed that people were not born sinful, but were born as blank slates. Their experiences and education shaped the nature they developed and the people they became. The Great Awakening was a renewal of the Christian faith that stressed piety and being emotionally united with God. Groups such as the Baptists, Presbyterians, and Methodists gained members. Both movements emphasized individualism and encouraged colonists to seek their independence.

CHAPTER 2 TEST, FORM B

Matching

1. F	2. H	3. J	4. A	5. D
6. G	7. E	8. I	9. B	10. C

Multiple Choice

11. D	12. C	13. D	14. C	15. C
16. D	17. B	18. D	19. C	20. C

Essay

21. In early colonial days, there was plenty of land for tobacco farmers, but not enough labor to work it. England had the opposite problem. The English enclosure movement had forced many peasants off the land. Many of them, hoping to acquire their own land in America, became indentured servants. They made labor contracts with colonists, agreeing to work for a set term, usually four years. In return, the colonists would pay for a servant's passage and provide food, clothing, and shelter until the contract expired.

22. Mercantilism gave the colonies a reliable market for some of their raw materials and an eager supplier of the manufactured goods they needed. However, it prevented them from selling goods to other nations, even if they could get a better price. Also, if a colony produced nothing the home country needed, the colony could not acquire gold or silver to buy manufactured goods.

SECTION QUIZ 3-1

Matching

1. D	2. B	3. E	4. A	5. C

Multiple Choice

6. C	7. A	8. D	9. B	10. D

SECTION QUIZ 3-2

Matching

1. E	2. D	3. A	4. B	5. C

Multiple Choice

6. A	7. C	8. D	9. B	10. D

SECTION QUIZ 3-3

Matching

1. A	2. C	3. D	4. E	5. B

Multiple Choice

6. B	7. A	8. D	9. D	10. A

SECTION QUIZ 3-4

Matching

1. D	2. E	3. C	4. A	5. B

Multiple Choice

6. B	7. A	8. C	9. D	10. D

SECTION QUIZ 3-5

Matching

1. D	2. E	3. A	4. C	5. B

Multiple Choice

6. C	7. A	8. B	9. D	10. D

CHAPTER 3 TEST, FORM A

Matching

1. E	2. C	3. B	4. A	5. G
6. F	7. D	8. J	9. I	10. H

Multiple Choice

11. B	12. B	13. A	14. B	15. C
16. B	17. C	18. C	19. C	20. A

Essay

21. The three branches of the federal government are the legislative, executive, and judicial branches. The two houses of Congress make up the legislative branch. They make the laws. The executive branch, headed by a president, implements and enforces the laws passed by Congress. The president performs other duties as well, such as serving as commander in chief of the armed forces. The judicial branch—a system of federal courts—interprets federal laws and renders judgment in cases involving those laws.

22. After the Revolutionary War, British merchants flooded America with goods at very low prices. This threw thousands of Americans out of work. Many states fought back by restricting British shipping and imports. Unfortunately, the states did not all impose the same duties and restrictions. Because the Confederation Congress was not allowed to regulate commerce, the states began setting up customs posts on their borders to prevent the British from exploiting the different trade laws. They also began to levy taxes on each other's goods to raise revenue for themselves. In effect, each state was beginning to act as a totally independent country, and this behavior threatened to tear apart the new United States.

CHAPTER 3 TEST, FORM B

Matching

1. H	**2.** I	**3.** G	**4.** C	**5.** B
6. E	**7.** A	**8.** F	**9.** J	**10.** D

Multiple Choice

11. B	**12.** C	**13.** B	**14.** B	**15.** D
16. B	**17.** C	**18.** B	**19.** C	**20.** B

Essay

21. The Sugar Act changed tax rates on some imported products and added new taxes on others. Merchants throughout the colonies complained that the act hurt trade. Many were also furious that the act violated several traditional English rights. Merchants accused of smuggling were presumed guilty until proven innocent. The act also let officials seize goods without due process in some circumstances, and prevented lawsuits by merchants whose goods had been improperly seized.

22. A republic is a form of government where power resides with a body of citizens entitled to vote, with this power exercised by elected officials or representatives who are responsible to the citizens and who must govern according to laws or a constitution.

SECTION QUIZ 4-1

Matching

1. D	**2.** B	**3.** E	**4.** A	**5.** C

Multiple Choice

6. B	**7.** D	**8.** A	**9.** A	**10.** C

SECTION QUIZ 4-2

Matching

1. E	**2.** A	**3.** B	**4.** C	**5.** D

Multiple Choice

6. B	**7.** D	**8.** B	**9.** C	**10.** D

SECTION QUIZ 4-3

Matching

1. D	**2.** A	**3.** E	**4.** B	**5.** C

Multiple Choice

6. A	**7.** C	**8.** B	**9.** D	**10.** A

CHAPTER 4 TEST, FORM A

Matching

1. E	**2.** A	**3.** D	**4.** B	**5.** C
6. B	**7.** A	**8.** A	**9.** B	**10.** B

Multiple Choice

11. B	**12.** D	**13.** A	**14.** C	**15.** A
16. D	**17.** D	**18.** A	**19.** B	**20.** A

Essay

21. To fund the Revolutionary War, the Confederation Congress had issued bonds. By 1789 the United States owed huge sums to American citizens as well as to other countries. Alexander Hamilton believed the only way for the new federal government to establish its credit was to make good on these debts. If it called in the old bonds and exchanged them at full value for new, interest-bearing ones, then the wealthy creditors, bankers, and merchants who held the bonds would have a stake in the federal government's success.

22. The first law required immigrants to wait 14 years before becoming citizens, thus weakening Republican support. The next two laws gave the president the power to deport without trial any alien deemed dangerous to the United States. The fourth made it a federal crime to utter or print anything "false, scandalous, and malicious" against the federal government or any federal official. In short, the act deprived citizens of their right to criticize public officials.

CHAPTER 4 TEST, FORM B

Matching

1. B   2. B   3. A   4. B   5. B
6. A   7. D   8. E   9. C   10. B

Multiple Choice

11. C   12. C   13. C   14. B   15. A
16. D   17. C   18. A   19. D   20. C

Essay

21. During the lean 1780s, many original bond purchasers such as farmers and Revolutionary War
veterans had been forced to sell their bonds at a
discount to speculators. Madison was outraged
that Northern speculators who had paid as little as
$10 for a $100 bond would now receive full value,
while the original buyers received nothing.
Furthermore, Northerners now owned roughly 80
percent of the bonds, but much of the tax money
that would be used to pay off the bonds would
come from the South.

22. The Monroe Doctrine was President Monroe's declaration that the American continents should no
longer be viewed as open to colonization. He
specifically advised Europe to respect the sovereignty of new Latin American nations. Monroe
issued the declaration in response to Spain's interest in regaining control of its Latin American
colonies, many of which were declaring independence, and Russia's announcement that its empire
extended south from Alaska to the Oregon Territory.
The Monroe Doctrine was a bold act. The United
States might not have been able to back up its new
policy if it had been challenged, but for years, the
doctrine would guide national foreign policy.

SECTION QUIZ 5-1

Matching

1. C   2. E   3. A   4. B   5. D

Multiple Choice

6. B   7. A   8. D   9. C   10. A

SECTION QUIZ 5-2

Matching

1. B   2. C   3. D   4. A   5. E

Multiple Choice

6. D   7. A   8. C   9. B   10. C

SECTION QUIZ 5-3

Matching

1. B   2. A   3. E   4. D   5. C

Multiple Choice

6. A   7. D   8. B   9. C   10. A

SECTION QUIZ 5-4

Matching

1. E   2. C   3. B   4. A   5. D

Multiple Choice

6. B   7. B   8. B   9. A   10. C

CHAPTER 5 TEST, FORM A

Matching

1. B   2. D   3. E   4. A   5. C
6. D   7. B   8. C   9. A   10. E

Multiple Choice

11. B   12. D   13. B   14. D   15. D
16. D   17. B   18. C   19. C   20. D

Essay

21. Manufacturing shifted from hand tools to large,
complex machines. Skilled artisans gave way to
organized workforces. Factories, often large
enough for hundreds of machines and workers,
replaced home-based workshops. Manufacturers
sold their wares nationwide or abroad instead of
just locally.

22. After winning independence from Mexico, Texans
voted overwhelmingly for annexation to the
United States. As proud as they were of their new
republic, most Texans still regarded themselves as
Americans. The revolution had also left the Texas
government with a large public debt. The people
knew, too, that growth depended on schools,
roads, and other improvements they could not
afford on their own. However, Texas wished to
enter the Union as a slave state, which antislavery
leaders opposed. In addition, Mexico continued to
claim ownership of Texas. To avoid conflict,
President Andrew Jackson made no move toward
annexation. Texas remained a republic for almost a
decade before becoming a state.

CHAPTER 5 TEST, FORM B

Matching

1. E   2. D   3. B   4. C   5. A
6. H   7. J   8. G   9. I   10. F

Multiple Choice

11. A   12. C   13. C   14. A   15. B
16. A   17. C   18. A   19. B   20. B

Essay

21. State slave codes forbade enslaved men and women from owning property, leaving a slaveholder's premises without permission, or testifying in court against a white person. Laws even banned them from learning to read and write.

22. In the 1700s, most economic activity took place in or near the home because most Americans lived on farms. Although husbands and wives had distinct chores, running the farm and raising the family was the focus of their efforts. The rise of factories and other work centers in the 1800s began to separate the home from the workplace. Men now left home to go to work, while women tended the house and children. Most believed the home was the proper place for women. Women often were viewed as more moral and charitable than men, and better able to serve as models of piety and virtue to their family. The idea that women had an important role to play in building a virtuous home was soon extended to making society more virtuous. As women became involved in the great reform movements and moral crusades of the era, some began to argue that they needed greater rights to promote their ideas. Women who shared this idea formed the first women's movement.

UNIT 1 POSTTEST, FORM A

Matching

1. I	2. D	3. G	4. B	5. H
6. E	7. C	8. J	9. A	10. F

Multiple Choice

11. D	12. D	13. C	14. B	15. B
16. B	17. B	18. B	19. D	20. C

Essay

21. After the War of 1812, the United States experienced an "Era of Good Feelings." The matter of statehood for Missouri, however, stirred up passionate disagreements, and the Era of Good Feelings began to dissolve. In 1819 the Union consisted of 11 free and 11 slave states. Admitting any new state, either slave or free, would upset the balance of political power in the Senate. The Missouri Compromise temporarily settled the dispute over the westward expansion of slavery, but the issue of slavery remained divisive. Another issue that increased sectional tension was the 1824 presidential election campaign of "favorite sons." In the disputed election of 1824, Andrew Jackson led in the popular vote and in the Electoral College but did not win the necessary majority of electoral votes. A supposed "corrupt bargain" between Henry Clay and John Quincy Adams led to Adams winning the election, which caused political par-

ties to break apart along sectional lines. A third reason for the sectional tension involved tariffs, which hurt Southern states that were mostly agricultural. When Congress levied the 1828 "Tariff of Abominations," South Carolina threatened to secede from the Union.

22. Alexander Hamilton believed the only way for the new federal government to establish its credit was to make good on these debts. If it called in the old bonds and exchanged them at full value for new, interest-bearing ones, then the wealthy creditors, bankers, and merchants who held the bonds would have a stake in the federal government's success. James Madison disagreed. During the lean 1780s, many original bond purchasers such as farmers and Revolutionary War veterans had been forced to sell their bonds at a discount to speculators. Madison was outraged that Northern speculators who had paid as little as $10 for a $100 bond would now receive full value, while the original buyers received nothing. Furthermore, Northerners now owned roughly 80 percent of the bonds, but much of the tax money that would be used to pay off the bonds would come from the South.

UNIT 1 POSTTEST, FORM B

Matching

1. D	2. C	3. F	4. I	5. H
6. G	7. J	8. A	9. B	10. E

Multiple Choice

11. D	12. C	13. B	14. C	15. D
16. B	17. C	18. C	19. B	20. C

Essay

21. In early colonial days, there was plenty of land for tobacco farmers, but not enough labor to work it. England had the opposite problem. The English enclosure movement had forced many peasants off the land. Many of them, hoping to acquire their own land in America, became indentured servants. They made labor contracts with colonists, agreeing to work for a set term, usually four years. In return, the colonists would pay for a servant's passage and provide food, clothing, and shelter until the contract expired. However, close to half of those who came to Virginia and Maryland died before earning their freedom. Of those who did become free, less than half acquired their own land.

22. Missouri's territorial government applied for statehood as a slave state. At the time, the Union consisted of 11 free and 11 slave states. Admitting any new state, either slave or free, would upset the balance of political power in the Senate. Many Northerners opposed extending slavery into the western territories because they believed that human bondage was morally wrong. The South feared that if slavery could not expand, new free states would eventually give the North enough votes to outlaw slaveholding. A solution that became known as the Missouri Compromise emerged when Maine sought statehood. The Senate decided to combine the two requests and admit Missouri as a slave state and Maine as a free state, thus preserving the balance. The Senate then added an amendment that would prohibit slavery in the rest of the Louisiana Territory north of Missouri's southern boundary. Southerners agreed, viewing this Northern region as unsuitable for farming anyway.

UNIT 2 PRETEST, FORM A

Matching

1. G	**2.** D	**3.** I	**4.** A	**5.** H
6. J	**7.** F	**8.** E	**9.** B	**10.** C

Multiple Choice

11. D	**12.** B	**13.** C	**14.** A	**15.** A
16. C	**17.** B	**18.** B	**19.** D	**20.** D

Essay

21. Under the Fugitive Slave Act, a slaveholder or slave-catcher had only to point out alleged run-aways to take them into custody. The accused then would be brought before a federal commissioner. With no right to testify on their own behalf, even those who had earned their freedom years earlier had no way to prove their case. An affidavit asserting that the captive had escaped from a slave-holder, or testimony by white witnesses, was all a court needed to order the person sent South. Furthermore, federal commissioners had a financial incentive to rule in favor of slaveholders; such judgments earned them a $10 fee, but only $5 for judgments in favor of the accused. The Fugitive Slave Act also required federal marshals to assist slave-catchers. Marshals could even deputize citizens on the spot to help them capture a fugitive. Anyone who refused to cooperate could be jailed.

22. The North's victory in the Civil War saved the Union and strengthened the power of the federal government over the states. It transformed American society by ending slavery, but it also left the South socially and economically devastated and many questions unresolved. No one yet knew how to bring the Southern states back into the Union, nor what the status of African Americans would be in Southern society.

UNIT 2 PRETEST, FORM B

Matching

1. F	**2.** H	**3.** I	**4.** J	**5.** A
6. G	**7.** D	**8.** E	**9.** C	**10.** B

Multiple Choice

11. A	**12.** A	**13.** C	**14.** B	**15.** B
16. A	**17.** D	**18.** D	**19.** B	**20.** B

Essay

21. Answers will vary. Students should recognize that there would likely be at least two countries in what is today the United States. Students should also note that the South would likely have continued, at least for many additional years, the institution of slavery. Some students may note that there would likely be ongoing tensions between the North and the South. Tensions would have arisen over the additions of land to each of their countries and over trade issues. Border states would have had to decide which side to support and a few additional states may have decided to leave the Union.

22. Answers will vary. Having won the war, the North had to determine how to treat the South. Political views varied on how much to punish the Southern states for seceding and how to begin allowing Southern states to rejoin the Union. In the South, state governments and economies had to be rebuilt. Also, the end of slavery freed African Americans, but left them with limited prospects. They needed jobs, education, and land. They also needed to be allowed full rights as citizens. Ongoing resentment by many Southerners made real gains by African Americans very difficult.

SECTION QUIZ 6-1

Matching

1. B	**2.** D	**3.** E	**4.** C	**5.** A

Multiple Choice

6. D	**7.** D	**8.** C	**9.** A	**10.** B

SECTION QUIZ 6-2

Matching

1. D	**2.** E	**3.** C	**4.** B	**5.** A

Multiple Choice

6. C	**7.** A	**8.** A	**9.** D	**10.** A

SECTION QUIZ 6-3

Matching

1. B	**2.** E	**3.** A	**4.** C	**5.** D

★ Answer Key

Multiple Choice

6. B   **7.** D   **8.** A   **9.** A   **10.** C

CHAPTER 6 TEST, FORM A

Matching

1. C   **2.** D   **3.** B   **4.** E   **5.** A

6. C   **7.** B   **8.** D   **9.** A   **10.** B

Multiple Choice

11. A   **12.** D   **13.** C   **14.** A   **15.** A

16. B   **17.** C   **18.** C   **19.** B   **20.** B

Essay

21. Clay's first pair of resolutions would allow California to come in as a free state, but organize the rest of the territory from Mexico without any restrictions on slavery. The second pair would settle a border between New Mexico and Texas in favor of New Mexico, but compensate Texas by having the federal government take on its debts. Clay's third pair would outlaw the slave trade in the District of Columbia, but not slavery itself. The final two resolutions were concessions to the South. Congress would be prohibited from interfering with the domestic slave trade and would pass a stronger law to help Southerners recover enslaved African Americans who had fled north.

22. Dred Scott was a Missouri slave who had been taken north to work in free territory for several years. After he returned with his owner to Missouri, Scott sued to end his slavery, arguing that living in free territory had made him a free man. The Supreme Court ruled against Scott. Chief Justice Taney first stated that African Americans could not be U.S. citizens and that Scott thus had no right to sue in the federal courts. Taney then held that Scott's residence in free territory did not alter his enslaved status. Furthermore, Taney said, Congress's ban on slavery in the western territories, enacted as part of the Missouri Compromise, was unconstitutional and void. The Court's ruling intensified sectional conflict. The Court had said that the federal government could not prohibit slavery in the territories.

CHAPTER 6 TEST, FORM B

Matching

1. B   **2.** B   **3.** A   **4.** B   **5.** A

6. A   **7.** B   **8.** B   **9.** B   **10.** B

Multiple Choice

11. D   **12.** B   **13.** B   **14.** A   **15.** D

16. C   **17.** D   **18.** A   **19.** A   **20.** C

Essay

21. Under the Fugitive Slave Act, a slaveholder or slave-catcher had only to point out alleged runaways to take them into custody. The accused then would be brought before a federal commissioner. With no right to testify on their own behalf, even those who had earned their freedom years earlier had no way to prove their case. An affidavit asserting that the captive had escaped from a slaveholder, or testimony by white witnesses, was all a court needed to order the person sent south. Furthermore, federal commissioners had a financial incentive to rule in favor of slaveholders; such judgments earned them a $10 fee, but only $5 for judgments in favor of the accused. The Fugitive Slave Act also required federal marshals to assist slave-catchers. Marshals could even deputize citizens on the spot to help them capture a fugitive. Anyone who refused to cooperate could be jailed.

22. If Douglas answered yes to this question, he would appear to be supporting popular sovereignty and opposing the *Dred Scott* ruling, which would cost him Southern support. If he said no, it would seem as if he had abandoned popular sovereignty, the principle on which he had built his national following. Douglas tried to avoid the dilemma by replying that he accepted the *Dred Scott* decision, but he argued that people could still keep out slavery by refusing to pass the laws needed to regulate and enforce it.

SECTION QUIZ 7-1

Matching

1. C   **2.** A   **3.** D   **4.** E   **5.** B

Multiple Choice

6. D   **7.** A   **8.** C   **9.** B   **10.** D

SECTION QUIZ 7-2

Matching

1. D   **2.** C   **3.** A   **4.** E   **5.** B

Multiple Choice

6. B   **7.** A   **8.** B   **9.** D   **10.** C

SECTION QUIZ 7-3

Matching

1. B   **2.** A   **3.** D   **4.** C   **5.** E

Multiple Choice

6. C   **7.** A   **8.** C   **9.** D   **10.** B

SECTION QUIZ 7-4

Matching

1. D **2.** E **3.** A **4.** C **5.** B

Multiple Choice

6. A **7.** D **8.** D **9.** C **10.** C

SECTION QUIZ 7-5

Matching

1. A **2.** D **3.** C **4.** B **5.** E

Multiple Choice

6. B **7.** C **8.** D **9.** A **10.** D

CHAPTER 7 TEST, FORM A

Matching

1. J **2.** D **3.** G **4.** E **5.** B

6. I **7.** C **8.** A **9.** H **10.** F

Multiple Choice

11. C **12.** B **13.** A **14.** D **15.** D

16. B **17.** B **18.** B **19.** C **20.** A

Essay

21. The Confederacy's financial situation was not good, and it became worse over time. Most Southern planters were in debt and unable to buy bonds. Southern banks were small and had few cash reserves, so they could not buy many bonds. The South's best hope to raise money was by taxing trade. Shortly after the war began, however, the Union Navy blockaded Southern ports, which reduced trade and revenues. The Confederacy then resorted to taxing its own people, but many Southerners refused to pay. The Confederacy also printed paper money, which caused rapid inflation, and the paper money became almost worthless.

22. The North's victory in the Civil War saved the Union and strengthened the power of the federal government over the states. It transformed American society by ending slavery, but it also left the South socially and economically devastated and many questions unresolved. No one yet knew how to bring the Southern states back into the Union, nor what the status of African Americans would be in Southern society.

CHAPTER 7 TEST, FORM B

Matching

1. H **2.** F **3.** C **4.** A **5.** G

6. E **7.** B **8.** J **9.** D **10.** I

Multiple Choice

11. C **12.** C **13.** C **14.** D **15.** C

16. D **17.** D **18.** A **19.** B **20.** C

Essay

21. Traditionally, troops would march in tight columns toward the enemy, firing in massed volleys. These tactics were necessary earlier in the century because soldiers used smoothbore muskets. These guns were very inaccurate except at close range. By the 1850s, French and American inventors had developed new inexpensive conoidal (cone-shaped) bullets that could be used in rifles. Rifles firing conoidal bullets were more accurate at much greater ranges. This meant that troops would be fired upon several times while charging enemy lines. At the same time, instead of standing in a line, troops defending positions in the Civil War began to use trenches and barricades to protect themselves. The combination of rifles and trenches often resulted in very high casualties to the attacking force.

22. The black codes varied from state to state, but all of them seemed to be intended to keep African Americans in a condition similar to slavery. African Americans were generally required to enter into annual labor contracts. Those who did not could be arrested for vagrancy and forced into involuntary servitude as punishment. Several state codes established specific hours of labor for African Americans and also required them to get licenses to work in non-agricultural jobs.

UNIT 2 POSTTEST, FORM A

Matching

1. B **2.** D **3.** C **4.** E **5.** G

6. I **7.** A **8.** J **9.** F **10.** H

Multiple Choice

11. A **12.** D **13.** D **14.** C **15.** B

16. A **17.** A **18.** D **19.** D **20.** C

Essay

21. The Underground Railroad was a key to many African Americans' escape from the South. This informal but well-organized network of sympathizers began to expand in the early 1830s and helped thousands of enslaved persons flee north. "Conductors" transported runaways in secret, gave them shelter and food along the way, and saw them to freedom in the Northern states or Canada with some money for a fresh start. Conductors used secret signals to communicate about how to proceed safely. The most famous conductor was Harriet Tubman, herself a runaway.

Again and again, she risked journeys into the slave states to bring people out. Levi Coffin, a Quaker, sheltered a reported 2,000 escaped African Americans in his home in Indiana and another 1,300 after he moved to Cincinnati, Ohio.

22. More than three-quarters of the United States Navy's officers came from the North. The crews of American merchant ships were almost entirely from the North. This provided a pool of trained sailors for the Union Navy. The North had several economic advantages as well. In 1860 the North had a much larger population, which gave it a great advantage in raising an army and in supporting the war effort. Almost 90 percent of the nation's factories were located in the North. Thus, the North more easily could provide its troops with ammunition and other supplies. In addition, the South had only half as many miles of railroad track as the North and had only one line connecting the western states of the Confederacy with the east. This made it much easier for Northern troops to disrupt the Southern rail system and prevent movement of food and troops. Financially, the North enjoyed several advantages. In addition to controlling the national treasury, the Union could expect continued revenue from tariffs. Many Northern banks also held large reserves of cash, which they loaned the government by buying bonds. In contrast, Southern planters were in debt and unable to buy bonds. Southern banks were small and had few cash reserves, so they were unable to buy many bonds. Soon after the war began, the Union Navy blockaded Southern ports, reducing the South's trade and therefore the revenue it could gain from taxing trade.

UNIT 2 POSTTEST, FORM B

Matching

1. I	**2.** G	**3.** D	**4.** H	**5.** J
6. F	**7.** C	**8.** E	**9.** B	**10.** A

Multiple Choice

11. D	**12.** A	**13.** B	**14.** A	**15.** B
16. C	**17.** D	**18.** D	**19.** B	**20.** C

Essay

21. Answers will vary. African Americans were now freedmen, but most lacked education, housing, and jobs. The Freedmen's Bureau helped provide food and began providing education to African Americans. African Americans worked to establish schools and start churches across the South.

Resentment in the South led to black codes that limited the rights of African Americans in most Southern states. The Fourteenth and Fifteenth Amendments to the Constitution gave legal protection to African Americans and brought many into the political process as voters and as elected officials.

Economic gains were difficult to achieve. Without land and with few skills, many African Americans became sharecroppers and tenant farmers. Both tended to keep African American farmers in poverty because the landlords demanded high rents or high shares of their crops.

22. Soldiers on both sides lived under difficult circumstances. Food was often scarce and many soldiers were poorly dressed. Soldiers often lacked such basic necessities as shoes and warm blankets. Unsanitary conditions in military camps led to outbreaks of disease. Many soldiers died from outbreaks of such things as smallpox, dysentery, typhoid, and pneumonia. New styles of fighting using trenches and barricades and improved rifles resulted in heavy casualties to attacking forces.

UNIT 3 PRETEST, FORM A

Matching

1. H	**2.** E	**3.** F	**4.** A	**5.** C
6. D	**7.** J	**8.** B	**9.** G	**10.** I

Multiple Choice

11. D	**12.** B	**13.** A	**14.** C	**15.** B
16. C	**17.** B	**18.** D	**19.** A	**20.** A

Essay

21. By calling the era the "Gilded Age," Twain was sounding an alarm. Something is "gilded" if it is covered in gold on the outside but made of cheaper material inside. A gilded age may appear to glitter, but Twain was trying to point out that beneath the surface lay corruption, swindles, poverty, crime, and great disparities in wealth between the rich and the poor.

22. News of a mineral strike in an area would start a stampede of prospectors desperately hoping to strike it rich. Almost overnight, the town near the strike would go from a frontier outpost to a boomtown of thousands of people. Shops, hotels, entertainment houses, and newspapers would open to serve the people. When the mineral veins were exhausted several years later, the mines would close. Without the mines the town's economy would collapse, and most townspeople would move on in search of new opportunities. The result was a ghost town. This cycle of boom and bust was repeated throughout the mountainous West.

UNIT 3 PRETEST, FORM B

Matching

1. D	**2.** B	**3.** C	**4.** J	**5.** G
6. I	**7.** H	**8.** A	**9.** F	**10.** E

Multiple Choice

11. B	**12.** C	**13.** B	**14.** D	**15.** D
16. D	**17.** D	**18.** B	**19.** C	**20.** A

Essay

21. The construction of railroads provided easy access to the Great Plains. Railroad companies sold land along the rail lines at low prices and provided credit to prospective settlers. Railroads opened offices throughout the United States and in major cities in Europe where land was scarce. Their posters and pamphlets proclaimed that booking passage to the Plains was a ticket to prosperity.

22. A corporation is an organization owned by many people but treated by law as though it were a single person. It can own property, pay taxes, make contracts, and sue and be sued. The people who own the corporation are called stockholders because they own shares of ownership called stock. Issuing stock allows a corporation to raise large amounts of money for big projects, while spreading out the risk.

SECTION QUIZ 8-1

Matching

1. D	**2.** E	**3.** C	**4.** A	**5.** B

Multiple Choice

6. D	**7.** A	**8.** C	**9.** D	**10.** A

SECTION QUIZ 8-2

Matching

1. E	**2.** A	**3.** C	**4.** B	**5.** D

Multiple Choice

6. B	**7.** B	**8.** D	**9.** C	**10.** A

SECTION QUIZ 8-3

Matching

1. A	**2.** D	**3.** B	**4.** E	**5.** C

Multiple Choice

6. D	**7.** A	**8.** B	**9.** C	**10.** D

CHAPTER 8 TEST, FORM A

Matching

1. E	**2.** F	**3.** G	**4.** C	**5.** A
6. D	**7.** B	**8.** H	**9.** I	**10.** J

Multiple Choice

11. C	**12.** B	**13.** D	**14.** B	**15.** C
16. B	**17.** C	**18.** D	**19.** C	**20.** A

Essay

21. News of a mineral strike in an area would start a stampede of prospectors desperately hoping to strike it rich. Almost overnight, the town near the strike would go from a frontier outpost to a boomtown of thousands of people. Shops, hotels, entertainment houses, and newspapers would open to serve the people. When the mineral veins were exhausted several years later, the mines would close. Without the mines the town's economy would collapse, and most townspeople would move on in search of new opportunities. The result was a ghost town. This cycle of boom and bust was repeated throughout the mountainous West.

22. The construction of railroads provided easy access to the Great Plains. Railroad companies sold land along the rail lines at low prices and provided credit to prospective settlers. Railroads opened offices throughout the United States and in major cities in Europe where land was scarce. Their posters and pamphlets proclaimed that booking passage to the Plains was a ticket to prosperity.

CHAPTER 8 TEST, FORM B

Matching

1. I	**2.** E	**3.** C	**4.** D	**5.** G
6. A	**7.** F	**8.** J	**9.** B	**10.** H

Multiple Choice

11. A	**12.** C	**13.** B	**14.** B	**15.** D
16. A	**17.** A	**18.** A	**19.** C	**20.** D

Essay

21. Before the Civil War, ranchers had little incentive to round up the longhorns roaming the grasslands. Beef prices were low, and moving the cattle to eastern markets was not practical. Two developments changed this situation: the Civil War and the construction of railroads. During the Civil War, eastern cattle were slaughtered in huge numbers to feed the armies. After the war, beef prices soared, making it worthwhile to round up the longhorns if a way could be found to move them east. By the end of the war, railroads had reached the Great Plains. Ranchers and livestock dealers realized that if the longhorns were rounded up and driven several hundred miles to the towns where the railroad lines ended, they could be sold for a huge profit and shipped east to market.

22. The Dakota Sioux had agreed to live on a small reservation in Minnesota in exchange for annuities,

or regular payments, from the United States government. The payments, however, were small, and much of the money ended up in the hands of white traders. These traders often claimed fabricated debts owed them by the Dakota and took the annuities in payment. Congress made things worse in 1862 by delaying the payments. As a result, some of the Dakota were starving. The Dakota rose up and slaughtered settlers in the area before troops put down the uprising.

SECTION QUIZ 9-1

Matching

1. E   2. C   3. A   4. B   5. D

Multiple Choice

6. C   7. B   8. A   9. D   10. B

SECTION QUIZ 9-2

Matching

1. D   2. A   3. E   4. B   5. C

Multiple Choice

6. B   7. D   8. A   9. C   10. D

SECTION QUIZ 9-3

Matching

1. C   2. B   3. E   4. A   5. D

Multiple Choice

6. A   7. C   8. C   9. B   10. D

SECTION QUIZ 9-4

Matching

1. C   2. D   3. B   4. E   5. A

Multiple Choice

6. B   7. D   8. B   9. C   10. A

CHAPTER 9 TEST, FORM A

Matching

1. E   2. F   3. C   4. H   5. A

6. G   7. D   8. B   9. J   10. I

Multiple Choice

11. C   12. D   13. B   14. D   15. B

16. A   17. B   18. C   19. B   20. C

Essay

21. The population growth stemmed from two causes—large families and a flood of immigrants. American industry began to grow at a time when social and economic conditions in China and Eastern Europe convinced many people to leave their nations and move to the United States in search of a better life. The population growth added to the growing industrial workforce, helping factories increase their production. At the same time, an increasing population created greater demand for the consumer goods that the factories produced.

22. A corporation is an organization owned by many people but treated by law as though it were a single person. It can own property, pay taxes, make contracts, and sue and be sued. The people who own the corporation are called stockholders because they own shares of ownership called stock. Issuing stock allows a corporation to raise large amounts of money for big projects, while spreading out the risk.

CHAPTER 9 TEST, FORM B

Matching

1. H   2. G   3. F   4. B   5. C

6. J   7. D   8. A   9. I   10. E

Multiple Choice

11. A   12. D   13. D   14. C   15. D

16. C   17. A   18. A   19. C   20. D

Essay

21. By linking the nation, railroads helped increase the size of markets, providing greater opportunities for many industries. Huge consumers themselves, the railroads also stimulated the economy by spending extraordinary amounts of money on steel, coal, and timber, among other needs.

22. Marxists argued that the basic force shaping capitalist society was the class struggle between workers and owners. Eventually, workers would revolt, seize control of the factories, and overthrow the government. After the revolution, the government would seize all private property and create a socialist society where wealth was evenly divided. Eventually, the state would whither away, leaving a Communist society where classes did not exist.

SECTION QUIZ 10-1

Matching

1. B   2. C   3. E   4. A   5. D

Multiple Choice

6. B   7. B   8. A   9. D   10. C

SECTION QUIZ 10-2

Matching

1. E   2. C   3. A   4. D   5. B

Multiple Choice

6. A   **7.** C   **8.** B   **9.** D   **10.** C

SECTION QUIZ 10-3

Matching

1. B   **2.** D   **3.** A   **4.** E   **5.** C

Multiple Choice

6. A   **7.** C   **8.** D   **9.** B   **10.** A

SECTION QUIZ 10-4

Matching

1. B   **2.** E   **3.** D   **4.** C   **5.** A

Multiple Choice

6. D   **7.** A   **8.** C   **9.** B   **10.** A

CHAPTER 10 TEST, FORM A

Matching

1. F   **2.** H   **3.** A   **4.** B   **5.** J
6. I   **7.** C   **8.** D   **9.** E   **10.** G

Multiple Choice

11. B   **12.** D   **13.** B   **14.** A   **15.** C
16. B   **17.** D   **18.** B   **19.** C   **20.** D

Essay

21. Many poor European farmers came simply because the United States had plenty of jobs available and few immigration restrictions. Many Europeans moved to avoid forced military service. Others, especially Jews living in Poland and Russia, fled to avoid religious persecution. By the late 1800s, most European states had made it easy to move to America. They had repealed laws that kept people from leaving. At the same time, moving to the United States offered a chance to break away from Europe's class system, and move to a democratic nation where newcomers had a chance to move up the social ladder.

22. By calling the era the "Gilded Age," Mark Twain and Charles Warner were sounding an alarm. Something is "gilded" if it is covered in gold on the outside but made of cheaper material inside. A gilded age may appear to glitter, but the writers were trying to point out that beneath the surface lay corruption, swindles, poverty, crime, and great disparities in wealth between the rich and the poor.

CHAPTER 10 TEST, FORM B

Matching

1. G   **2.** J   **3.** H   **4.** C   **5.** A
6. I   **7.** F   **8.** E   **9.** D   **10.** B

Multiple Choice

11. C   **12.** A   **13.** C   **14.** C   **15.** D
16. C   **17.** B   **18.** B   **19.** B   **20.** D

Essay

21. Crime and violence, fire, disease, and pollution posed threats to city dwellers. The rapid growth of cities made these problems worse. Pickpockets, swindlers, and thieves thrived in crowded urban living conditions. Major crimes such as murder increased as well. Alcohol contributed to violent crime, both inside and outside the home. Improper sewage disposal contaminated city drinking water and triggered epidemics of typhoid fever and cholera. Pollution resulted from horse waste that fell in the streets, smoke belching from chimneys, and soot and ash from coal and wood fires.

22. Charles Darwin had argued that plant and animal life evolved over the years by the process of natural selection. In this process, those species that cannot adapt to the environment in which they live gradually die out, while those that adapt best thrive. Social Darwinists took this theory of biology, intended to explain developments over millions of years, and applied it to human society, arguing that human society also evolved through competition and natural selection. They argued that society progressed and became better because only the fittest people survived.

SECTION QUIZ 11-1

Matching

1. D   **2.** B   **3.** E   **4.** A   **5.** C

Multiple Choice

6. D   **7.** C   **8.** C   **9.** A   **10.** B

SECTION QUIZ 11-2

Matching

1. B   **2.** E   **3.** C   **4.** A   **5.** D

Multiple Choice

6. B   **7.** C   **8.** A   **9.** D   **10.** B

SECTION QUIZ 11-3

Matching

1. D   **2.** A   **3.** E   **4.** B   **5.** C

Multiple Choice

6. C   **7.** D   **8.** B   **9.** A   **10.** A

CHAPTER 11 TEST, FORM A

Matching

1. J	**2.** H	**3.** C	**4.** G	**5.** A
6. I	**7.** D	**8.** F	**9.** B	**10.** E

Multiple Choice

11. C	**12.** C	**13.** A	**14.** D	**15.** A
16. A	**17.** D	**18.** A	**19.** D	**20.** A

Essay

21. Governments impose tariffs to protect weak domestic industries from foreign competition. Tariffs have the effect of raising the prices of manufactured goods. While protecting weak domestic manufacturing after the Civil War may have made sense, many questioned the necessity of maintaining high tariffs in the 1880s when large American companies were fully capable of competing internationally. High tariffs also forced other nations to respond in kind, making it difficult for farmers to export their surpluses.

22. "Deflation" is an increase in the value of money and a decrease in the general level of prices. Deflation hit farmers especially hard. Most farmers had to borrow money for seeds and other supplies to plant their crops. Because money was in short supply, interest rates began to rise, which increased the amount farmers owed. For those who wanted to expand their farms, rising interest rates also made mortgages more expensive. The falling prices of the period of deflation meant that farmers sold their crops for less. Nevertheless, they still had to make the same mortgage payments to the banks.

CHAPTER 11 TEST, FORM B

Matching

1. C	**2.** F	**3.** I	**4.** D	**5.** G
6. H	**7.** A	**8.** J	**9.** E	**10.** B

Multiple Choice

11. D	**12.** B	**13.** C	**14.** B	**15.** D
16. B	**17.** B	**18.** D	**19.** B	**20.** B

Essay

21. One reason farmers could not charge higher prices for their crops was that there were so many farmers in competition. If a farmer raised prices, a buyer could always go elsewhere and pay less. When they joined a cooperative, farmers pooled their crops and held them off the market in order to force the price up. Because a cooperative controlled a large quantity of farm products, it could also negotiate better shipping rates from the railroads.

22. Booker T. Washington proposed that African Americans concentrate on achieving economic goals rather than legal or political ones. In his famous speech known as the Atlanta Compromise, he urged his fellow African Americans to postpone the fight for civil rights and instead concentrate on preparing themselves educationally and vocationally for full equality. W.E.B. Du Bois challenged Washington's ideas. He pointed out that white Southerners continued to strip African Americans of their civil rights, in spite of the progress they were making in education and vocational training. Du Bois argued that African Americans could regain that lost ground and achieve full equality only by demanding their rights. Du Bois was particularly concerned with protecting and exercising voting rights.

UNIT 3 POSTTEST, FORM A

Matching

1. G	**2.** C	**3.** I	**4.** E	**5.** D
6. A	**7.** B	**8.** J	**9.** F	**10.** H

Multiple Choice

11. C	**12.** C	**13.** A	**14.** D	**15.** B
16. D	**17.** D	**18.** B	**19.** D	**20.** C

Essay

21. Southern states disfranchised African Americans using a variety of voting restrictions. They instituted literacy tests, made owning property a voting requirement, or added a poll tax. To ensure that the restrictions did not severely restrict the rights of poor white voters, some states included a grandfather clause that allowed people to avoid the voting restrictions if they had an ancestor who was on the voting rolls in 1867.

African Americans responded in a variety of ways. Some protested, and some protests turned violent. Others focused on making economic gains, ignoring political and civil rights. Still others focused on educational and vocational training, while advocating full rights as citizens.

22. Crime and violence, fire, disease, and pollution posed threats to city dwellers. The rapid growth of cities made these problems worse. Pickpockets, swindlers, and thieves thrived in crowded urban living conditions. Major crimes such as murder increased as well. Alcohol contributed to violent crime, both inside and outside the home. Improper sewage disposal contaminated city drinking water and triggered epidemics of typhoid fever and cholera. Pollution resulted from horse waste that fell in the streets, smoke belching from chimneys, and soot and ash from coal and wood fires.

UNIT 3 POSTTEST, FORM B

Matching

1. I	**2.** H	**3.** A	**4.** F	**5.** E
6. B	**7.** D	**8.** G	**9.** J	**10.** C

Multiple Choice

11. B	**12.** D	**13.** A	**14.** D	**15.** C
16. D	**17.** C	**18.** A	**19.** C	**20.** B

Essay

21. Student answers will vary. Most students will focus on the rapid industrialization that occurred after the Civil War. As companies built large factories, workers needed to live near the factories. Cities grew up around the factories. Some students may also note that the free enterprise system allowed corporations to grow. Corporations could raise the money needed to build ever larger factories and attract more workers, including huge numbers of immigrants, to work in the factories.

22. Student answers will vary. Students may select individualism and note that Horatio Alger wrote "rags to riches" novels developing the idea that poor individuals can be successful, wealthy, or powerful. Other students may select realism and mention the works of William Dean Howells, Mark Twain, Henry James, or Edith Wharton. All presented a realistic look at life in America. Twain focused on honest appraisals of pre-Civil War American society, while James and Wharton wrote novels describing the real lives of the upper class. Students may focus on naturalism and mention the works of Stephen Crane, Frank Norris, Jack London, and Theodore Dreiser. Naturalists expressed the idea that some people did not succeed because they were caught in circumstances that were out of their control.

UNIT 4 PRETEST, FORM A

Matching

1. G	**2.** H	**3.** E	**4.** F	**5.** I
6. J	**7.** C	**8.** B	**9.** D	**10.** A

Multiple Choice

11. C	**12.** A	**13.** D	**14.** C	**15.** D
16. B	**17.** A	**18.** B	**19.** C	**20.** B

Essay

21. Theodore Roosevelt believed in a strong global military presence. He insisted that displaying American power to the world would make nations think twice about fighting, thus promoting global peace. He often expressed this belief with a West African saying, "Speak softly and carry a big stick." The voyage of the Great White Fleet was one application of this policy, showcasing the nation's mighty fleet to the world. Another example was the use of the United States military to aid the revolt in Panama.

22. Progressivism was not a tightly organized political movement. Progressives often disagreed with each other, although they generally believed that industrialism and urbanization had created many social problems. Progressives belonged to both major political parties and usually were urban, educated, middle-class Americans. Some progressives saw corruption and inefficiency in government. They focused on making government more efficient by applying principles of scientific management to it. Other progressives wanted to make elected officials more responsive to the concerns of voters. They pushed for reforms such as direct primaries and direct election of senators. Other groups saw the unequal status of women and focused on gaining women the right to vote. Some progressives wanted to solve problems such as crime, illiteracy, drunkenness, and threats to health and safety. They pushed for social welfare reform, such as child labor laws, health and safety codes, and prohibition.

UNIT 4 PRETEST, FORM B

Matching

1. H	**2.** D	**3.** I	**4.** J	**5.** G
6. C	**7.** A	**8.** F	**9.** E	**10.** B

Multiple Choice

11. D	**12.** D	**13.** D	**14.** A	**15.** B
16. D	**17.** D	**18.** A	**19.** D	**20.** C

Essay

21. The United States desired new markets and sought to increase its influence in Latin America. It wanted to let European powers know that it was the dominant power in the region. Some believed that the United States and Latin American countries should work together. This belief was known as Pan-Americanism. Others believed that the United States should dominate the relationship by annexing territory. This group viewed Latin Americans as less civilized.

As Americans became more involved in world affairs, they also saw the strategic importance of the Caribbean, especially the Panama Canal Zone. The United States developed a policy of policing the region by stepping in to maintain political and economic stability in Latin American countries.

22. Answers will vary. Students should note that women now had a political voice in the United States. They could express their political views by supporting candidates who favored their positions.

They could run and be elected to office at all levels of government. Politicians had to consider how their positions would affect women. Issues important to women such as issues related to family and education received more attention from many politicians.

SECTION QUIZ 12-1

Matching

1.	B	**2.**	C	**3.**	A	**4.**	E	**5.**	D

Multiple Choice

6.	B	**7.**	D	**8.**	A	**9.**	C	**10.**	A

SECTION QUIZ 12-2

Matching

1.	D	**2.**	E	**3.**	C	**4.**	A	**5.**	B

Multiple Choice

6.	C	**7.**	D	**8.**	A	**9.**	B	**10.**	B

SECTION QUIZ 12-3

Matching

1.	E	**2.**	B	**3.**	D	**4.**	A	**5.**	C

Multiple Choice

6.	A	**7.**	C	**8.**	B	**9.**	D	**10.**	A

CHAPTER 12 TEST, FORM A

Matching

1.	J	**2.**	G	**3.**	B	**4.**	E	**5.**	A
6.	H	**7.**	D	**8.**	C	**9.**	I	**10.**	F

Multiple Choice

11.	B	**12.**	C	**13.**	B	**14.**	D	**15.**	C
16.	B	**17.**	D	**18.**	C	**19.**	A	**20.**	B

Essay

21. Economic and military competition from other nations, as well as a growing feeling of cultural superiority, led the shift in American opinion toward imperialism. Several European nations were expanding their power overseas, forming colonies and protectorates to protect their new markets and investments in other nations. In the United States, the Western frontier was filling up, and many Americans concluded that the nation had to develop new overseas markets to keep its economy strong. Influential author Alfred T. Mahan argued that the United States needed to build a large navy to protect its merchant ships and to defend its right to trade with other countries. To support the navy, the United States had to acquire territory for overseas bases. At the same time, many Americans began to believe in Anglo-Saxonism—the idea that English-speaking nations had superior character, ideas, and systems of government, and were destined to dominate the planet.

22. Puerto Rico's status as an unincorporated territory meant that Puerto Ricans were not citizens and had no constitutional rights, and that Congress could pass whatever laws it wanted for the island. From 1901 to 1904, in a series of cases known as the Insular Cases, the Supreme Court ruled that the Constitution did not cover "unincorporated" territories, and that the people in these territories received only those civil rights that Congress granted to them.

CHAPTER 12 TEST, FORM B

Matching

1.	D	**2.**	I	**3.**	H	**4.**	B	**5.**	A
6.	F	**7.**	E	**8.**	J	**9.**	C	**10.**	G

Multiple Choice

11.	A	**12.**	C	**13.**	D	**14.**	C	**15.**	A
16.	B	**17.**	A	**18.**	D	**19.**	D	**20.**	A

Essay

21. The Platt Amendment specified that: (a) Cuba could not make any treaty with another nation that would weaken its independence or allow another foreign power to gain territory in Cuba; (b) Cuba had to allow the United States to buy or lease naval stations in Cuba; (c) Cuba's debts had to be kept low to prevent foreign countries from landing troops to enforce payment; and (d) the United States would have the right to intervene to protect Cuban independence and keep order.

22. Theodore Roosevelt believed in a strong global military presence. He insisted that displaying American power to the world would make nations think twice about fighting, thus promoting global peace. He often expressed this belief with a West African saying, "Speak softly and carry a big stick." The voyage of the Great White Fleet was one application of this policy, showcasing the nation's mighty fleet to the world. Another example was the use of the United States military to aid the revolt in Panama.

SECTION QUIZ 13-1

Matching

1.	B	**2.**	D	**3.**	E	**4.**	C	**5.**	A

Multiple Choice

6.	D	**7.**	A	**8.**	D	**9.**	C	**10.**	B

SECTION QUIZ 13-2

Matching

1. C   2. E   3. A   4. D   5. B

Multiple Choice

6. B   7. D   8. A   9. C   10. A

SECTION QUIZ 13-3

Matching

1. C   2. D   3. B   4. A   5. E

Multiple Choice

6. B   7. A   8. D   9. C   10. B

SECTION QUIZ 13-4

Matching

1. D   2. E   3. C   4. A   5. B

Multiple Choice

6. B   7. B   8. C   9. A   10. D

CHAPTER 13 TEST, FORM A

Matching

1. D   2. B   3. C   4. A   5. E
6. A   7. F   8. B   9. D   10. C

Multiple Choice

11. C   12. A   13. B   14. B   15. C
16. D   17. A   18. C   19. B   20. B

Essay

21. In an era before modern pharmaceuticals had been developed, many companies patented and marketed potions they claimed would cure a variety of ills. Many patent medicines were little more than alcohol, colored water, and sugar. Others contained caffeine, opium, cocaine, and other dangerous compounds. Consumers had no way to know what they were taking, nor received any assurance the potions worked as claimed. In 1905 a series of articles in *Collier's* magazine helped focus public attention on the problem. An outraged Roosevelt pushed for federal legislation. In 1906 the Pure Food and Drug Act was passed, prohibiting the manufacture, sale, or shipment of impure or falsely labeled food and drugs.

22. Roosevelt and Taft were very different kinds of men. Roosevelt was a dynamic person who loved the spotlight and the rough-and-tumble world of politics. He had grand ideas and schemes, but left the details of administering them to others. Taft was in many ways the opposite. He was a skillful administrator and judge. He disliked political maneuvering, and preferred to avoid conflict with others. Unlike Roosevelt, who acted quickly and decisively on issues, Taft responded slowly, approaching problems from a legalistic point of view.

CHAPTER 13 TEST, FORM B

Matching

1. H   2. E   3. J   4. F   5. I
6. A   7. G   8. B   9. D   10. C

Multiple Choice

11. B   12. C   13. A   14. A   15. D
16. C   17. C   18. D   19. C   20. D

Essay

21. Progressivism was not a tightly organized political movement. Progressives had many different views about how to fix the problems they believed existed in American society. They often disagreed with each other, although they generally believed that industrialism and urbanization had created many social problems. They responded to these problems by demanding changes in the law and the Constitution. The issues progressives cared about varied widely, but as a group, they generally agreed the solution lay in pushing for a more active role on the part of the government to solve society's problems. Progressives belonged to both major political parties and usually were urban, educated, middle-class Americans.

22. Roosevelt accepted the economic power of the trusts as a fact of life and proposed a more powerful federal government and a strong executive to regulate them. Wilson criticized Roosevelt's program as one that supported "regulated monopoly." Monopolies, Wilson believed, were evils to be destroyed, not regulated. Wilson argued that Roosevelt's approach gave the federal government too much power in the economy, and did nothing to restore competition.

SECTION QUIZ 14-1

Matching

1. D   2. C   3. A   4. B   5. E

Multiple Choice

6. A   7. C   8. B   9. D   10. C

SECTION QUIZ 14-2

Matching

1. C   2. E   3. B   4. A   5. D

Multiple Choice

6. C   7. B   8. D   9. A   10. D

SECTION QUIZ 14-3

Matching

1. B **2.** D **3.** A **4.** E **5.** C

Multiple Choice

6. D **7.** A **8.** D **9.** B **10.** A

SECTION QUIZ 14-4

Matching

1. B **2.** A **3.** D **4.** E **5.** C

Multiple Choice

6. C **7.** A **8.** D **9.** B **10.** B

CHAPTER 14 TEST, FORM A

Matching

1. D **2.** F **3.** A **4.** J **5.** B

6. I **7.** G **8.** E **9.** H **10.** C

Multiple Choice

11. D **12.** A **13.** C **14.** B **15.** B

16. B **17.** B **18.** D **19.** C **20.** C

Essay

21. To try to cut off supplies going to Britain, the Germans announced in 1915 that their U-boats would sink without warning any ship found in the waters around Britain. This announcement outraged the United States because it violated an international treaty requiring military vessels to reveal their intentions to merchant ships and provide for the safety of the people aboard before sinking the ships. In implementing their policy, the Germans sank the British passenger liner *Lusitania* in the war zone, killing 1,200, including 128 Americans. In 1916 a U-boat torpedoed the French passenger ship *Sussex*, injuring several Americans on board. In 1917 British intelligence intercepted a telegram from Arthur Zimmermann, a German official. It proposed to offer the Mexican government its "lost territory in Texas, New Mexico, and Arizona" if Mexico sided with Germany in the event that the United States entered the war. Furious, many Americans now concluded war with Germany was necessary.

22. In the first five points, President Wilson proposed to eliminate the general causes of war through free trade, disarmament, freedom of the seas, impartial adjustment of colonial claims, and open diplomacy instead of secret agreements. The next eight points addressed the right of self-determination. They also required the Central Powers to evacuate all of the countries invaded during the war. The fourteenth point called for the creation of the League of Nations. The League's member nations would help preserve peace and prevent future wars by pledging to respect and protect each other's territory and political independence.

CHAPTER 14 TEST, FORM B

Matching

1. A **2.** C **3.** B **4.** B **5.** A

6. A **7.** A **8.** C **9.** B **10.** B

Multiple Choice

11. C **12.** A **13.** D **14.** C **15.** D

16. A **17.** D **18.** B **19.** B **20.** D

Essay

21. The purpose of the War Industries Board was to organize industry to increase efficiency and maximize production. It set priorities, told manufacturers what they could and could not make, controlled the flow of raw materials, ordered the construction of new factories, and occasionally, with the president's approval, set prices. The purpose of the National War Labor Board was to maintain cooperation between industry management and labor unions. It attempted to mediate labor disputes that might otherwise lead to strikes. It frequently pressured industry to grant concessions to workers in exchange for the agreement of labor leaders not to disrupt war production with strikes and other disturbances.

22. When the war ended, government agencies removed their controls on the economy. This released pent up demand. People raced to buy goods that had been rationed, while businesses rapidly raised prices they had been forced to keep low during the war. The result was rapid inflation. Workers wanted to raise their wages to keep up with inflation. On the other hand, companies wanted to hold down wages because inflation was also driving up their operating costs. These competing desires helped spark the wave of strikes.

UNIT 4 POSTTEST, FORM A

Matching

1. C **2.** I **3.** H **4.** B **5.** G

6. E **7.** J **8.** D **9.** A **10.** F

Multiple Choice

11. C **12.** D **13.** D **14.** B **15.** A

16. D **17.** D **18.** A **19.** D **20.** D

Essay

21. Many supporters of annexing the Philippines emphasized the economic and military benefits of taking the islands. They would provide the United States with a naval base in Asia, a stopover on the way to China, and a large market for American goods. Other supporters believed Americans had a duty to teach "less civilized" peoples how to live properly.

22. In January 1917, a German official named Arthur Zimmermann cabled the German ambassador in Mexico, instructing him to make an offer to the Mexican government. Zimmermann proposed that Mexico ally itself with Germany in the event of war between Germany and the United States. In return, Mexico would regain its "lost territory in Texas, New Mexico, and Arizona" after the war. Germany hoped, if war came, Mexico would tie down the American forces and prevent them from being sent to Europe. British Intelligence intercepted the Zimmermann telegram. Shortly afterward, it was leaked to American newspapers. Furious, many Americans now concluded war with Germany was necessary.

UNIT 4 POSTTEST, FORM B

Matching

1.	G	**2.**	C	**3.**	F	**4.**	H	**5.**	J
6.	B	**7.**	E	**8.**	D	**9.**	A	**10.**	I

Multiple Choice

11.	D	**12.**	C	**13.**	D	**14.**	A	**15.**	D
16.	A	**17.**	D	**18.**	A	**19.**	B	**20.**	C

Essay

21. Banks have to keep a portion of their deposits in a regional reserve bank, which provides a financial cushion against unanticipated losses. The Federal Reserve Board of Governors can set the interest rates the reserve banks charge other banks, thereby indirectly controlling the interest rates of the entire nation and the amount of money in circulation. This gives the Board the ability to fight inflation by raising interest rates and to stimulate the economy during a recession by lowering interest rates.

22. The Food Administration, run by Herbert Hoover, was responsible for increasing food production while reducing civilian consumption. Instead of using rationing, Hoover encouraged Americans to save food on their own. Using the slogan "Food Will Win the War—Don't Waste It," the Food Administration encouraged families to "Hooverize" by "serving just enough" and by having Wheatless Mondays, Meatless Tuesdays, and Porkless Thursdays and Saturdays. Hoover also encouraged citizens to plant victory gardens to raise their own vegetables, leaving more for the troops. The Food Administration also set high prices for wheat and other grains to encourage farmers to increase production.

UNIT 5 PRETEST, FORM A

Matching

1.	I	**2.**	D	**3.**	H	**4.**	J	**5.**	G
6.	F	**7.**	E	**8.**	C	**9.**	A	**10.**	B

Multiple Choice

11.	C	**12.**	D	**13.**	B	**14.**	D	**15.**	B
16.	D	**17.**	A	**18.**	C	**19.**	A	**20.**	B

Essay

21. Supporters of Prohibition believed that it would help reduce unemployment, domestic violence, and poverty. However, after the law took effect, Americans persisted in blatantly ignoring it. People flocked to secret bars called speakeasies where they could buy alcohol. Organized crime specialized in supplying and often running these speakeasies, which popped up all over the country.

22. Cars revolutionized American life. The auto industry created jobs in related industries, such as rubber, plate glass, nickel, and petroleum. Cars also created new small-business opportunities, such as garages and gas stations. Cars eased the isolation of rural life, putting towns within reach of many farmers and the countryside a mere ride away for city dwellers. Cars also enabled people to live farther away from work. An entirely new kind of consumer and worker, the auto commuter, appeared. Commuters lived in growing suburban communities and drove to work in the city.

UNIT 5 PRETEST, FORM B

Matching

1.	J	**2.**	G	**3.**	F	**4.**	I	**5.**	B
6.	E	**7.**	A	**8.**	D	**9.**	C	**10.**	H

Multiple Choice

11.	B	**12.**	C	**13.**	A	**14.**	A	**15.**	A
16.	A	**17.**	D	**18.**	A	**19.**	A	**20.**	C

Essay

21. Most economists agree that overproduction was a key cause of the Depression. Increasingly efficient machinery greatly sped the production of factory and farm goods. Most Americans, however, did not earn enough to buy up the flood of goods they helped produce. As consumers bought more on the installment plan, the debt forced some to reduce their other purchases. As sales slowed, manufacturers cut production and laid off employees. Jobless workers had to cut back purchases even more, causing business activity to spiral downward.

22. The main goal of the Social Security Act was to provide some security for the elderly and for

unemployed workers. Its framers viewed it primarily as an insurance bill, with workers earning the right to receive benefits by paying premiums. The law provided modest welfare payments to other needy people, including those with disabilities and poor families with young dependent children. The core of Social Security was the monthly retirement benefit, which people could collect when they stopped working at age 65. The plan also included unemployment insurance, providing temporary income to unemployed workers looking for new jobs.

SECTION QUIZ 15-1

Matching

1. D	**2.** C	**3.** A	**4.** B	**5.** E

Multiple Choice

6. A	**7.** D	**8.** C	**9.** C	**10.** B

SECTION QUIZ 15-2

Matching

1. C	**2.** E	**3.** D	**4.** A	**5.** B

Multiple Choice

6. A	**7.** C	**8.** B	**9.** D	**10.** D

SECTION QUIZ 15-3

Matching

1. B	**2.** D	**3.** C	**4.** E	**5.** A

Multiple Choice

6. B	**7.** D	**8.** C	**9.** A	**10.** D

CHAPTER 15 TEST, FORM A

Matching

1. F	**2.** E	**3.** B	**4.** C	**5.** H
6. J	**7.** D	**8.** I	**9.** G	**10.** A

Multiple Choice

11. C	**12.** A	**13.** D	**14.** C	**15.** D
16. B	**17.** B	**18.** C	**19.** D	**20.** A

Essay

21. Based on the bar graph, the United States would accept the most new immigrants from Britain and the least from Serbia. The law set quotas at 2 percent of each national group already residing in the United States in 1890. Although the law seemed to limit immigrants from all countries, it actually favored immigrants from regions already heavily represented in the United States. Because more immigrants from northwestern European countries lived in the United States as of the 1890 census, a larger portion of the quota would go to new immigrants from this region than from southern or eastern Europe.

22. America's youth loved cars because they made them more independent and allowed them to escape the careful watch of their parents. Instead of socializing with family, many youths used cars to seek new forms of entertainment with their friends and to find privacy.

CHAPTER 15 TEST, FORM B

Matching

1. I	**2.** F	**3.** J	**4.** C	**5.** E
6. H	**7.** A	**8.** G	**9.** B	**10.** D

Multiple Choice

11. C	**12.** D	**13.** B	**14.** C	**15.** A
16. D	**17.** C	**18.** B	**19.** A	**20.** C

Essay

21. In the 1920s, Americans persisted in blatantly ignoring Prohibition laws. People flocked to secret bars called speakeasies where they could buy alcohol. Organized crime specialized in supplying and often running these speakeasies, which popped up all over the country. The great demand for liquor meant that huge profits could be made. Because making and selling liquor were illegal, legitimate businesses could not fill this need. As a result, supplying the demand for liquor became a billion-dollar industry for gangsters.

22. Although not the typical American woman, the young, unconventional "flapper" personified women's quest for personal freedom in the 1920s. While flappers pursued social freedoms, other women sought financial independence by entering the workforce. Many single and working class women worked simply because they needed the wages for themselves or for their family, but for some young, single women, work was a way to break away from parental authority and establish a personal identity. Work also provided the wages that allowed women to participate in the consumer culture. Many women who attended college in the 1920s found support for their emerging sense of independence. Women's colleges, in particular, encouraged their students to pursue careers and to challenge traditional ideas about the nature of women and their role in society.

SECTION QUIZ 16-1

Matching

1. E	**2.** B	**3.** D	**4.** A	**5.** C

Multiple Choice

6. B   7. A   8. C   9. B   10. A

SECTION QUIZ 16-2

Matching

1. D   2. C   3. A   4. E   5. B

Multiple Choice

6. A   7. C   8. B   9. A   10. D

SECTION QUIZ 16-3

Matching

1. E   2. C   3. A   4. B   5. C

Multiple Choice

6. B   7. D   8. A   9. C   10. B

CHAPTER 16 TEST, FORM A

Matching

1. D   2. F   3. H   4. E   5. G
6. I   7. A   8. J   9. C   10. B

Multiple Choice

11. C   12. D   13. B   14. B   15. B
16. A   17. D   18. D   19. D   20. D

Essay

21. Technological advances enabled farmers to produce more, but higher yields without a corresponding increase in demand meant that they received lower prices. The cost to farmers of the improved technology, meanwhile, continued to increase. Many factors contributed to the "quiet depression" in American agriculture. During the war, the government had urged farmers to produce more to meet the great need for food supplies in Europe. Many farmers borrowed heavily to buy new land (at inflated prices) and new machinery in order to raise more crops. After the war, however, European farm output rose, and the debt-ridden countries of Europe had little to spend on American farm products anyway. Then Congress passed a tariff law in 1922 that provoked a reaction in foreign markets against American agricultural products. Farmers in the United States could no longer sell as much of their output overseas, and prices tumbled.

22. Supporters of supply-side economics, such as Secretary of the Treasury Mellon, believed that high taxes reduced the money available for private investment and prevented business expansion. Mellon argued that high tax rates actually reduced the amount of tax money the government collected. If taxes were lower, businesses and con-

sumers would spend and invest their extra money, causing the economy to grow. As the economy grew, Americans would earn more money, and the government would actually collect more taxes at a lower rate than it would if it kept tax rates high.

CHAPTER 16 TEST, FORM B

Matching

1. D   2. B   3. A   4. C   5. C
6. B   7. F   8. D   9. E   10. A

Multiple Choice

11. D   12. A   13. B   14. C   15. C
16. B   17. C   18. B   19. C   20. A

Essay

21. The contrast between Harding and Coolidge could not have been greater. Harding had enjoyed the easy conversation and company of old friends. He drank, smoked, and played poker in the White House with his friends. Coolidge, joked a critic, could be "silent in five languages." "Silent Cal" had a simple and frugal manner.

22. Cars revolutionized American life. The auto industry spurred growth in other large industries, such as rubber, plate glass, nickel, and lead. Automaking alone consumed 15 percent of the nation's steel, and the flood of cars stimulated a tremendous expansion of the petroleum industry. Cars also created new small-business opportunities, such as garages and gas stations. Cars eased the isolation of rural life, putting towns within reach of many farmers and the countryside a mere ride away for city dwellers. Cars also enabled people to live farther away from work. An entirely new kind of consumer and worker, the auto commuter, appeared. Commuters lived in growing suburban communities and drove to work in the city.

SECTION QUIZ 17-1

Matching

1. B   2. E   3. A   4. C   5. D

Multiple Choice

6. C   7. D   8. A   9. B   10. D

SECTION QUIZ 17-2

Matching

1. D   2. A   3. B   4. C   5. E

Multiple Choice

6. B   7. C   8. D   9. A   10. B

SECTION QUIZ 17-3

Matching

1. C	**2.** E	**3.** B	**4.** A	**5.** D

Multiple Choice

6. A	**7.** D	**8.** D	**9.** A	**10.** B

CHAPTER 17 TEST, FORM A

Matching

1. G	**2.** E	**3.** F	**4.** H	**5.** D
6. C	**7.** I	**8.** A	**9.** J	**10.** B

Multiple Choice

11. B	**12.** C	**13.** D	**14.** D	**15.** A
16. D	**17.** C	**18.** B	**19.** A	**20.** B

Essay

21. When buying stock on margin, investors made only a small cash down payment—as low as 10 percent of the price. With $1,000, an investor could buy $10,000 worth of stock. The other $9,000 would come as a loan from a stockbroker. If the stock price rose to, say, $12,000, the investor could sell it, pay off the $9,000 loan, and make a quick $2,000 profit on the $1,000 investment. However, if the stock price dropped to, say, $8,000, the broker might issue a margin call, demanding the investor repay the loan at once. In this case, the investor may not be able to repay the loan. After selling the stock and giving the broker the $8,000, the investor would still have to come up with $1,000 of his or her own money to pay off the $9,000 loan. Not only would the investor have lost his or her initial $1,000 investment, but with the additional $1,000 paid to the stockbroker, the investor's total loss would be $2,000.

22. Most economists agree that overproduction was a key cause of the Depression. Increasingly efficient machinery greatly sped the production of factory and farm goods. Most Americans, however, did not earn enough to buy up the flood of goods they helped produce. As consumers bought more on the installment plan, the debt forced some to reduce their other purchases. As sales slowed, manufacturers cut production and laid off employees. Jobless workers had to cut back purchases even more, causing business activity to spiral downward. A second cause was the loss of export sales. American banks were making lucrative loans to speculators instead of to foreign companies. This fact, along with the Hawley-Smoot Tariff that dampened foreign sales in the United States, caused foreign countries to buy fewer American products. A third cause was mistakes by the Federal Reserve. Instead of raising interest rates to curb excessive speculation, it lowered rates. This action encouraged banks to make risky loans and encouraged businesses to borrow more money to expand production, adding to the problem of over-production.

CHAPTER 17 TEST, FORM B

Matching

1. B	**2.** C	**3.** J	**4.** F	**5.** G
6. A	**7.** D	**8.** I	**9.** E	**10.** H

Multiple Choice

11. A	**12.** B	**13.** A	**14.** B	**15.** D
16. C	**17.** D	**18.** C	**19.** B	**20.** C

Essay

21. Most banks make a profit by lending out money received from depositors and collecting interest on the loans. The bank holds only a fraction of the depositors' money to cover everyday business, such as occasional withdrawals. Ordinarily that reserve is enough to meet the bank's needs, but if too many people withdraw their money at the same time, the reserves will not be sufficient to cover the withdrawals, and the bank will eventually collapse.

22. The problem was that someone had to pay for public works projects. If the government raised taxes to pay for them, it would take money away from consumers and hurt businesses that were already struggling. If the government decided to keep taxes low and run a budget deficit instead, it would have to borrow the money from banks. If the government did this, less money would be available for businesses that wanted to expand and for consumers who wanted mortgages or other loans. Hoover feared that deficit spending would actually delay an economic recovery.

SECTION QUIZ 18-1

Matching

1. B	**2.** A	**3.** E	**4.** D	**5.** C

Multiple Choice

6. B	**7.** C	**8.** A	**9.** B	**10.** D

SECTION QUIZ 18-2

Matching

1. E	**2.** D	**3.** C	**4.** B	**5.** A

Multiple Choice

6. C	**7.** A	**8.** C	**9.** D	**10.** D

SECTION QUIZ 18-3

Matching

1.	D	**2.**	B	**3.**	C	**4.**	A	**5.**	E

Multiple Choice

6.	D	**7.**	B	**8.**	A	**9.**	A	**10.**	A

SECTION QUIZ 18-4

Matching

1.	C	**2.**	D	**3.**	A	**4.**	E	**5.**	B

Multiple Choice

6.	B	**7.**	A	**8.**	B	**9.**	C	**10.**	D

CHAPTER 18 TEST, FORM A

Matching

1.	H	**2.**	B	**3.**	I	**4.**	G	**5.**	E
6.	C	**7.**	A	**8.**	F	**9.**	D	**10.**	J

Multiple Choice

11.	C	**12.**	B	**13.**	A	**14.**	C	**15.**	B
16.	B	**17.**	A	**18.**	B	**19.**	A	**20.**	C

Essay

21. Americans saw in Roosevelt an energy and optimism that gave them hope despite the tough economic times. His serenity and confidence amazed many people, and his "fireside chats" helped reassure them. Also, many people believed that his struggle with polio had given him a better understanding of their hardships. Roosevelt's confidence that he could make things better contrasted sharply with Hoover's apparent failure to do anything effective. In his campaign for president, Roosevelt revealed the approach he would take as president: "Above all, try something." He implemented his campaign promise with a flurry of bills to Congress during the first "Hundred Days." Unlike the public impression of Hoover, Roosevelt was "doing something."

22. Source of funding: workers' pay. Groups receiving benefits (order not important): (1) people with disabilities and poor families with young dependent children; (2) retirees (or the elderly); (3) unemployed workers looking for new jobs. Those left out: many farm and domestic workers.

The framers of the Social Security Act viewed it primarily as an insurance bill, with workers earning the right to receive benefits by paying premiums. The law provided modest welfare payments to other needy people, including those with disabilities and poor families with young dependent children. The core of Social Security was the monthly retirement benefit, which people could collect when they stopped working at age 65. The plan also included unemployment insurance, providing temporary income to unemployed workers looking for new jobs. Social Security initially left out many of the neediest members of society— farm and domestic workers, many of whom were African American workers.

CHAPTER 18 TEST, FORM B

Matching

1.	D	**2.**	A	**3.**	B	**4.**	H	**5.**	C
6.	E	**7.**	G	**8.**	I	**9.**	F	**10.**	J

Multiple Choice

11.	D	**12.**	C	**13.**	C	**14.**	B	**15.**	C
16.	A	**17.**	D	**18.**	D	**19.**	B	**20.**	B

Essay

21. The act guaranteed workers the right to organize unions without interference from employers and to bargain collectively. The law set up the National Labor Relations Board, which organized factory elections by secret ballot to determine whether workers wanted a union. The NLRB then certified the successful unions. The new law also set up a process whereby dissatisfied union members could take their complaints to binding arbitration, in which a neutral party would listen to both sides and decide the issues. The NLRB was authorized to investigate the actions of employers and could issue "cease and desist" orders against unfair practices.

22. The New Deal had only limited success in ending the Depression. Unemployment remained high, and economic recovery was not complete until after World War II. Even so, the New Deal gave many Americans a stronger sense of security and stability. The New Deal tended to operate so that it balanced competing economic interests. Business leaders, farmers, workers, consumers, homeowners, and others now looked to government to protect their interests. This "broker" role in mediating among competing interests has continued under the administrations of both parties ever since. Also, the New Deal programs created a "safety net" that protected people against economic disaster. After the Roosevelt years, the American people felt that the government had a duty to maintain this safety net, even though it required a larger, more expensive federal government.

UNIT 5 POSTTEST, FORM A

Matching

1.	D	**2.**	G	**3.**	H	**4.**	I	**5.**	C
6.	B	**7.**	E	**8.**	F	**9.**	A	**10.**	J

Multiple Choice

11. A	**12.** D	**13.** B	**14.** A	**15.** C
16. D	**17.** A	**18.** B	**19.** B	**20.** A

Essay

21. In the 1920s, Americans persisted in blatantly ignoring the Volstead Prohibition law. People flocked to secret bars called speakeasies where they could buy alcohol. Organized crime specialized in supplying and often running these speakeasies, which popped up all over the country. The great demand for liquor meant that huge profits could be made. Because making and selling liquor were illegal, legitimate businesses could not fill this need. As a result, supplying the demand for liquor became a billion-dollar industry for gangsters.

22. Increasingly efficient machinery greatly sped the production of factory and farm goods. Most Americans, however, did not earn enough to buy up the flood of goods they helped produce. As consumers bought more on the installment plan, their debt forced some to reduce their other purchases. As sales slowed, manufacturers cut production and laid off employees. Jobless workers had to cut back purchases even more, causing business activity to spiral downward.

UNIT 5 POSTTEST, FORM B

Matching

1. J	**2.** I	**3.** B	**4.** H	**5.** A
6. G	**7.** E	**8.** C	**9.** D	**10.** F

Multiple Choice

11. D	**12.** B	**13.** D	**14.** D	**15.** D
16. A	**17.** A	**18.** B	**19.** C	**20.** A

Essay

21. Henry Ford adopted the assembly line, which enormously increased manufacturing efficiency. Ford's system divided operations into simple tasks that unskilled workers could do, and it cut unnecessary motion to a minimum. In 1914 he installed the first moving assembly line, which enabled workers to build a car in a fraction of the time required only one year before. These mass production methods lowered the cost per car, which lowered prices for consumers. As lower prices increased sales volume, prices could be reduced even more, leading to affordable cars for the majority of Americans.

22. The main goal of the Social Security Act was to provide some security for the elderly and for unemployed workers. Its framers viewed it primarily as an insurance bill, with workers earning the right to receive benefits by paying premiums. The law provided modest welfare payments to other needy people, including those with disabilities and poor families with young dependent children. The core of Social Security was the monthly retirement benefit, which people could collect when they stopped working at age 65. The plan also included unemployment insurance, providing temporary income to unemployed workers looking for new jobs.

UNIT 6 PRETEST, FORM A

Matching

1. D	**2.** H	**3.** J	**4.** I	**5.** E
6. A	**7.** B	**8.** G	**9.** F	**10.** C

Multiple Choice

11. C	**12.** D	**13.** C	**14.** B	**15.** A
16. D	**17.** A	**18.** D	**19.** C	**20.** C

Essay

21. One of Truman's advisers opposed using the bomb because it would kill civilians indiscriminately. Instead, he believed an economic blockade and conventional bombing might convince Japan to surrender. Another adviser wanted to warn the Japanese about the bomb while at the same time telling them that they could keep the emperor if they surrendered, which is what Japan wanted. Another adviser wanted to drop the bomb without any warning to shock Japan into surrendering. All his advisers warned President Truman to expect massive casualties if the United States invaded Japan. Truman decided to drop the bomb because he believed it was his duty as president to use every weapon available to save American lives.

22. As television gained popularity, movies lost viewers. Throughout the 1950s, Hollywood struggled to recapture its audience. It tried contests, door prizes, and advertising, but most of these tactics failed to lure people out of their living rooms. Then Hollywood tried to make films more exciting by introducing 3-D films. These worked temporarily, but viewers soon tired of them. Cinemascope, movies shown on large, panoramic screens, finally gave Hollywood a reliable lure. Hollywood eventually began to film programs especially for television and also sold old movies, which could be cheaply rebroadcast, to the networks.

UNIT 6 PRETEST, FORM B

Matching

1. J	**2.** G	**3.** D	**4.** I	**5.** F
6. C	**7.** H	**8.** A	**9.** E	**10.** B

Multiple Choice

11. C	**12.** C	**13.** D	**14.** B	**15.** A
16. D	**17.** D	**18.** D	**19.** B	**20.** D

Essay

21. The Great Depression had hit Germany especially hard. Millions of people had lost their jobs, and Germany's economy teetered on the edge of collapse. Germans rallied around Adolf Hitler, who gained popularity by exploiting people's concern about unchecked inflation and severe unemployment. During the Depression, many Japanese also grew frustrated with their government's failure to solve economic problems. As a result, military leaders rose to power in the early 1930s. These leaders thought they would solve Japan's problems by expanding Japanese power in Asia, so they invaded Manchuria.

22. For the first time, large numbers of women served in the military during World War II. These women did not fight in combat—most performed clerical tasks or worked as nurses—but they played important roles in the war effort. In addition, many women joined the workforce, working in factories to ensure that war materials continued to be manufactured.

SECTION QUIZ 19-1

Matching

1. B	**2.** A	**3.** D	**4.** C	**5.** E

Multiple Choice

6. A	**7.** C	**8.** B	**9.** B	**10.** C

SECTION QUIZ 19-2

Matching

1. A	**2.** E	**3.** C	**4.** D	**5.** B

Multiple Choice

6. D	**7.** B	**8.** A	**9.** C	**10.** C

SECTION QUIZ 19-3

Matching

1. D	**2.** C	**3.** B	**4.** E	**5.** A

Multiple Choice

6. A	**7.** D	**8.** B	**9.** C	**10.** A

SECTION QUIZ 19-4

Matching

1. D	**2.** C	**3.** E	**4.** A	**5.** B

Multiple Choice

6. C	**7.** A	**8.** D	**9.** B	**10.** C

CHAPTER 19 TEST, FORM A

Matching

1. G	**2.** E	**3.** F	**4.** J	**5.** I
6. B	**7.** D	**8.** H	**9.** A	**10.** C

Multiple Choice

11. A	**12.** C	**13.** C	**14.** C	**15.** C
16. D	**17.** A	**18.** D	**19.** C	**20.** D

Essay

21. Fascism was a kind of aggressive nationalism. Fascists believed that the nation was more important than the individual. They argued that individualism made countries weak, and that a strong government led by a dictator was needed to impose order on society. Fascists believed a nation became great by expanding its territory and building up its military. Fascism was also strongly anti-Communist.

22. After trapping the British and French forces in Belgium, the Germans began to drive them toward the English Channel. The Germans had captured nearly all of the ports except the one at Dunkirk in northern France. As German forces closed in on Dunkirk, Hitler suddenly ordered them to stop. No one is sure why. Historians know he was nervous about risking his tank forces, and he wanted to wait until more infantry arrived. Perhaps Hitler believed Herman Goering that aircraft alone could destroy the soldiers trapped near Dunkirk. There is also some evidence that Hitler thought that the British would be more willing to accept peace if the Germans did not humiliate them by destroying their forces at Dunkirk. In any case, his order provided a three-day delay. In that time, the British sent 850 ships of all sizes, some as small a sailboats operated by civilian volunteers. They were able to save an estimated 338,000 British and French soldiers, a feat referred to as the "Miracle of Dunkirk."

CHAPTER 19 TEST, FORM B

Matching

1. D	**2.** A	**3.** B	**4.** C	**5.** A
6. C	**7.** B	**8.** F	**9.** E	**10.** D

Multiple Choice

11. D	**12.** B	**13.** D	**14.** B	**15.** A
16. D	**17.** C	**18.** C	**19.** C	**20.** D

Essay

21. In his book, Hitler called for the unification of all Germans under one government. He claimed that certain Germans, particularly blond, blue-eyed Germans, were descendants of a "master race"

★ Answer Key

called Aryans. He argued that these Germans needed more lebensraum, or living space, and called for Germany to expand east into Poland and Russia. According to Hitler, the Slavic people of Eastern Europe belonged to an inferior race, which Germans should enslave. He believed that Jews were responsible for many of the world's problems. In particular, he blamed them for Germany's defeat in World War I.

22. Students should identify five of the following as factors most historians consider as possibly contributing to the Holocaust: the German people's sense of injury after World War I; severe economic problems; Hitler's grip on the German nation; the lack of a strong tradition of representative government in Germany; German fear of Hitler's secret police; and a long history of anti-Jewish prejudice and discrimination in Europe.

SECTION QUIZ 20-1

Matching

| 1. B | 2. E | 3. C | 4. A | 5. D |

Multiple Choice

| 6. A | 7. C | 8. D | 9. A | 10. D |

SECTION QUIZ 20-2

Matching

| 1. D | 2. B | 3. E | 4. A | 5. C |

Multiple Choice

| 6. D | 7. B | 8. A | 9. B | 10. D |

SECTION QUIZ 20-3

Matching

| 1. E | 2. B | 3. A | 4. D | 5. C |

Multiple Choice

| 6. C | 7. A | 8. D | 9. B | 10. A |

SECTION QUIZ 20-4

Matching

| 1. B | 2. C | 3. D | 4. E | 5. A |

Multiple Choice

| 6. B | 7. A | 8. C | 9. D | 10. C |

SECTION QUIZ 20-5

Matching

| 1. C | 2. E | 3. B | 4. A | 5. D |

Multiple Choice

| 6. B | 7. A | 8. D | 9. C | 10. A |

CHAPTER 20 TEST, FORM A

Matching

| 1. J | 2. F | 3. C | 4. A | 5. D |
| 6. B | 7. H | 8. G | 9. I | 10. E |

Multiple Choice

| 11. B | 12. D | 13. C | 14. C | 15. B |
| 16. B | 17. B | 18. D | 19. C | 20. D |

Essay

21. President Roosevelt wanted to bomb Tokyo to raise the morale of the American people. American planes, however, could reach Tokyo only if an aircraft carrier brought them close enough. Unfortunately, Japanese ships in the North Pacific prevented carriers from getting close enough to Japan to launch their short-range bombers. A military planner suggested replacing the carriers' usual short-range bombers with long-range B-25 bombers that could attack from farther away. Although the B-25s could take off from a carrier, they could not land on its short deck. After attacking Japan, they would have to land in China. The raid resulted in the first American bombs to fall on Japan.

22. The United Nations was designed to have two branches: the General Assembly and the Security Council. In the General Assembly, every member nation in the world would have one vote. The Security Council would have 11 members. Five countries would be permanent members: Britain, France, China, the Soviet Union, and the United States. Each permanent member would have veto power. The General Assembly could vote on resolutions, choose non-permanent members of the Security Council, and vote on the UN budget. The Security Council was responsible for international peace and security. It could investigate any international problem and propose settlements to countries that had disputes with each other. It could also take action to preserve the peace, including asking its members to use military force to uphold a UN resolution.

CHAPTER 20 TEST, FORM B

Matching

| 1. C | 2. J | 3. G | 4. F | 5. D |
| 6. I | 7. H | 8. E | 9. A | 10. B |

Multiple Choice

| 11. C | 12. B | 13. A | 14. B | 15. D |
| 16. C | 17. C | 18. A | 19. B | 20. D |

Essay

21. A zoot suit had an overstuffed jacket that had wide lapels and reached to the knees, with very baggy, pleated pants. Accessories included a wide-brimmed hat and a long key chain. Zoot-suit wearers usually wore their hair long, gathered into a ducktail. The zoot suit angered many Americans. In order to save fabric for the war, most men wore a "victory suit," which had no vest, no cuffs, a short jacket, and narrow lapels. By comparison, the zoot suit seemed unpatriotic. Also, crimes committed by young people had been rising dramatically across the nation. The fact that many young Mexican Americans adopted the zoot suit linked racism as well as fear of juvenile crime to the zoot suit. In Los Angeles, this mix resulted in violence against Mexican American teenagers.

22. One adviser opposed using the bomb because it would kill civilians indiscriminately. Instead, he believed an economic blockade and conventional bombing might convince Japan to surrender. Another adviser wanted to warn the Japanese about the bomb while at the same time telling them that they could keep the emperor if they surrendered. Another adviser wanted to drop the bomb without any warning to shock Japan into surrendering. All his advisers warned President Truman to expect massive casualties if the United States invaded Japan. Truman decided to drop the bomb because he believed it was his duty as president to use every weapon available to save American lives.

SECTION QUIZ 21-1

Matching

1. D	2. B	3. A	4. E	5. C

Multiple Choice

6. A	7. C	8. D	9. B	10. C

SECTION QUIZ 21-2

Matching

1. C	2. A	3. B	4. E	5. D

Multiple Choice

6. D	7. A	8. C	9. B	10. A

SECTION QUIZ 21-3

Matching

1. E	2. C	3. B	4. A	5. D

Multiple Choice

6. B	7. C	8. D	9. C	10. A

SECTION QUIZ 21-4

Matching

1. E	2. A	3. B	4. C	5. D

Multiple Choice

6. B	7. D	8. A	9. D	10. B

CHAPTER 21 TEST, FORM A

Matching

1. F	2. J	3. I	4. E	5. B
6. A	7. C	8. H	9. G	10. D

Multiple Choice

11. C	12. C	13. D	14. A	15. C
16. D	17. A	18. D	19. B	20. C

Essay

21. Until 1950, the United States had preferred to use political pressure and economic aid to contain communism. After the Korean War began, the United States embarked on a major military buildup. The Korean War also helped expand the Cold War to Asia. Before 1950, the United States had focused on Europe as the most important area to contain communism. After the Korean War began, the United States became more militarily involved in Asia. The United States signed defense agreements with several Asian nations and began to send aid to the French forces fighting Communist guerrillas in Vietnam.

22. The Korean War had convinced Eisenhower that the United States could not contain communism by fighting a series of small wars. Instead, these wars had to be prevented from happening in the first place. The best way to do that seemed to be to threaten to use nuclear weapons if a Communist state tried to seize territory by force. This policy came to be called "massive retaliation." "Brinkmanship" was the willingness to go to the brink of war to force the other side to back down. Eisenhower used these two concepts in international confrontations. In Korea, for example, he quietly let the Chinese know that the United States might continue the Korean War "under circumstances of our own choosing." The message was a hint at nuclear attack. The threat to go to the brink of nuclear war seemed to work, because negotiators soon signed an armistice.

CHAPTER 21 TEST, FORM B

Matching

1. I	2. G	3. F	4. E	5. H
6. B	7. C	8. A	9. J	10. D

Multiple Choice

| **11.** A | **12.** B | **13.** B | **14.** D | **15.** C |
| **16.** D | **17.** B | **18.** B | **19.** D | **20.** D |

Essay

21. Soviet Union's main concern: security

Soviet Union's ideology: communism

United States's main concern: economic problems

United States's ideology: democracy (or free enterprise)

As the war ended, Soviet leaders became concerned about security. Germany had invaded Russia twice in less than 30 years. The Soviets did not want it to happen again. They wanted to keep Germany weak and make sure that the countries between Germany and the Soviet Union were under Soviet control. The Soviet leaders also believed that communism was superior and would eventually replace capitalism, and that they should encourage communism in other nations. They also accepted Lenin's theory that capitalism causes wars and would try to destroy communism. American leaders believed that the Depression had caused World War II. It helped Hitler rise to power and caused Japan to seek to expansion to get the resources it needed. American leaders believed that economic growth was the key to world peace, and that increasing world trade would promote growth. For similar reasons, American leaders wanted to promote democracy, believing that it was the best way to stability and prosperity.

22. When McCarthy became chairman of the Senate subcommittee on investigations, he used the power of his committee to force government officials to testify about alleged Communist influences. He turned the investigation into a witch hunt, insinuating disloyalty based on flimsy evidence and irrational fears. He blackened reputations with vague and unfounded charges. His theatrics and sensational accusations drew the attention of the press, which put him in the headlines and quoted him widely. Relishing the spotlight, he became bolder. When he questioned witnesses, McCarthy would badger them and then refuse to accept their answers. His tactics left a cloud of suspicion that McCarthy and others interpreted as guilt. Furthermore, people were afraid to challenge him for fear of becoming targets themselves.

SECTION QUIZ 22-1

Matching

| **1.** E | **2.** B | **3.** C | **4.** D | **5.** A |

Multiple Choice

| **6.** C | **7.** A | **8.** C | **9.** D | **10.** B |

SECTION QUIZ 22-2

Matching

| **1.** D | **2.** B | **3.** A | **4.** E | **5.** C |

Multiple Choice

| **6.** C | **7.** A | **8.** D | **9.** A | **10.** B |

SECTION QUIZ 22-3

Matching

| **1.** C | **2.** A | **3.** D | **4.** E | **5.** B |

Multiple Choice

| **6.** B | **7.** C | **8.** A | **9.** C | **10.** B |

SECTION QUIZ 22-4

Matching

| **1.** B | **2.** A | **3.** D | **4.** E | **5.** C |

Multiple Choice

| **6.** A | **7.** D | **8.** B | **9.** C | **10.** C |

CHAPTER 22 TEST, FORM A

Matching

| **1.** E | **2.** I | **3.** H | **4.** D | **5.** J |
| **6.** A | **7.** C | **8.** G | **9.** F | **10.** B |

Multiple Choice

| **11.** C | **12.** A | **13.** C | **14.** D | **15.** D |
| **16.** C | **17.** B | **18.** C | **19.** C | **20.** D |

Essay

21. Eisenhower showed his conservative side by appointing several business leaders to his cabinet. He ended government price and rent controls and tried to curb the federal budget by vetoing a school construction bill and slashing government aid to public housing. To accompany these cuts, he supported some modest tax reductions. In other conservative actions, he abolished the Reconstruction Finance Corporation and slashed funding for the Tennessee Valley Authority. He displayed his activism by advocating passage of the Federal Highway Act and authorizing construction of the Great Lakes-St. Lawrence Seaway. Although President Eisenhower cut federal spending and worked to limit the federal government's role in the nation's economy, he agreed to extend the Social Security system to an additional 10 million people. He also extended unemployment compensation, increased the minimum wage, and continued to provide some government aid to farmers.

22. Several factors contributed to the baby boom. First, young couples who had delayed marriage during World War II and the Korean War could now marry, buy homes, and begin their families. In addition, the government encouraged the growth of families by offering generous GI benefits for home purchases. Finally, on television and in magazines, popular culture celebrated pregnancy, parenthood, and large families.

CHAPTER 22 TEST, FORM B

Matching

1.	D	2.	C	3.	G	4.	J	5.	H
6.	A	7.	E	8.	I	9.	B	10.	F

Multiple Choice

11.	A	12.	B	13.	D	14.	D	15.	B
16.	A	17.	B	18.	A	19.	B	20.	B

Essay

21. Some whites moved to the suburbs to escape the crime and congestion of the city. Others viewed life in the suburbs as a move up to a better life. Also, the GI Bill offered low-interest loans, making new housing quite affordable during the postwar period. Equally attractive was the government's offer of income tax deductions for home mortgage interest payments and property taxes. For millions of Americans, the suburbs came to symbolize the American dream. They owned their homes, sent their children to good schools, lived in safe communities, and were economically secure.

22. As television gained popularity, movies lost viewers. Throughout the 1950s, Hollywood struggled to recapture its audience. It tried contests, door prizes, and advertising, but most of these tactics failed to lure people out of their living rooms. Then Hollywood tried to make films more exciting by introducing 3-D films. These worked temporarily, but viewers soon tired of them. Cinemascope, movies shown on large, panoramic screens, finally gave Hollywood a reliable lure. Hollywood eventually began to film programs especially for television and also sold old movies, which could be cheaply rebroadcast, to the networks.

UNIT 6 POSTTEST, FORM A

Matching

1.	H	2.	J	3.	B	4.	D	5.	A
6.	C	7.	I	8.	F	9.	G	10.	E

Multiple Choice

11.	B	12.	D	13.	A	14.	B	15.	B
16.	A	17.	D	18.	A	19.	D	20.	D

Essay

21. In his book, Hitler called for the unification of all Germans under one government. Hitler believed that certain Germans, particularly blond, blue-eyed Germans, were descendants of a "master race" called Aryans. According to Hitler, the Slavic people of Eastern Europe belonged to an inferior race, which Germans should enslave. Most likely these beliefs contributed to his actions toward expanding in Eastern Europe and Poland, justifying his acts by claiming that Germans needed more lebensraum, or living space. Hitler believed that Jews were responsible for many of the world's problems. In particular, he blamed them for Germany's defeat in World War I. Acting on his hatred toward Jews, Hitler set in motion a plan for killing millions of Europe's Jews in what became known as the Holocaust.

22. McCarthyism was named after its main perpetrator, Senator Joseph McCarthy, who embarked on a witch hunt for Communist influences in the United States. He accused many Americans of disloyalty based on flimsy evidence and irrational fears, blackening reputations with vague and unfounded charges. His theatrics and sensational accusations drew the attention of the press, which put him in the headlines. When he questioned witnesses, McCarthy would badger them and then refuse to accept their answers. His tactics left a cloud of suspicion that McCarthy and others interpreted as guilt. Furthermore, people were afraid to challenge him for fear of becoming targets themselves. When McCarthy began to look for Soviet spies in the United States Army, the army, alerted to his intentions, had already done its own investigations and found no spies. During weeks of televised Army-McCarthy hearings, millions of Americans watched McCarthy bully witnesses, and his popular support began to fade. His attempt to ruin the career of a young army lawyer outraged spectators. Later that year, the Senate passed a vote of censure against him.

UNIT 6 POSTTEST, FORM B

Matching

1.	H	2.	F	3.	A	4.	G	5.	E
6.	I	7.	D	8.	B	9.	J	10.	C

Multiple Choice

11.	C	12.	C	13.	C	14.	D	15.	B
16.	B	17.	B	18.	C	19.	D	20.	B

Essay

21. The Doolittle Raid was an early bombing raid on Tokyo. President Roosevelt wanted to bomb Tokyo to raise the morale of the American people.

American planes, however, could reach Tokyo only if an aircraft carrier brought them close enough. Unfortunately, Japanese ships in the North Pacific prevented carriers from getting close enough to Japan to launch their short-range bombers. A military planner suggested replacing the carriers' usual short-range bombers with long-range B-25 bombers that could attack from farther away. Although the B-25s could take off from a carrier, they could not land on its short deck. After attacking Japan, they would have to land in China. The raid resulted in the first American bombs to fall on Japan and an instant boost to sagging American morale. However, the bombers did not have enough fuel to reach friendly airfields, so they had to crash land or bail out, and only 71 of the 80 crew members survived.

22. Some whites moved to the suburbs to escape the crime and congestion of the city. Others viewed life in the suburbs as a move up to a better life. Also, the GI Bill offered low-interest loans, making new housing quite affordable during the postwar period. Equally attractive was the government's offer of income tax deductions for home mortgage interest payments and property taxes. For millions of Americans, the suburbs came to symbolize the American dream. They owned their homes, sent their children to good schools, lived in safe communities, and were economically secure.

UNIT 7 PRETEST, FORM A

Matching

1. H	**2.** F	**3.** G	**4.** I	**5.** J
6. C	**7.** A	**8.** E	**9.** B	**10.** D

Multiple Choice

11. D	**12.** B	**13.** C	**14.** C	**15.** D
16. A	**17.** C	**18.** C	**19.** C	**20.** A

Essay

21. Dr. Martin Luther King, Jr., was the pastor at Dexter Avenue Baptist Church in Montgomery, Alabama. He emerged as the leader of the Montgomery bus boycott after Rosa Parks's arrest and later as one of the most inspirational leaders of the civil rights movement. He believed that the only moral way to end segregation and racism was through nonviolent passive resistance. King drew upon the philosophy of Mohandas Gandhi, who had used nonviolent resistance effectively in his struggle against British rule in India. Like Gandhi, King encouraged his followers to disobey unjust laws. Believing in the ability of people to transform themselves spiritually, King was certain that public opinion would eventually force government officials to end segregation.

22. Since the American military was extremely strong, it marched into Vietnam initially with great confidence. However, the war soon turned into a bloody stalemate. Lacking the firepower of the Americans, the Vietcong used ambushes, booby traps, and hit-and-run tactics. The Vietcong also frustrated American troops by blending in with the general population in the cities and the countryside and then quickly vanishing. As one journalist put it, "It's a war where nothing is ever quite certain and nowhere is ever quite safe." To counter the enemy's tactics, American troops went on "search-and-destroy" missions. They tried to find enemy troops, bomb their positions, destroy their supply lines, and force them out into the open for combat. American forces also sought to take away the Vietcong's ability to hide in the thick jungles by literally destroying the landscape. American planes dropped napalm and Agent Orange, a chemical that strips leaves from trees and shrubs, turning the farmland and forest into wasteland.

UNIT 7 PRETEST, FORM B

Matching

1. E	**2.** A	**3.** H	**4.** D	**5.** F
6. J	**7.** B	**8.** I	**9.** G	**10.** C

Multiple Choice

11. B	**12.** D	**13.** D	**14.** C	**15.** A
16. B	**17.** C	**18.** C	**19.** D	**20.** D

Essay

21. Students' answers should show an understanding of the group and explain why they chose this group over others. Students may choose from any of the following groups: Freedom Riders with the Congress of Racial Equality; sit-ins at lunch counters with the Student Nonviolent Coordinating Committee; integrating universities or other schools; civil rights marches with Martin Luther King, Jr., and the Southern Christian Leadership Conference; Malcolm X and the Nation of Islam (Black Muslims); Stokely Carmichael and advancement of Black Power; the Black Panther Party.

22. The Berlin Wall, built by the East Germans with Soviet backing, closed the borders between Communist-controlled East Berlin and free West Berlin. The Berlin Wall cut communication between the two parts of the city, and it came to symbolize Communist repression and the division between the East and West during the Cold War.

SECTION QUIZ 23-1

Matching

1. E	**2.** C	**3.** A	**4.** D	**5.** B

Multiple Choice

| 6. D | 7. A | 8. B | 9. C | 10. B |

SECTION QUIZ 23-2

Matching

| 1. D | 2. E | 3. B | 4. C | 5. A |

Multiple Choice

| 6. C | 7. D | 8. A | 9. A | 10. B |

SECTION QUIZ 23-3

Matching

| 1. A | 2. D | 3. E | 4. B | 5. C |

Multiple Choice

| 6. C | 7. D | 8. B | 9. A | 10. C |

CHAPTER 23 TEST, FORM A

Matching

| 1. B | 2. E | 3. A | 4. D | 5. F |
| 6. C | 7. A | 8. C | 9. B | 10. D |

Multiple Choice

| 11. C | 12. B | 13. B | 14. A | 15. B |
| 16. C | 17. B | 18. C | 19. D | 20. B |

Essay

21. Kennedy and Nixon differed in many ways. Kennedy, a Catholic, came from a Massachusetts family of wealth and influence. Nixon, a Quaker, was a Californian from a financially struggling family. Kennedy seemed outgoing and relaxed, while Nixon struck many as formal and even stiff in manner. Although the candidates presented different styles, they differed little on the two main issues. Both promised to boost the economy and both portrayed themselves as "Cold Warriors" determined to stop the forces of communism.

22. Latin American governments were often in the hands of the wealthy few, and many of their citizens lived in extreme poverty. These conditions sometimes spurred the growth of left-wing movements aimed at overthrowing their governments. The United States often tried to help the existing governments stay in power in order to prevent Communist movements from flourishing. Poor Latin Americans resented this intrusion, just as they resented American corporations that had business operations in their countries, a presence that was seen as a kind of imperialism.

CHAPTER 23 TEST, FORM B

Matching

| 1. F | 2. J | 3. I | 4. A | 5. G |
| 6. D | 7. E | 8. C | 9. B | 10. H |

Multiple Choice

| 11. D | 12. D | 13. A | 14. A | 15. B |
| 16. C | 17. B | 18. C | 19. D | 20. C |

Essay

21. John Kennedy captured the imagination of the American public as few presidents before him had. Many people were taken with his youth and optimism. He reinforced this impression in his Inaugural Address, in which he wore neither coat nor hat on a cold day and declared, "The torch has been passed to a new generation." He called on his fellow Americans to take an active role in making the United States a better place. Kennedy's looks, his glamorous wife, and their young children seemed to have been created for media coverage. Newspeople followed the family everywhere. Plus, Kennedy himself was a master of the media, particularly television. His charisma inspired people with "a feeling that he was moving, and the world with him, toward a better time."

22. Johnson was a man of impressive stature who spoke directly, convincingly, and even roughly at times. His style was more that of a persuasive and personable politician than of the elegant society man. Finding it difficult to gain acceptance from the Eastern establishment in the nation's capital, he often reveled in his rough image. He honed his style in long years of public service. As he moved up the political ladder, Johnson developed a reputation as a man who got things done. He did favors, twisted arms, bargained, flattered, and threatened. The tactics he used to persuade others became known throughout Washington as the "Johnson treatment." It was often an overpowering and intimidating style. With every technique he could think of, he sought to find consensus. His ability to build coalitions had made him one of the most effective and powerful leaders in the Senate's history.

SECTION QUIZ 24-1

Matching

| 1. C | 2. B | 3. E | 4. D | 5. A |

Multiple Choice

| 6. A | 7. C | 8. B | 9. B | 10. D |

SECTION QUIZ 24-2

Matching

1. B	**2.** E	**3.** D	**4.** A	**5.** C

Multiple Choice

6. D	**7.** B	**8.** C	**9.** A	**10.** C

SECTION QUIZ 24-3

Matching

1. A	**2.** D	**3.** E	**4.** C	**5.** B

Multiple Choice

6. A	**7.** C	**8.** B	**9.** A	**10.** B

CHAPTER 24 TEST, FORM A

Matching

1. B	**2.** A	**3.** C	**4.** D	**5.** A
6. C	**7.** E	**8.** F	**9.** D	**10.** B

Multiple Choice

11. B	**12.** C	**13.** A	**14.** D	**15.** D
16. A	**17.** B	**18.** C	**19.** B	**20.** A

Essay

21. The "Letter from a Birmingham Jail" was an eloquent defense of nonviolent protest. In it, Dr. King explained that although the protesters were breaking the law, they were following a higher moral law, based on divine justice. To the charge that the protests created racial tensions, King argued that the protests "merely bring to the surface the hidden tension that is already alive." Injustice, he insisted, had to be exposed "to the light of human conscience and the air of national opinion before it can be cured."

22. A few African Americans interpreted black power to mean that physical self-defense and even violence were acceptable in defense of one's freedom, which was a clear rejection of Dr. King's philosophy. To most, the term meant that they should control the social, political, and economic direction of their struggle for equality. Black power also stressed pride in the African American cultural group. It emphasized racial distinctiveness instead of cultural assimilation. Pride in their racial heritage was manifested in new Afro hairstyles and African-style clothing, as well as the adoption of African names and a demand that African and African American Studies courses be adopted as part of the standard school curriculum.

CHAPTER 24 TEST, FORM B

Matching

1. G	**2.** I	**3.** F	**4.** E	**5.** A
6. B	**7.** D	**8.** H	**9.** C	**10.** J

Multiple Choice

11. C	**12.** D	**13.** A	**14.** A	**15.** B
16. D	**17.** C	**18.** A	**19.** D	**20.** A

Essay

21. Before World War I, the vast majority of African Americans lived in the South, where they were largely excluded from voting. During the Great Migration, many African Americans moved to Northern cities where they were allowed to vote. Increasingly, Northern politicians sought the votes of African Americans and listened to their concerns. During the Great Depression, many African Americans benefited from Franklin Roosevelt's New Deal programs and voted for him in record numbers. Their votes gave the Democratic Party new strength in the North, where Republicans had dominated ever since the Civil War. They forced the Democratic Party to pay attention to civil rights issues and helped counter the powerful Southern Democrats, many of whom strongly supported segregation.

22. The Civil Rights Act of 1964 was the most comprehensive civil rights law ever enacted. It gave the federal government broad power to prevent racial discrimination in a number of areas. The law outlawed segregation in most places of public accommodation, and it gave citizens of all races and nationalities equal access to such facilities as restaurants, parks, libraries, and theaters. The law gave the attorney general more power to bring lawsuits to force school desegregation, and it required private employers to end discrimination in the workplace. It also established the Equal Employment Opportunity Commission as a permanent agency in the federal government, which would oversee the ban on job discrimination by race, religion, gender, or national origin.

SECTION QUIZ 25-1

Matching

1. B	**2.** E	**3.** C	**4.** A	**5.** D

Multiple Choice

6. B	**7.** C	**8.** D	**9.** A	**10.** A

SECTION QUIZ 25-2

Matching

1. E	**2.** D	**3.** C	**4.** A	**5.** B

Multiple Choice

| 6. | B | 7. | C | 8. | D | 9. | A | 10. | C |

SECTION QUIZ 25-3

Matching

| 1. | D | 2. | A | 3. | B | 4. | E | 5. | C |

Multiple Choice

| 6. | A | 7. | C | 8. | B | 9. | C | 10. | B |

SECTION QUIZ 25-4

Matching

| 1. | D | 2. | B | 3. | C | 4. | A | 5. | E |

Multiple Choice

| 6. | D | 7. | B | 8. | A | 9. | C | 10. | D |

CHAPTER 25 TEST, FORM A

Matching

| 1. | J | 2. | F | 3. | B | 4. | E | 5. | I |
| 6. | H | 7. | A | 8. | D | 9. | C | 10. | G |

Multiple Choice

| 11. | D | 12. | A | 13. | B | 14. | A | 15. | D |
| 16. | C | 17. | A | 18. | C | 19. | D | 20. | C |

Essay

21. Lacking the firepower of the Americans, the Vietcong used ambushes, booby traps, and hit-and-run tactics. The Vietcong also frustrated American troops by blending in with the general population in the cities and the countryside and then quickly vanishing. As one journalist put it, "It's a war where nothing is ever quite certain and nowhere is ever quite safe." To counter the enemy's tactics, American troops went on "search-and-destroy" missions. They tried to find enemy troops, bomb their positions, destroy their supply lines, and force them out into the open for combat. American forces also sought to take away the Vietcong's ability to hide in the thick jungles by literally destroying the landscape. American planes dropped napalm and Agent Orange, a chemical that strips leaves from trees and shrubs, turning the farmland and forest into wasteland.

22. The circle graphs show that African Americans made up about 20% of the American combat deaths in 1967—about twice their proportion of the population within the United States at that time (10%). An unfair draft system may have contributed to this situation. At the beginning of the war, a college student was often able to defer military service until after graduation. By contrast, young people with limited education from low-income families were more likely to be sent to Vietnam because they were unable to afford college. This meant minorities, particularly African Americans, made up a disproportionately large number of the soldiers in Vietnam.

CHAPTER 25 TEST, FORM B

Matching

| 1. | H | 2. | I | 3. | E | 4. | G | 5. | B |
| 6. | A | 7. | F | 8. | C | 9. | D | 10. | J |

Multiple Choice

| 11. | D | 12. | C | 13. | B | 14. | D | 15. | D |
| 16. | B | 17. | C | 18. | B | 19. | A | 20. | D |

Essay

21. Students should fill in one side of the graphic organizer with "military" or "government" and the other with "media" or "television."

    Initially, public support for the war was strong, but it dropped as the war dragged on. A significant cause was suspicion of the government's truthfulness about the war. Throughout the early years of the war, the American commander in South Vietnam, General Westmoreland, reported that the enemy was on the brink of defeat. He said things like "we have reached an important point where the end begins to come into view." Contradicting such reports were less optimistic media accounts, especially on television. Vietnam was the first "television war," with footage of combat appearing nightly on the evening news. Day after day, millions of families saw images of wounded and dead Americans and began to doubt government reports. A "credibility gap" had developed. It was hard to believe what the Johnson administration said about the war.

22. The Tet offensive was a massive surprise attack by the Vietcong and North Vietnamese on virtually all American airbases and most cities in the South. Militarily, Tet turned out to be a disaster for the Communist forces. Politically, however, they had scored a major victory. The American people were shocked that an enemy supposedly on the verge of defeat could launch such a large-scale attack. When General Westmoreland requested a huge number of additional troops, it seemed another admission that the United States could not win the war. After Tet, the mainstream media, which had tried to remain balanced in their war coverage, began openly criticizing the effort. Public opinion no longer seemed with the president. His approval ratings plummeted. The administration's credibility gap now seemed too wide to repair. Most likely, Tet contributed to Johnson's decision not to run for a second term.

SECTION QUIZ 26-1

Matching

1. D	**2.** C	**3.** B	**4.** E	**5.** A

Multiple Choice

6. C	**7.** A	**8.** D	**9.** B	**10.** D

SECTION QUIZ 26-2

Matching

1. E	**2.** D	**3.** A	**4.** C	**5.** B

Multiple Choice

6. C	**7.** B	**8.** A	**9.** C	**10.** B

SECTION QUIZ 26-3

Matching

1. E	**2.** C	**3.** A	**4.** B	**5.** D

Multiple Choice

6. A	**7.** C	**8.** D	**9.** C	**10.** A

SECTION QUIZ 26-4

Matching

1. E	**2.** C	**3.** B	**4.** D	**5.** A

Multiple Choice

6. C	**7.** A	**8.** C	**9.** B	**10.** C

CHAPTER 26 TEST, FORM A

Matching

1. F	**2.** E	**3.** H	**4.** J	**5.** B
6. I	**7.** C	**8.** D	**9.** G	**10.** A

Multiple Choice

11. D	**12.** B	**13.** D	**14.** C	**15.** B
16. D	**17.** C	**18.** D	**19.** B	**20.** A

Essay

21. The counterculture generation dressed in costumes rather than in occupational or class uniforms. The colorful, beaded, braided, patched, and fringed garments that both men and women wore turned the fashion industry upside down. The international fashion world took its cues from young men and women on the street. Men's clothing became more colorful and women's clothing became more comfortable. Protest often expressed itself in clothing. The counterculture adopted military surplus attire not only because it was inexpensive, but also because it expressed rejection of materialist values and blurred the lines of social class. For the same reasons, clothing of another age was recycled, and worn-out clothing repaired with patches. Ethnic clothing was also popular. Beads and fringes imi-

tated Native American costumes; tie-dyed shirts borrowed techniques from India and Africa. Long hair was a particularly potent symbol of the era. Once the initial shock wore off, longer hair on men and more individual clothes for both men and women became generally accepted. What was once clothing of defiance soon became mainstream.

22. Supporters of nuclear energy hailed it as a cleaner and less expensive alternative to fossil fuels, which have a limited supply. Opponents warned of the risks nuclear energy posed, in particular, the devastating consequences of an accidental radiation release into the air.

An accident at Three Mile Island, a nuclear facility outside of Harrisburg, Pennsylvania, moved the debate to the nation's forefront. A reactor overheated after its cooling system failed. As a result, low levels of radiation escaped from the reactor. Officials evacuated many nearby residents, while others fled on their own. Citizens and community groups expressed outrage in protest rallies. Officials closed down the reactor and sealed the leak. The federal regulatory agency eventually declared the plant safe. Yet this accident had a powerful impact and left much of the public in great doubt about the safety of nuclear energy. Such doubts have continued. Since Three Mile Island, 60 nuclear power plants have been shut down and no new facilities have been built since 1973.

CHAPTER 26 TEST, FORM B

Matching

1. G	**2.** J	**3.** H	**4.** C	**5.** B
6. A	**7.** I	**8.** D	**9.** F	**10.** E

Multiple Choice

11. D	**12.** B	**13.** C	**14.** C	**15.** B
16. A	**17.** A	**18.** C	**19.** D	**20.** C

Essay

21. The nuclear arms race between the United States and Soviet Union made many of the nation's youth uneasy about their future. This concern led many young people to become more active in social causes, from the civil rights movement to President Kennedy's Peace Corps. As a result of the baby boom, a larger percentage of the American population was less than 34 years old in the 1960s than ever before. Because of the economic boom of the 1950s, many more families could afford to send their children to college, so enrollments soared in the 1960s. College life empowered young people with a new-found sense of freedom and independence. It also allowed them to meet and bond with others who shared their feelings about society and fears about the future. It was on the college cam-

puses across the nation where the protest movements would rage the loudest.

22. By the early 1960s, many women were increasingly resentful of old stereotypes of a world where newspaper ads separated jobs by gender, where clubs refused them separate memberships, where banks routinely denied them credit, and where they often were paid less for the same work. Generally, women found themselves shut out of the higher-paying and prestigious professions, such as law, medicine, and accounting. About three-fourths of the women in the workforce in the 1960s worked in lower-paying and routine clerical, sales, or factory jobs, or as cleaning women and hospital attendants. Even in the civil rights and antiwar movements, women were often restricted to menial tasks and rarely had a say in any policy decisions. Awareness of these kinds of inequalities sparked a new and energetic feminist movement.

UNIT 7 POSTTEST, FORM A

Matching

| 1. | D | 2. | F | 3. | A | 4. | J | 5. | H |
| 6. | I | 7. | E | 8. | B | 9. | C | 10. | G |

Multiple Choice

| 11. | B | 12. | B | 13. | A | 14. | B | 15. | D |
| 16. | D | 17. | A | 18. | B | 19. | C | 20. | A |

Essay

21. The Great Society improved thousands if not millions of lives. Still, debate continues over whether it was truly a success. Many of the programs grew so quickly that they became unmanageable and difficult to evaluate. Groups eligible for aid began to expect significant and immediate benefits, but were often left frustrated. Other Americans opposed the massive growth of federal programs and criticized the Great Society for intruding too much into their lives. Lack of funding also hurt the programs, as the Vietnam War required an ever-increasing share of the federal budget. Some Great Society initiatives continue, such as Medicare and Medicaid. An important legacy of the Great Society was the questions it produced. How can the federal government help its disadvantaged citizens? How much government help can a society have without weakening the private sector? How much help can people receive without losing motivation to help themselves?

22. President Johnson announced that North Vietnamese torpedo boats had fired on two American destroyers in the Gulf of Tonkin. Two days later he announced another similar attack. He insisted that the attacks were unprovoked and immediately ordered American aircraft to attack

North Vietnamese ships and naval facilities. He did not reveal that the American warships had been assisting the South Vietnamese in electronic spying and commando raids on North Vietnam. Johnson then asked Congress to authorize the use of force to defend American forces. Congress passed the Gulf of Tonkin Resolution, authorizing the president to "take all necessary measures to repel any armed attack" against United States forces. In effect, Congress handed its war powers over to the president. Soon the Vietcong began to attack American bases. Johnson responded by bombing North Vietnam. Soon, the first American combat troops were ordered into Vietnam.

UNIT 7 POSTTEST, FORM B

Matching

| 1. | B | 2. | F | 3. | I | 4. | E | 5. | D |
| 6. | C | 7. | G | 8. | J | 9. | A | 10. | H |

Multiple Choice

| 11. | C | 12. | C | 13. | B | 14. | D | 15. | A |
| 16. | C | 17. | B | 18. | D | 19. | D | 20. | C |

Essay

21. The Nation of Islam, commonly known as the Black Muslims, was led by Elijah Muhammad. They did not hold the same beliefs as mainstream Muslims. They preached black nationalism, believing that African Americans should separate themselves from whites and form their own self-governing communities. The Black Muslims viewed themselves as a nation and attempted to make themselves as economically self-sufficient as possible. They ran their own businesses, organized their own schools, established their own weekly newspaper, and encouraged their members to respect each other and to strengthen their families. Although Black Muslims did not advocate violence, they did advocate self-defense. Malcolm X was a powerful and charismatic leader who gained national attention for the Nation of Islam.

22. Throughout the 1960s, thousands of mostly white youths turned away from their middle- and upper-class existence and created a new lifestyle—one that promoted the virtues of flamboyant dress, rock music, drug use, and free and independent living. With their alternative ways of life, these young people became known as the counterculture and were commonly called "hippies." Originally, hippie culture represented a rebellion against the dominant culture. This included a rejection of Western civilization, of rationality, order, and the traditional values of the middle class. At its core, the counterculture held up a utopian ideal: the ideal of a society that was freer, closer to nature,

and full of love, empathy, tolerance, and cooperation. When the movement grew larger, many of the
newcomers did not always understand these original ideas of the counterculture. For them, what
mattered were the outward signs that defined the
movement, such as long hair, shabby jeans, and
drugs. Many hippies formed group living arrangements called communes. Thousands flocked to San
Francisco's Haight-Ashbury district.

UNIT 8 PRETEST, FORM A

Matching

1.	G	**2.**	B	**3.**	I	**4.**	F	**5.**	C
6.	A	**7.**	D	**8.**	H	**9.**	E	**10.**	J

Multiple Choice

11.	B	**12.**	D	**13.**	C	**14.**	C	**15.**	C
16.	D	**17.**	A	**18.**	C	**19.**	B	**20.**	B

Essay

21. Watergate was a scandal that arose from the Nixon
Administration's attempts to cover up its involvement in the break-in at the Democratic National
Committee headquarters at the Watergate
apartment-office complex. Five Nixon supporters
broke into the headquarters in an effort to steal
campaign information that might help Richard
Nixon win re-election. The burglars were caught,
and as investigations and hearings proceeded, it
became clear that Nixon was involved. Nixon's
own tapes of conversations in the White House
helped to implicate him. When impeachment and
conviction seemed inevitable, Nixon resigned the
presidency in disgrace. The scandal left many
Americans with a deep distrust of their public officials. On the other hand, some Americans saw the
Watergate affair as proof that in the United States,
no person is above the law.

22. In the 1980s, cable and satellite television rapidly
expanded. Dozens of channels offered programs
for specialized audiences. Ted Turner Cable News
Network became the first all-news television network. In 1981 MTV went on the air, mixing songs
with video images to create music videos. Home
video games developed quickly, and video arcades
became the new spot for young people to meet in
the 1980s.

UNIT 8 PRETEST, FORM B

Matching

1.	F	**2.**	I	**3.**	A	**4.**	G	**5.**	H
6.	J	**7.**	D	**8.**	E	**9.**	B	**10.**	C

Multiple Choice

11.	B	**12.**	C	**13.**	C	**14.**	D	**15.**	B
16.	A	**17.**	C	**18.**	B	**19.**	B	**20.**	D

Essay

21. Students' answers should show an understanding
of the situation. President Jimmy Carter was a
human rights president who took a stand against
the Soviets when they invaded Afghanistan. The
games were to be held in Moscow. Many argued,
however, that the Olympic Games are not political;
as sports events designed to bring countries
together, the Olympic spirit should have been hon-
ored by the United States.

22. During the 1980s, China's Communist government
began to reform its economy, but it refused to
make political reforms. In May 1989, students and
workers in China held demonstrations calling for
more democracy. As the protests spread, the country seemed on the verge of a revolution. The
Chinese government sent troops to crush the
uprising. In early June 1989, soldiers and tanks
killed protesters gathered in Tiananmen Square in
the center of Beijing. World leaders condemned the
slaughter. Although President George Bush halted
arms sales and reduced diplomatic contacts with
China, he refused harsher measures, believing that
trade and diplomacy would eventually moderate
China's behavior.

SECTION QUIZ 27-1

Matching

1.	E	**2.**	C	**3.**	B	**4.**	D	**5.**	A

Multiple Choice

6.	A	**7.**	B	**8.**	D	**9.**	C	**10.**	B

SECTION QUIZ 27-2

Matching

1.	D	**2.**	A	**3.**	B	**4.**	E	**5.**	C

Multiple Choice

6.	C	**7.**	A	**8.**	C	**9.**	A	**10.**	B

SECTION QUIZ 27-3

Matching

1.	D	**2.**	C	**3.**	E	**4.**	B	**5.**	A

Multiple Choice

6. D	7. C	8. A	9. B	10. D

SECTION QUIZ 27-4

Matching

1. B	2. E	3. D	4. C	5. A

Multiple Choice

6. A	7. B	8. D	9. C	10. B

CHAPTER 27 TEST, FORM A

Matching

1. J	2. G	3. H	4. D	5. B
6. F	7. I	8. E	9. A	10. C

Multiple Choice

11. C	12. D	13. A	14. D	15. C
16. B	17. C	18. A	19. B	20. A

Essay

21. Revenue sharing was a series of bills passed by Congress that granted federal funds to state and local agencies. Revenue sharing was intended to give state and local agencies more power. Over time, however, it actually increased the power of the federal government. As states came to depend on federal funds, the federal government could impose conditions on the states. Unless they met those conditions, their funds would be cut off.

22. Disenchanted with the conventional religions of their parents, some young people sought fulfillment through the host of secular movements and activities that made up the New Age movement. New Age enthusiasts embraced the idea that people were responsible for and capable of everything from self-healing to creating the world. They believed spiritual enlightenment could be found in common practices, not just in traditional churchgoing. They tried activities like yoga, martial arts, and chanting to achieve fuller spiritual awareness. The New Age movement took many different paths to transform individuals and society. Some New Agers extolled the power of crystals and gemstones to improve life; others touted astrology. Some were inspired by the Eastern belief in reincarnation, which taught that people could be reborn many times until reaching greater perfection. Awareness of former lives was supposed to bring knowledge of the true inner self.

CHAPTER 27 TEST, FORM B

Matching

1. F	2. E	3. H	4. B	5. J
6. C	7. D	8. I	9. G	10. A

Multiple Choice

11. B	12. B	13. C	14. D	15. B
16. A	17. D	18. D	19. C	20. D

Essay

21. The Watergate crisis prompted a series of new laws intended to limit the power of the executive branch and reestablish a greater balance of power in government. The Federal Campaign Act Amendments limited campaign contributions and established an independent agency to administer stricter election laws. The Ethics in Government Act required financial disclosure by high government officials in all three branches of government. The FBI Domestic Security Investigation Guidelines restricted the bureau's political intelligence-gathering activities. After Watergate, Congress also established a mechanism for appointing an independent counsel to investigate and prosecute wrongdoing by high government officials. Despite these efforts, Watergate left many Americans with a deep distrust of their public officials. On the other hand, some Americans saw Watergate as proof that in the United States, no person is above the law.

22. The softer sounds of disco music replaced rock 'n' roll as the music of the 1970s youth. T-shirts bearing personalized messages, skateboards, and mood rings were also popular with 1970s Americans. Mood rings changed color, supposedly to match the wearer's changing moods. CB radios in vehicles became popular. These systems allowed drivers to talk to each other within a range of a few miles. Many truck drivers used them to warn each other of police speed traps. Soon average drivers purchased them, mostly for entertainment, as they talked to each other in CB jargon and code words. Fitness was another trend, especially aerobics. It was a way to stay fit while having fun and interacting socially. Running also attracted fitness enthusiasts in the 1970s.

SECTION QUIZ 28-1

Matching

1. C	2. D	3. A	4. E	5. B

Multiple Choice

6. C	7. D	8. A	9. C	10. B

SECTION QUIZ 28-2

Matching

| 1. | E | 2. | D | 3. | A | 4. | C | 5. | B |

Multiple Choice

| 6. | A | 7. | C | 8. | D | 9. | A | 10. | B |

SECTION QUIZ 28-3

Matching

| 1. | B | 2. | A | 3. | D | 4. | C | 5. | E |

Multiple Choice

| 6. | D | 7. | C | 8. | B | 9. | A | 10. | A |

SECTION QUIZ 28-4

Matching

| 1. | B | 2. | D | 3. | C | 4. | A | 5. | E |

Multiple Choice

| 6. | D | 7. | C | 8. | B | 9. | C | 10. | A |

CHAPTER 28 TEST, FORM A

Matching

| 1. | E | 2. | G | 3. | H | 4. | F | 5. | C |
| 6. | I | 7. | A | 8. | J | 9. | D | 10. | B |

Multiple Choice

| 11. | C | 12. | D | 13. | B | 14. | C | 15. | B |
| 16. | B | 17. | D | 18. | A | 19. | C | 20. | C |

Essay

21. Liberals generally support high taxes on the wealthy, partly because the taxes weaken the power of the rich and partly because the government can transfer the wealth to other Americans to keep society more equal. They believe that most social problems have their roots in economic inequality. Conservatives generally oppose high taxes and government programs that transfer wealth from the rich to those less wealthy. They believe that taxes and government programs not only discourage investment and take away people's incentive to work hard but also reduce the amount of freedom in society.

22. In the 1980s, cable and satellite television rapidly expanded. Dozens of channels offered programs for specialized audiences. Ted Turner Cable News Network became the first all-news television network. In 1981 MTV went on the air, mixing songs with video images to create music videos. Home video games developed quickly, and video arcades became the new spot for young people to meet in the 1980s.

CHAPTER 28 TEST, FORM B

Matching

| 1. | I | 2. | F | 3. | B | 4. | G | 5. | A |
| 6. | J | 7. | D | 8. | E | 9. | H | 10. | C |

Multiple Choice

| 11. | B | 12. | A | 13. | A | 14. | C | 15. | D |
| 16. | A | 17. | B | 18. | B | 19. | C | 20. | C |

Essay

21. The new conservative coalition held a common belief that American society had somehow lost its way. The Watergate scandal, high taxes, and special interest politics had undermined many Americans' faith in their government. Rising unemployment, rapid inflation, and the energy crisis had undermined their confidence in the economy. Riots, crime, and drug abuse suggested that society itself was falling apart. The retreat from Vietnam, the hostage crisis in Iran, and the Soviet invasion of Afghanistan made the nation look weak and helpless internationally. Many Americans were tired of change and upheaval. They wanted stability and a return to what they remembered as a better time. The "new conservativism" and its most prominent spokesperson, Ronald Reagan, offered hope to a nation in distress.

22. As the Soviet threat faded, the United States began reducing its armed forces. Many former military personnel now had to find civilian jobs. Meanwhile, the government canceled orders for military equipment. This forced defense factories to lay off thousands of workers.

SECTION QUIZ 29-1

Matching

| 1. | C | 2. | B | 3. | E | 4. | A | 5. | D |

Multiple Choice

| 6. | A | 7. | C | 8. | D | 9. | B | 10. | C |

SECTION QUIZ 29-2

Matching

| 1. | D | 2. | E | 3. | C | 4. | B | 5. | A |

Multiple Choice

| 6. | B | 7. | C | 8. | B | 9. | A | 10. | D |

SECTION QUIZ 29-3

Matching

1. B	2. C	3. E	4. A	5. C

Multiple Choice

6. D	7. C	8. D	9. A	10. A

SECTION QUIZ 29-4

Matching

1. D	2. A	3. E	4. C	5. B

Multiple Choice

6. C	7. A	8. B	9. D	10. C

SECTION QUIZ 29-5

Matching

1. E	2. C	3. B	4. A	5. D

Multiple Choice

6. B	7. D	8. A	9. C	10. A

CHAPTER 29 TEST, FORM A

Matching

1. G	2. C	3. E	4. D	5. J
6. A	7. I	8. B	9. H	10. F

Multiple Choice

11. C	12. D	13. A	14. D	15. B
16. D	17. D	18. B	19. B	20. B

Essay

21. In one scandal, Clinton was accused of arranging illegal loans for Whitewater Development—an Arkansas real estate company. Later, a new scandal emerged involving a personal relationship between the president and a White House intern. Some evidence suggested that the president had committed perjury about the relationship. After examining the evidence, Kenneth Starr, the independent counsel appointed to look into the issues, submitted a report that argued that Clinton had obstructed justice, abused his power as president, and committed perjury. Clinton's supporters charged that Starr's report was politically motivated. The House passed two articles of impeachment, one for perjury and one for obstruction of justice, moving the case to trial in the Senate. There the vote was fairly even, but well short of the two-thirds needed to remove the president from office. Still, Clinton's reputation had suffered.

22. The voting in the 2000 election was so close in the pivotal state of Florida that officials authorized a hand recount of the votes. Problems arose, however, because of chads—little pieces of cardboard that voters had to punch out of their ballot to make their votes. Vote counters had to decide how to count a ballot when the chad was still partially attached. On some ballots, the chad was still in place, and the voter had left only a dimple on the surface of the ballot. When looking at the ballots, vote counters had to determine what the voter intended, and different counties used different standards to judge the ballots.

CHAPTER 29 TEST, FORM B

Matching

1. G	2. H	3. D	4. A	5. C
6. J	7. I	8. F	9. B	10. E

Multiple Choice

11. B	12. B	13. C	14. A	15. C
16. A	17. A	18. C	19. C	20. D

Essay

21. Many experts believe carbon dioxide emissions from factories and power plants cause global warming, but others disagree. Some question whether global warming even exists. The issue is very controversial because the cost of controlling emissions would affect the global economy. Industries would have to pay the cost of further reducing emissions, and those costs would eventually be passed on to consumers. Developing nations trying to industrialize would be hurt the most, but economic growth in wealthier nations would be hurt, too.

22. Bin Laden's experience against the Russians in Afghanistan convinced him that superpowers could be beaten. He also believed that Western ideas had contaminated Muslim society. He was outraged when Saudi Arabia allowed American troops on Saudi soil after Iraq invaded Kuwait. Bin Laden dedicated himself and his terrorist organization to driving Americans and other non-Muslims out of the Middle East.

UNIT 8 POSTTEST, FORM A

Matching

1. C	2. I	3. J	4. H	5. F
6. G	7. E	8. B	9. D	10. A

Multiple Choice

11. A	12. D	13. C	14. A	15. C
16. B	17. C	18. C	19. B	20. C

Essay

21. Nixon believed in shaping a foreign policy rooted in practical approaches rather than ideologies. He felt the nation's decades-long anti-Communist

crusade had created a foreign policy that was too rigid and often worked against the nation's interests. While he wanted to continue to contain communism, he believed that engagement and negotiation offered a better way for the United States to achieve its international goals. Though Nixon was still staunchly anti-Communist, over the years he had come to reject the notion of a bipolar world, in which the superpowers of the United States and Soviet Union confronted each other. He believed the United States needed to understand the growing role that China, Japan, and Western Europe would soon begin playing. This "multipolar" world of the future demanded a different approach to American foreign policy. Nixon fashioned an approach called détente, or relaxation of tensions between the United States and its two major Communist rivals, the Soviet Union and China.

22. Conservatives fundamentally distrust the power of government, particularly the federal government. They support the original intent of the Constitution, and they believe that government power should be divided into different branches and split between the state and federal level to limit its ability to intrude on people's lives. Conservatives believe that if the government regulates the economy, it makes the economy less efficient, resulting in less wealth and more poverty. They believe that free enterprise is the best way to achieve a higher standard of living for everyone. For this reason, conservatives generally oppose high taxes and government programs that transfer wealth from the rich to the poor. These taxes and programs, they believe, discourage investment and take away people's incentive to work hard. The more that government regulates the economy, conservatives argue, the more it will have to regulate every aspect of people's behavior. Ultimately, they fear, the government will so restrict people's economic freedom that Americans will no longer be able to improve their standard of living and get ahead in life.

UNIT 8 POSTTEST, FORM B

Matching

1. H	**2.** B	**3.** A	**4.** C	**5.** G
6. D	**7.** I	**8.** J	**9.** E	**10.** F

Multiple Choice

11. C	**12.** B	**13.** D	**14.** D	**15.** B
16. A	**17.** D	**18.** A	**19.** B	**20.** D

Essay

21. During the Watergate hearings, White House aide Alexander Butterfield testified that Nixon had ordered a taping system installed in the White House to record all conversations. All the groups investigating the scandal sought access to the tapes. The tapes would tell them exactly what the president knew and when he knew it. Nixon tried of avoid handing them over by pleading executive privilege. Special prosecutor Archibald Cox took Nixon to court to force him to give up the recordings. Nixon had Cox fired, but the new special prosecutor, Leon Jaworski, pressed for the tapes as well. Nixon then released edited transcripts of the tapes. Finally the Supreme Court ruled that Nixon had to turn over the tapes themselves, which he did. The tapes gave investigators the link to Nixon that they were looking for. The tapes revealed that Nixon had ordered the CIA to stop the FBI's investigation of the break-in. With this news, impeachment and conviction now seemed inevitable. Nixon resigned in disgrace.

22. As oil became important to the American economy in the 1920s, the United States invested heavily in the oil industry in the Middle East. This industry brought great wealth to the ruling families in some Middle Eastern kingdoms, but it left most of the people poor. Some became angry at the United States for supporting the wealthy kingdoms and families. The growth of the oil industry increased the Middle East's contact with Western society. As Western ideas spread through the region, many devout Muslims—followers of the region's dominant religion—feared that their traditional values and beliefs were being weakened. Throughout the Middle East, new movements arose calling for a return to traditional Muslim religious laws. These movements sought to overthrow pro-Western governments in the Middle East and hoped to establish a pure Islamic society. The Muslim fundamentalist militants of these movements began using terrorism to achieve their goals.